GW00383661

The author is a retired UK solicitor and an international lawyer who was born in Nairobi, Kenya, in 1948. He was the youngest of three brothers, who were very close and attached to one another. They suffered the unhappy and broken marriage of their parents, lack of love, rejection and abandonment first by their mother then by their father and the wretchedness and misery of living in orphanages. Two brothers were victims of sexual abuse. The eldest brother committed suicide at 39 and the middle brother died of a massive heart attack at 47. The author was the youngest brother and sole survivor who endured terrible traumatisms, insecurity, inferiority complex, guilt complexes, depressions, various setbacks and post-traumatic stress disorder over several decades before attaining resilience, greater confidence in life and serenity with his wife, three offspring and four grandsons.

Dedicated to my two beloved deceased brothers, in affectionate memory, and for my marvellous wife, my wonderful two sons and daughter, and my four magnificent grandsons.

"Hold very tenderly in your hand at all times throughout your life the hand of the child that you once were."
— Anonymous

"Memory is the scribe of the soul."
— Aristotle

"One does not fully recover from one's unhappy childhood."
— Jean Ferrat, French poet, composer and singer

"Rejection in childhood has the most strong and consistent negative effect on personality and development."
— Research Professor Ronald Rohner,
University of Connecticut, United States
of America

"Dark secrets must be divulged one day, otherwise they will devour you. Deep wounds must be treated, otherwise they will kill you."
— Philippe Benson, French writer

Amlodd Meyrick

THREE BROTHERS –
THREE DESTINIES

A novel based on and inspired by a true story

AUSTIN MACAULEY PUBLISHERS™

LONDON * CAMBRIDGE * NEW YORK * SHARJAH

A CIP catalogue record for this title is available from the British Library.

ISBN 9781788783156 (Paperback)
ISBN 9781788783163 (Hardback)
ISBN 9781788783170 (E-Book)

www.austinmacauley.com

First Published (2018)
Austin Macauley Publishers Ltd
25 Canada Square
Canary Wharf
London
E14 5LQ

Table of Contents

Chapter 1

Bad Times in Nairobi

'Push harder, my dear, push harder! I can see the top of the wee head at the entrance!' exclaimed Sally MacCleod, the Scottish expatriate nurse and mid-wife, to Mrs Rosamund Walton-Mornick, in as sympathetic and encouraging a tone as she could muster. She knew that it was very unpleasant, disappointing and saddening for the future mother to have to give birth to her third child in Nairobi Hospital on that morning of September 7th 1948 without having the assuring, strong, confident and masculine presence of the child's father, her husband, who had not kept his promise to be there for the birth.

'The entire head is through, now for the shoulders. Keep pushing, while taking in a deep breath of air and exhaling as low down in the stomach as possible, which will help to accelerate the expulsion of the baby into his or her new world !' cried the nurse, who was very excited now.

She became exhilarated as the reddish, purple coloured little body slid out into her awaiting arms so that she could see the genitalia. She glanced at the gynaecologist, Dr Manfield, as if asking for his permission to be able to announce to the exhausted mother the gender of her new-born, but in a male-dominated world the gynaecologist reacted immediately to this threat to his masculine pre-eminence by leaning very close to Mrs Walton-Mornick's face and whispering, rather sheepishly and apprehensively, in her left ear, 'Dearest Rosamund, my heartiest congratulations on the birth of your third son!'

As Rosamund made a heart-rending grimace and turned languidly on to her right side, with a groan, a mournful sigh and then a sad burst of tears, Dr Manfield gently placed his hand on to her upraised left shoulder and simply rubbed it up and down without attempting to say anything more, for he knew that no words of his would be able to comfort her in this double distress of giving birth alone without her husband being there and to a third son, whereas she had so desperately hoped and prayed that her third child would be a girl. Dr Manfield had known her and her husband, Adrian, since having met them at one of the parties of the British colonial set in Nairobi, the capital city of Kenya, soon after their arrival from South Africa in 1943. Having been recommended to Rosamund by one of the other wives of a white settler as being, by far, the most talented and reliable white gynaecologist in the city, he had not only become a friend of the couple but had also officiated, with the very competent assistance of Sally MacCleod, at the births in 1944 of their eldest son, Neil, and in 1946 of their second son, Justin, in this very hospital.

'Rosamund, take him into your arms and see how chubby and lovely he is,' Dr Manfield pleaded after Sally had done all the necessary chores of bathing the baby, cleaning him well and swaddling him in a fresh white towel. Despite his entreaty, Rosamund remained lying on her right side with her back turned to him and would not lie on her back to become receptive to holding this precious, individual, inoffensive tiny baby boy to whom she had given life and painful birth.

It was only much later and with a tremendous mental effort that she accepted to take him finally into her arms and breast-feed him. However, deep down in his heart and entire being, the innocent new-born baby could feel with his ultra-sensitivity and innate intuition that the seeds of rejection, lack of acceptance, abandonment and virtual treachery from the beginning, which would hound and haunt him and plague his life for so many long years, had already been sown.

Dr Manfield did not say anything to the devoted and caring Sally MacCleod, but he felt somewhat perturbed and worried about the negative reaction of Rosamund Walton-Mornick to the arrival of this baby boy. He had been aware for some time that the marriage between Rosamund and Adrian was difficult and fraught with differences of character, temperament and personality and that this unhappy situation had already greatly affected young Neil and Justin.

Further, the tenuous marital harmony had suffered progressively from the increased occasions of infidelity to one another, in the vein of the social climate of the so-called « Happy Valley » set which had prevailed among the white settlers in Kenya since the 1920s, involving frequent wild and licentious parties, safari weekends and barbecues in one or other of the immaculately manicured English style gardens in the residential parts of Nairobi, where the temptation to embark on sexual adventures and barely disguised affairs was not only strongly present but extremely rarely resisted.

Adrian did return from his mysterious adventures and did make the effort to come to the hospital in his rather old, dirty and worse-for-wear Land Rover to collect Rosamund and their tiny baby boy five days after the birth and drove them home to their small but charming English-style stone and wood, three-bedroomed house in a suburb of Nairobi. He had left Neil and Justin in the care of the family's only servant, Shelia, a black girl from the Kikuyu tribe whose family lived in a poor suburb of Nairobi. Shelia combined in her tiny frame the exhausting roles of cook, house cleaner and nursemaid to the boys, for Adrian and Rosamund could not afford to pay for the services of another servant.

Adrian, now thirty years old, was a tall, slim, handsome, aristocratic man of predominantly Welsh descent, with a small percentage of Scottish blood. He had a high, intelligent forehead, elongated face, perfectly shaped narrow, aquiline nose, broad shoulders and slender, strong body. He possessed bright blue eyes which, matched with his almost jet black hair, flashing, seductive smile and charming demeanour, made him very popular not only with women but also with the local community of white men, many of whom met up at

regular intervals at one of the social clubs in Nairobi, in particular the Muthaiga Club, which the British settlers had established and developed over time with their unrivalled capability for creating a club as soon as two or more of the expatriates in any foreign country within the expansive British empire became acquainted.

Rosamund had met Adrian at a house party down on the Cape in South Africa, where certain members of both their families possessed secondary residences, their principal homes being situated in Wales, Scotland and England. However, Rosamund's parents had been living in Cape Town permanently for several years. Rosamund was also of both Welsh and Scottish descent. Whilst being pretty and attractive in a comely way, she had a somewhat round face and curiously sad brown eyes, had to fight constantly against a problem of gaining weight, which ran through generations of her family, was not very tall and could not be considered to be a classically beautiful woman. She had always wondered how she had managed to ensnare Adrian, who could have made the choice of settling down with any one of the many women that he was acquainted with, and she had always felt a nagging complex of inferiority and a painful lack of self-confidence, especially when she saw various women, including the wives of other men, flitting around Adrian and making it vulgarly obvious that they considered him to be a first-rate male specimen and singularly attractive potential lover.

Up until now, Neil and Justin had enjoyed a bedroom each whilst their parents occupied the third bedroom. With the arrival of their baby brother, they were obliged to share one bedroom, with Justin moving into Neil's bedroom, for Rosamund decided that the baby should have his cot placed in the bedroom directly adjoining that of his parents. This decision caused a flaming row between her and Adrian, for he was of the opinion that Neil should have the privilege of keeping his own bedroom, enjoying the status of the eldest son, and that the cot of the new-born should be placed in Justin's room. However, Rosamund remained adamant in her argument that the baby should have the entire peace and calm of sleeping, without any risk of disturbance from Justin, in the bedroom which was right beside theirs, so that she could go to him if she heard him crying, coughing or being perturbed during the night in any way whatsoever.

As both Adrian and Rosamund possessed an excessive degree of pride and obstinacy as well as a hot temper, this new argument, the latest in a long line of antagonisms between them over the years, blazed on for many hours and caused a heavy, smoulderingly aggressive and unpleasant atmosphere in the house, disturbing further what little harmony existed and causing Neil and Justin to feel very sad and wretched at this most recent illustration of the unhappy relationship between their parents.

In the end, Adrian conceded the point, in a petulant huff, after Rosamund had screamed at the top of her voice, 'You do not know everything, you arrogant sod, and you can believe me that a mother always knows what is best

for her child, so this baby will have the room to himself next to ours, and if you don't like it you can go and get lost!'

Yet another storm brew when the couple realised that they had not got round to discussing the name that they wanted for their third child, since Adrian, in agreement for once on a subject with his wife, had concurred with her desire to have a girl, so they had not researched alternative names for a boy.

Rosamund said with great conviction that she wanted him to be named George, as that was the Christian name of her paternal grandfather, whom she loved and admired very deeply.

'Oh, no!' roared Adrian. 'That's such a common and over-used name. The British Royal Family has already displayed a distinct lack of imagination on that subject, as the country and empire have already gone through so many Kings called George over the centuries and are now presently on their sixth!'

When Adrian proposed to name his baby boy Archibald, the name of his own father, Rosamund yelled that that was an atrocious, old-fashioned, Victorian and utterly unacceptable name for her son.

Much bitter haggling followed, which their other two cringing and trembling sons had to endure, for the house was so small and the insulation between the rooms so poor that they heard everything coming from any room, especially as their parents almost always raised their voices at one another, like two growling or barking dogs.

Eventually, Rosamund calmed down when Adrian suggested that they name their third son after himself, firstly because it was a name that she liked very much and, secondly and more importantly, because she hoped deep inside herself that such a big concession to her husband's personal pride would have a positive effect and cause him in return be more loving, gentler, kinder and, hope against hope, faithful towards her.

'What a lovely suggestion!' beamed Rosamund, as she threw her arms around her husband and gave him a passionate kiss on the lips while holding him for several seconds in a python-strong embrace.

Regaining her breath and laughing coquettishly as he gasped for breath himself, she stretched up her arms, took his head between her hands, looked up at him with an adoring gaze and said in as seductive a voice as possible, 'Yes, my beloved, I really do like that – I will run and tell Neil and Justin that their baby brother's name is Adrian!'

* * *

When he was just two years old, young Adrian caught a very bad cold, then after a few days he had shaking fits and teeth-chattering chills in his body, followed by a cough, a high fever, nausea and vomiting, an awful diarrhoea, with a fast heartbeat and difficulty breathing. When the doctor came to their home at Rosamund's request, he recognised the symptoms rapidly and told Rosamund that Adrian had become very ill with pneumonia after a heavy cold and he prescribed a treatment with medicine and total rest in bed, as an

infection in a lung was also part of the pneumonia condition. During the first few days of the illness, the doctor came to visit him in his bedroom at home, but when his condition deteriorated, the doctor had him transported to Nairobi Hospital. After two weeks or so of hospital treatment, it appeared that the illness was subsiding and that Adrian was getting much better, so his mother was allowed to take him home for his convalescence.

However, after several days, the symptoms of the pneumonia returned with a vengeance. Rosamund was in a state of panic and when the doctor came to visit and checked Adrian's condition, he was gravely concerned and had him re-admitted to hospital. The situation worsened dramatically and the doctor eventually told Rosamund that Adrian had what was called a "double pneumonia", as both lungs had now been infected, which killed several dozens of young children each year in Kenya. He told her in as gentle and sympathetic a manner as he could that she and the family had to expect the worst and that, due to the gravity of his condition, it would be a miracle if Adrian beat the illness and survived.

A while later, Rosamund knelt down beside Adrian's little hospital bed, took his burning, feverish right hand in hers, stroked it gently and lovingly and whispered to her small son, 'My darling Adrian, I am sure that you can hear me and understand what I am saying. Be brave and strong, be a fighter, hang in there and I am very sure that you will pull through and will beat off this dreadful illness and be able to come home very soon and play again with your two brothers, who miss you very much. I love you, my adorable son. I will come back to stay for periods here beside you as often as I can in the days to come for as long as it takes, and I will pray to God for your speedy and full recovery, so be strong, hang on to life and get well again.'

The fever seemed to worsen. Poor Adrian had even greater difficulty to breathe than before, and the doctor feared one night that he was losing his battle and would not be alive by the morning. Rosamund returned in the early morning, after giving Neil and Justin their breakfasts and she held young Adrian's limp and almost lifeless hand in hers for what seemed many hours as she sat beside his bed on a chair and prayed silently and constantly that she would not lose her beloved youngest son.

In the early evening, she told the doctor that she was going back home to prepare supper for her two other sons and herself, confiding to him that she had no idea where her husband was, and would come back to the hospital as quickly as possible. She arranged for a bed to be placed for her beside Adrian's little bed, saying to the doctor that if he had to die during that coming night she wanted to be there with him right up until the end of the dreadful ordeal.

However, during that night the fever subsided a little, the following day it went down even more and over the next five days Adrian's overall condition improved almost miraculously. He was kept in hospital for one more week, then the doctor diagnosed that the double pneumonia had been beaten and Rosamund was allowed to taken Adrian home where he could enjoy his family

surroundings and be with his brothers again whilst he completed his convalescence.

When his father came home again one day, after an unexplained, protracted absence, Rosamund said proudly to her husband, 'Our little Adrian is a survivor. I know that, after beating off this life-threatening illness, he will be able to face and overcome any trials and tribulations that may hit him during his life.'

Little did Rosamund realise just how prophetic her words were, in light of the dramas, traumas and tragedies that were to strike in the years and decades to come. Albeit being very proud of little Adrian for overcoming his battle against death and surviving the awful ordeal, she was very ashamed of her husband and noted with deep sadness and anger his cold detachment and distance from and very little concern for his son during the dreadful illness which very nearly killed him.

***

Little Adrian was now just three years old and loved walking anywhere with either of his parents and running around their small but neat and pleasant garden with Neil and Justin. His English was already very good and his parents were very proud of the fact that he was also learning and assimilating many words in the Swahili language, largely through the devoted efforts of their servant Shelia as well as the teaching of Neil and Justin who proudly seized on every opportunity to demonstrate their progressively extended knowledge of the African language. On several occasions, Adrian had seen a grey squirrel scampering across the lawn and running up into the branches of a fig tree in one corner of the garden and he pointed to the lovely creature calling out "kindi, kindi", as he knew that the grey squirrel was called kindi in Swahili. He also knew that the fig tree was named mkuyu in Swahili.

As with his two brothers before him, Adrian was in fact able to swim even before he could walk, as their father had taken each of his sons when he was less than two years old to the large swimming pool at the Muthaiga Club and had literally thrown him in at the deep end, obliging the boy to adopt automatically the "doggy paddle" movement in order to stop himself from drowning, whilst his father dived in, surfaced, turned and swam leisurely towards him, and then took the poor flailing boy, coughing, spluttering, and entirely panicked, into his arms before he sank for the third time below the surface.

Following a few such visits to the swimming pool, when each son had gained a certain amount of confidence and proficiency with the doggy paddle technique, Adrian took him on a long weekend trip to the shore of the magnificent Diani Beach near Mombasa on the Indian Ocean coast, took him by the scruff of his hair and his swimming trunks and threw him into the crashing and noisy waves of the immense sea, where he had to fend for himself to regain the shore.

So, by the time young Adrian was three years old, both his elder brothers were very strong swimmers and he had a true love of water, just like them, and all three of them thoroughly enjoyed participating in various swimming races in the pool at the Muthaiga Club.

In particular, they loved watching their athletic father winning many of the swimming races at the weekends, for he was renowned as the overall champion. And they laughed with glee every time he won so easily the wonderful race of swimming breast-stroke for four lengths while blowing a tiny table-tennis ball before him with great dexterity as it bobbed and dinked in an amusing manner on the surface of the water.

Such moments of sharing swimming pleasures with their father brought immense joy to all three boys, but they had to cherish and make the most of those occasions, for he was, to their dismay and enormous sadness, a very distant, aloof and absent father for a good part of the time. Indeed, he would disappear for several days at a time whilst their mother simply told them that he was obliged to travel in the context of his work as an engineer. They were observant, sensitive and perspicacious and did not fail to note the anguished look in their mother's eyes nor the fact that the absences of their beloved father became more frequent and more prolonged.

Further, on the occasions when their father was at home for several days, the three boys were desperately anguished and huddled together in trembling fear and in tears as their parents screamed at one another and their father frequently beat their mother with his open hand, or his clenched fist or on some occasions with a flat, wooden cheese board that he took from a drawer in the kitchen. Finally, the three sons were deeply pained and wretchedly unhappy when their mother stopped sleeping in the same bedroom as their father and moved into young Adrian's bedroom where she slept on a second bed beside his own.

As the increasingly heavy, tense and unhappy atmosphere caused by his warring parents became more and more difficult for him to cope with, Adrian, who was only three and a half years old, started becoming incontinent, urinated in his pyjamas each night and became victim to increasingly violent nightmares and grave difficulty in falling off to sleep.

One night, when he was still awake and lying in his usual position on his right side facing his mother's bed and the bedroom door beyond it, he heard and saw the door open, as his eyes were accustomed to the darkness in the room. He pulled up the sheet just below the level of his eyes and watched, without moving his body or even his eyelids, as two people tiptoed into the bedroom. He knew that one of them was his mother and could just see, sense and even smell that the other presence was that of a white man. He watched silently and secretly as the man took his mother into his arms and kissed her passionately, then fondled her body with his hands and unbuttoned her blouse and the belt of her skirt, hastily undressing her.

Horrified, he observed his mother opening the man's shirt, taking it off, undoing his belt, pulling his trousers and underpants off. Then kneeling in front

of the man and stroking gently then energetically a large and long protuberance hanging between the man's legs with her hand, which she then took into her mouth and started sucking, whilst making a slurpy noise.

He heard the sighs and moans which the man emitted as his mother continued to suck and pull on the long and thick object, then similar sighs and moans which came from his mother's mouth when the man tipped her onto the bed and placed his head between her legs. He almost screamed out in horror and anguish when the man then seemed to attack his mother by lying on her and penetrating her body with his long protuberance and he prepared himself to leap out of his bed, grab his bedside lamp and hit the man over the head with it in his rage and overwhelming desire to defend his mother from this dreadful attack.

But he cringed and remained motionless in an entirely confused state beneath the sheets as he saw his mother and the man move their bodies in a rhythmic cycle, caress each other with their hands and kiss one another with passion on the lips, then emit the same soft, moaning, sighing and groaning sounds as before, whilst gyrating faster and faster until their violent movements subsided, slowed then ceased and they lay calmly in each other's arms, until the man stood up, dressed, kissed his mother one last time then left the room. Adrian's mother spent quite a while in the bathroom, then returned to the bedroom, lay down on her bed and subsided rapidly into a deep sleep.

Young Adrian knew that the man who had been intimate with his mother was not his father. Even though he was little and not yet four years old, he knew instinctively and from what he had personally observed that what the unknown man had done to his mother had pleased and contented her and he was filled with a dreadful fear that it would be extremely harmful to the already difficult and unstable relationship between his parents and would have prejudicial consequences for his brothers and himself. He cried silently in his bed, his body rocking from side to side as he became overwhelmed by sadness, despair, anger, confusion and an engulfing feeling that he and his brothers had been betrayed and terribly badly treated over time by the attitudes and behaviour of both their parents.

He never mentioned one word to his mother, his father or his two brothers about what he had seen that night, but worse was to follow, as his father's absences became more frequent and similar unbearable scenes occurred over many nights, with several different men in his mother's bed just next to his, over the coming months. And young Adrian became increasingly perturbed, agitated and disturbed by his mother's actions and her sheer abandonment to such men in these adventures late at night and by the ever growing distance and coldness between his parents and the increasing absences of his father.

Whilst most of the men that his mother brought home for late night sex were white men who lived in the colonialist settlement of the city, on more than one occasion Adrian observed from his secret spying position, lying in his bed with the sheet drawn up to just below his eyes, that the casual lover was a black man. And each time his mother seemed to abandon herself with even

18

greater lasciviousness and to derive even more pleasure from the sexual coupling with a black man than when she was in bed having intercourse with a white man.

Adrian wondered where his mother met such black men but he could guess that in a city with a predominantly black population, there must have been many places where she could easily pick up black men. The shock and the traumatism that his mother's disgusting, shameless and ever-increasing promiscuous behaviour caused to his system were very grave and deep and the images of his mother with those various men and the growing hatred, contempt and distance between his parents were to disturb, haunt and torture him for many long years.

Whilst he revered his two elder brothers and felt very close to them, he wanted to preserve them from the awful pains and feelings of hurtful betrayal and rejection that he suffered, so he maintained his silence, keeping the traumatisms and anguish hidden deep within himself as dreadful and appalling secrets.

Chapter 2

Mau Mau Terror in Nyeri Region

Adrian Walton-Mornick had been travelling between Nairobi and some other places in Kenya for quite some time and his wife Rosamund was becoming very concerned that he kept the whole family in the dark and gave no explanations for his movements or about the nature of his activities.

One evening, whilst they were in the kitchen with Shelia, who was busy preparing their supper, Neil, Justin and Adrian all suddenly looked at one another with panic in their eyes, stopped chattering and strained their ears so that they could hear their parents shouting at one another in the living room.

'What on earth are you telling me?' Rosamund screamed at her husband. 'You have bought a small farm in the Nyeri region and want us all to move up there? What a scatter-brained, crazy and idiotic idea! Our lives are here, we love Nairobi and Neil and Justin are happy in their school here and have made some good friends. Why would we want to move away up north, for goodness sake!'

'I am sick and tired of my present job as an engineer!' retorted Adrian as he raised his voice even higher in an aggressive manner. 'As I told you when we first met, I was given the opportunity to come out to Africa from England when I was seventeen in order to work on a sisal farm. I enjoyed that experience and it was only under pressure from certain people insisting that I had to obtain a professional qualification that I studied to become an engineer. However, I miss the work on the land and in a stroke of good luck an opportunity came my way to purchase a small farming homestead with some land in the very fertile region of Nyeri. But I was given very little time to take the decision as several other expatriate families were interested, so I went ahead and bought the farm. You will see, more and more white families are moving to that area and Nyeri is a pleasant, small town which is developing fast. A primary school has been created in a village not far from where we will live and later on, the boys will be able to attend the secondary school in Nyeri. You will see, we can make a new life for our family up there and build up a profitable farming enterprise.'

'As you seem to have firmly taken the decision, it is important that we tell the boys that a big and important change is about to happen in their lives.'

'We will talk to them about it after they have eaten their supper,' concluded Adrian with an imperious wave of his hand in the direction of the kitchen.

'There is no need to tell us, for we already know,' shouted Neil, as he burst into the living room from the kitchen. 'Since you were both screaming at each

other, as you never just talk but are only capable of shouting, screaming and raising your voices all the time, Justin, Adrian and I could not help but overhear your slanging match. As you always bully mother and impose on her decisions that you make in your arrogant and domineering way, what can we say? So we will just have to follow your orders, but I have a strong feeling that you are about to ruin our lives!'

With tears welling in his sensitive blue eyes, Neil reeled away and ran out of the room in the direction of his bedroom. Justin and little Adrian stood there silently for a small moment, each looking up to his father with a pleading look in his eyes, but as he merely adopted a cold, marble stare in those powerful, steely blue eyes empty of any emotion, they both glanced at one another, shuddered and ran out of the room in pursuit of Neil. The sounds of sobbing and distress soon came from the boys' bedrooms, Rosamund covered her eyes in despair with both hands, but Adrian just glared at her then turned on his heels and walked out into the garden. Once more, the lack of communication between them and the feeling of contempt bordering on enmity that they seemed to have for one another was palpable, pathetic and destructive.

***

Several months later, the small house in Nairobi had been sold, and all the furniture and other personal belongings of the entire family, as well as the meagre personal items of Shelia, who had accepted to accompany them, had been moved to and installed in the rambling farmhouse fifteen miles from the small town of Nyeri and five miles from the nearest village where Neil and Justin were taken on a ramshackle, old bus to the little primary school every day.

As the youngest brother, Adrian was still too young to go to primary school and out there in the bush there did not exist as yet any infant school or kindergarten for him to attend.

Rosamund worked hard to create some semblance of a pleasant family life for herself and her three young boys, and she did like the farmhouse and its very lovely garden, which previous owners had created and quite evidently had enjoyed developing. However, she was profoundly unhappy, although she never said a word to her husband, whom she resented more than ever for having forced them all to abandon their pleasant, comfortable life in Nairobi to move up here into the countryside.

Most of all, she anguished over the loss of her several lovers left behind in Nairobi and she wondered how she would be able to meet attractive young men and bring them back to the farmhouse in order to satisfy her insatiable sexual appetite, as she no longer slept with her husband but craved for a renewed experience of being in a man's arms and having him satisfy not only her bodily but her emotional needs as well.

Adrian was in his element and plunged with great enthusiasm and energy into the work on the farm and he met up regularly with other white settlers in

the area to discuss their experiences and exchange and pool ideas as to the most efficient methods of farming. He bought a horse, so that he could visit other farms in the neighbourhood on horseback.

Little Adrian would laugh and point his finger as his father rode away and would shout to his brothers 'There goes Dad on his *farasi*' so he could show off to his brothers his expanding Swahili vocabulary.

He and his brothers loved watching the *kigengen*, as the chameleon was known in Swahili, crawling very slowly along a branch then unfurling its long tongue in an incredibly fast movement, catching an unsuspecting fly or other insect and changing the colour of its skin instantaneously whenever it was necessary to blend into its surrounding environment. They also enjoyed tending the eight goats, which their father had bought, and they even helped Shelia milk the *mbuzi*, which she taught them was the Swahili name for the goat.

As he had kept the sturdy Land Rover, which was still performing well despite its very old age, Adrian sometimes drove down to Nyeri to purchase provisions and equipment. On many occasions, he did not return at night and Rosamund felt certain that he spent each of those nights in the arms of some welcoming woman whom he had met on his frequent visits to the town, including undoubtedly the wives of some residents when the husbands were away travelling on business.

Rosamund began to think to herself that she was ready to bet that Adrian had deliberately chosen to make them move out to this god-forsaken country retreat so that she would become a prisoner out there, since she had never learnt to drive a car nor to ride a horse. Whilst he would be footloose and fancy free to do whatever pleased him, to roam wherever he liked at the wheel of the Land Rover or on horseback, and to seek out romantic adventures with other women to his heart's delight and his body's nourishment.

'What a fool I have been!' she said to herself, now regretting that she had never been able to learn to drive nor to ride a horse. 'I hate you more and more, Adrian Walton-Mornick! You wait, you selfish, rotten scoundrel, my time for vengeance will come. As soon as all the boys have finished their education and become young men, I will drop you like a hot potato!'

***

As Adrian had bought a radio, he and Rosamund were able to hear the information on the development of the extremely disturbing *Mau Mau* Uprising. In addition, Adrian drove down on occasions to the Muthaiga Club in Nairobi, where he met up with other white settlers and exchanged with them all the up-to-date news concerning the discontentment of the black community in Kenya. He was also kept informed on the subject by several white farmers each time that he went into the town of Nyeri.

Since early 1952, a movement called the *Mau Mau* Uprising, or the *Mau Mau* Rebellion or the *Mau Mau* Revolt, had gathered pace as an insurgency by Kenyan black rebels against the British colonial administration. The main

backbone of the resistance was made up of members of the Kikuyu ethnic group, along with smaller numbers of the Embu and Meru tribes. The uprising occurred as a consequence of a long period of simmering political, economic and racial tensions coupled with the apparent lack of any peaceful political solution.

Through their various sources, Adrian and Rosamund discovered that over the past several decades, an increasing point of contention and resentment on the part of the black community in Kenya was the occupation of land by British settlers. Most of the land in question was in the central highlands and in all the large area around the Nyeri fertile region, which had a relatively cool climate compared to the rest of the country, and was inhabited primarily by the Kikuyu tribe.

Adrian and Rosamund were astounded to learn that by 1948 approximately 1,250,000 Kikuyu were restricted to about 2,000 square miles, while a small number of 30,000 white settlers occupied roughly 12,000 square miles, and, just as importantly, the very best and most desirable agricultural land was almost entirely held in the hands of settlers. Sometime after 1948, a campaign of civil disobedience was organised involving all of the Kikuyu in order to protest the land issue.

After a demand for Kenyan independence from British rule made in May 1950, followed by arrests of the leaders then many strikes by blacks culminating in a general strike, the black movement became radicalised and led to a revolutionary climate dedicated to the use of violence in order to overthrow colonial rule. As from end 1951, the houses of European settlers were randomly set on fire and their livestock was hamstrung or taken away, leading to a large increase over several months in the destruction of settlers' properties, many attacks on Africans considered by *Mau Mau* members to be loyalists to the British rule, including simple servants of white settlers, and a veritable war of liberation launched by *Mau Mau* leaders.

The so-called Land and Freedom Armies, named after the two issues that the Kikuyu considered were the most essential and important, were principally equipped with spears, *simis*, which were short swords, *kikobos*, which were rhino hide whips, and *pangas*, a type of machete. Adrian and Rosamund learned to their dismay that the *panga*, a common agricultural tool in large supply, was the most widely used weapon of the *Mau Mau*.

In mid-January 1953, Adrian was told one day by another settler, whom he happened to come across over a late-morning drink in a bar in Nyeri, that reports had confirmed that a reasonably small but menacing band of *Mau Mau* insurgents were marauding and prowling in the countryside south of the town and would soon be reaching some of the villages not far from Nyeri. Although it was not feared that they would enter the town itself and attempt to attack any white households, since they would not be any match for the much larger population of white settlers in Nyeri if the latter decided to group together and mount a defence against any attack.

A few hours later in the afternoon, the Land Rover drew up to a halt on the gravel driveway in front of the house and Rosamund spotted Adrian through the kitchen window going to the back of the vehicle with two long dog leads in his hand, opening the back flap and attaching each lead to a large dog. "Large" was in fact an under-statement, for when the two animals jumped lithely out of the Land Rover onto the gravel Rosamund was astonished to see that they were two huge and very athletic-looking Alsatians.

'What on earth are you doing with those great beasts?' Rosamund shouted to Adrian as she rushed out through the front door. 'And where did you get them from?'

'A fellow in town told me that a band of *Mau Mau* warriors may be heading this way very soon, armed apparently with spears and *pangas*. I remembered that a policeman in Nyeri had told me some while ago that the local police force had acquired several Alsatian dogs and had given them a thorough training in chasing and catching black thieves, as the incidence of break-ins and burglaries by blacks looting the homes of white settlers in the town and in some of the surrounding villages had increased considerably. The policeman had said that the properly trained Alsatians were ferocious and struck terror into the hearts of all the blacks that they chased and inflicted dreadful wounds on them if they caught them. So, I have just been over to the police station and I asked whether they might be able to sell me any trained Alsatians. The chief police officer said that they could only spare me two dogs, which they have named Romulus and Remus, after the two wolves in Rome in ancient history, we haggled over a fair price, and here they are! If the band of *Mau Mau* decide to attack this place, we will have a big surprise waiting for them!'

'Well, I do hope that they will efficiently defend us against any attack, but I warn you that I am not going to touch them. You should not allow the boys to come near them in case they turn on and bite them, and it is your entire responsibility to look after, handle and feed these beasts, which I imagine are going to cost us a fortune in meat and dog biscuits, judging by the enormous size of them!'

***

The attack occurred a short while after dusk one day a few weeks later.

A warning had reached Adrian from another farm not very far away that the small *Mau Mau* band, estimated to be about ten young and very fit men, was walking steadfastly in the direction of his property. As there were two farmhouses situated between Adrian's house and the outskirts of Nyeri, the other two farmers, Jim McCauly and Ray Pollock, told the police chief earlier in the day that they were going to drive over to Adrian's place, each armed with a shotgun, several rounds of bullets, and *pangas*, in case hand-to-hand fighting became necessary, in order to give Adrian some support. They asked the police to send patrols over to their farms to check that all was in order and

their families would be safe while they were absent, to which the police chief in Nyeri readily agreed.

As soon as Jim and Ray arrived during the late afternoon, Adrian started giving his orders in anticipation of an attack, which they all agreed would probably be staged after sunset, when the darkness of night would rapidly descend on the garden and the surrounding fields.

'As for our positions, Ray should remain in waiting at the front of the house, in the dining room with the window just open enough for him to fire his shotgun. And Jim and I will each hide in the pantry and the laundry room at the back, both of which have windows we can open enough to fire our shotguns, for I am ready to bet that at least six of the *Mau Mau* group will come at us from behind the house. Furthermore, each of us must also place his *panga* very near him, just in case, God forbid, any of these black renegades manages to break into the house and there are no bullets left for our guns.'

'Rosamund, please, will you firstly light several spirit lamps, turn them up to their maximum and place them on the window-sills around the house, so that the reflection of their light will show up the silhouettes of the approaching attackers as much as possible?'

'Then, you and Shelia must take the three boys upstairs and hide with them in our bedroom, with the door locked, and it is vital for the protection of your lives that you all remain silent and do not move around in the room.'

'I will immediately tell Shelia to go upstairs with the boys,' Rosamund replied, 'but there is no way that I am going to hide away like a coward. Surely, I can make myself useful in some way?'

'Yes, you can,' Jim McCauly interjected. 'We have a certain number of rounds of bullets between Adrian's stock and those that Ray and I have brought with us, but it will be difficult for us to hold many bullets in our pockets and hands, use our shotguns to best effect at the same time and know how many bullets each of us will need depending on the intensity of the fighting. If you do not mind standing in the kitchen, out of sight, well away from the window but near the inside open door, guarding a good quantity of bullets, each of us can call to you when we need more bullets and you can rush over crouched down to our position to hand them to us. What do you think, Adrian, are you prepared to let her do that?'

'Yes, all right, it is, in effect, quite a good idea, so let us give to Rosamund all the bullets that we cannot keep on us at the outset.'

Later on, after the sun had set, dusk had settled in and darkness had shrouded the exterior surroundings, upstairs in the master bedroom, as soon as the first gunshots rang out and screams were heard from three *Mau Mau* who had been hit, Neil rushed to the window, opened it and peered out, longing to follow what was going on in the fight as far as the reflections from the lit spirit lamps downstairs would permit.

'Please, Neil,' whispered the terrified Shelia, 'you heard what your father said: you must remain hidden under the bed or in the cupboard, so shut the window and come away from it.'

'I am nine years old!' retorted Neil proudly in a low but growling voice. 'I am not a small kid anymore and I insist on seeing what is going on out there as well as can be in the dark, so I am staying here with the window open. You hide like a coward if you want to, but I am not afraid.'

'Neither are we,' both Justin and little Adrian whispered in unison. 'Make some room for us, Neil, so that we can see some of the action as well.'

Both seven-year-old Justin and five-year-old Adrian grabbed a bedside table from each side of the large bed, stood on tip-toes on the table and did manage to get some glimpses of the fighting that was going on down below as their father and the other two farmers shot at *Mau Mau* approaching in the garden.

All of a sudden, and entirely unexpectedly, a crashing noise of splintering wood and broken glass resounded through the house, as the locked French-windows in the living room gave way under the massive weight and strength of a tall and bulky *Mau Mau*.

Before Ray, who was in the neighbouring dining-room, could fully realise what was happening and point his shotgun properly in the direction of the noise, the *Mau Mau* rushed at him, sliced off the first arm then the second one with his razor-sharp *panga*, pushed him to the ground and hacked at his chest several times then killed him with a savage *panga* blow deep in his neck.

As Adrian, Jim and Rosamund all left their positions and came rushing towards the dining-room, terrified by the awful screams emitted by Ray then the chilling silence, they all stopped in their tracks as both Romulus and Remus pounced onto the *Mau Mau* warrior. Romulus ripped open his face, Remus bit very deeply into his chest on the left side and his teeth ground through the muscle, sinews and rib cage and started searching for his heart, as if he had done this type of thing before.

The *Mau Mau* could barely howl his agonising pain as most of his jaw, mouth and tongue were savagely ripped away by Romulus. And it was only seconds before his rib cage was bitten through and his heart torn out by Remus, leaving the man writhing and twitching on the floor, until he gave his last breath and joined Ray in death.

'Oh, my God!' Adrian yelled. 'I had totally forgotten about the dogs. If I had only let them loose outside earlier on, we might have avoided having this vermin crashing in here and killing Ray. What a bloody fool I am!'

Rosamund screeched: 'Look out!'

And she hid behind Adrian's back as two other *Mau Mau*, one carrying a spear and another wielding a *panga*, clambered over the broken French-window on the living room floor and rushed with fierce yells and murderous grimaces towards them. However, Romulus and Remus both pounced on them in unison and with lightning speed, jumping up at the chest, knocked each man over.

Adrian then shot one in the head and Jim dispatched the other with a shot in the heart.

Now in control of his wits again, Adrian immediately called to the dogs, 'Go get the remaining bastards out there, boys!'

At the same time, he stretched out an arm in the direction of the space left by the destroyed French-windows. Both Alsatians reacted instantaneously to the order, rushed out into the garden and high-pitched screams were heard as the four *Mau Mau*, still on their feet, ran away from the property as fast as they could, with the dogs yapping and nipping at their heels until the men had run so far that the dogs gave up the chase and came back into the living-room.

By this time, Shelia, Neil, Justin and little Adrian had all come rushing downstairs after hearing the dreadful noises and commotion. They stood, very shocked and shaking with emotion, as they surveyed the gory scene of Ray's dreadfully mutilated body, one *Mau Mau* with half of his face ripped off and his rib-cage gaping open and his heart lying on the floor in a massive pool of blood, and the other two *Mau Mau* prostrated on the floor with deep bullet wounds.

Whilst Neil and Justin both put on a brave face and acted with great stoicism, looking at this dreadful carnage, little Adrian tumbled over to where Ray lay, sagged down onto his knees, started weeping uncontrollably, then wailed aloud and rocked his body from side to side, whilst wrapping his arms across his chest, as if a great physical pain overwhelmed him together with the extreme anguish and emotional distress. Neil and Justin glanced at each other, then rushed over together to try to give some comfort to Adrian, all three brothers being very close and adoring one another.

However, Rosamund got to him first, picked him up, cradled him in her arms and carried him up rapidly to his bedroom, where she continued to hold him in her arms, lying on the bed, with him doubled up in a foetal position pressed against her warm body, until his frantic, anguished spasms of weeping and emotional agony calmed down and he finally slipped into a feverish but welcome and soothing sleep.

The funeral for Ray was organised a few days later and the entire white population of Nyeri and the surrounding villages came to the service in the Nyeri Protestant Church in support of Ray's widow Maureen and their two children, and accompanied them to the nearby cemetery for the burial service.

The local police had been contacted and had driven out in a large van the day after the attack and had taken away the bodies of the six *Mau Mau* invaders who had lost their lives. Adrian and Jim did not want to know what happened to the bodies of these men and, like them, the other members of the local white community did not care about the manner in which the bodies were disposed of by the police and forensic authorities.

***

After the tragedy, everyone in the community did their best to ensure that life took on some semblance of normality again, although the traumas and the scars were very deep. There were reports that another farm of a white settler had

been attacked, but that was much farther north, so the Walton-Mornick family and their friends and acquaintances in the Nyeri region decided to remain wary but not obsessed about any threat of further *Mau Mau* attacks in the vicinity.

Despite Rosamund's objections that Romulus and Remus were costing them in upkeep a lot of money that they could ill-afford, Adrian insisted firmly that it was only prudent and sensible to keep them for the time being, as the *Mau Mau* rebellion had not yet been defeated by the military and police forces or terminated through a settlement process negotiated by the political authorities. Rosamund had to give way and accept his decision, which she had become reluctantly accustomed to doing in their tempestuous and difficult relationship.

One day, about three months after the *Mau Mau* attack on their farm, Adrian was away for a good part of the day in Nyeri, attending an agricultural fair coupled with conferences. Neil and Justin were absent from home at their local primary school, Rosamund had accepted an invitation from another white settler's wife to allow her to collect her in her van and spend some hours together over at that wife's place, whilst young Adrian had gone to play with some children roughly his own age at a neighbouring farm, where his father dropped him off on his way to Nyeri, saying he would collect him again on his way home after the agricultural fair was finished during the afternoon.

After a pleasant light lunch, then the usual siesta, followed by some more fun and games with his pals, little Adrian decided that he had had enough and did not want to wait for his father to pick him up and said to his hosts that he was going to walk home. They did not find this untoward, as all the children in the farming community were used to walking and even running quite long distances cross-country. When he arrived at his home, Adrian called out to Shelia as he walked up the garden path, saying he was thirsty and asking if she had a cool drink for him. There was no reply, to his great surprise, as Shelia was always in the house carrying out some task or other. He was also amazed that Romulus and Remus, who adored him, did not come running out to greet him for he was sure they would be at home, as his father had not taken them with him to Nyeri and his mother, who merely tolerated the dogs but did not have any great affection for them, would never have allowed them to accompany her on her outing.

As Adrian entered the house, he had the enormous shock of seeing Remus lying dead on his side in the living room in a pool of reddish, blackening blood, and he saw three or four wide gashes in his side and throat and a large chunk of red, raw meat stuck between his jaws, into which his long teeth had sunk deeply. Looking around, he then saw Romulus, also prostrated, lying dead in a wide pool of his blood, and also bearing several wide gashes on his body and a large chunk of raw meat clamped between his jaws.

In a state of shock, great distress and incomprehension, Adrian started sweating profusely and running around the room in circles, screaming: 'Shelia! Shelia! What is happening? Where are you? Where are you? Why are the dogs dead?'

There was a heavy, mournful silence. Shelia did not reply, and in a fit of anxiety and apprehension, Adrian rushed into the kitchen, stumbled over something lying on the floor and fell sprawling headlong with a crash and through a wide patch of drying blood into the small dustbin kept under the kitchen sink. He was dazed and almost fainted, but when he recovered his senses, he turned around and just could not believe what he saw. Shelia was lying on her back, her eyes were closed, the green dress which Adrian saw her wearing that morning had disappeared and she was stark naked. The full length of her body had been butchered with deep lacerations and gashes across her forehead, her shoulders, her breasts, her stomach, her thighs and her lower legs. The blood in all the wounds was drying and congealing and flies were settling in hoards in each of the gashes. A flash appeared before Adrian's eyes of the dreadful gashes he had seen on Ray's body, but they were nothing compared to the horrendous wounds which had been inflicted on Shelia and had killed her.

This was far too much pain to bear. Adrian had loved Shelia and she had been so good and kind to him and his brothers.

With his heart breaking, he simpered 'Shelia! Shelia!', burst out crying, then emitted a loud, anguished wail, and collapsed down beside her slain and bloodied body. He cupped up her left, lifeless and cold hand in both his small hands covered also in blood, curled his body into a foetal position facing her with her hand and his hands clasped against his heart and kept sobbing, with his chest heaving and his body shaking, for what seemed like hours.

It was, in actual fact, only about half an hour later when Neil and Justin jumped out of the small, ramshackle bus, which conveyed them and other children in the outlying homesteads to and from their primary school. In their turn, they discovered with enormous shock and dismay the two dead dogs then they fell upon the horrendous scene of Shelia's lacerated and bloodied body and little Adrian curled up beside her with his blood-stained body trembling and his eyes red from tears and his voice hoarse and barely audible from his repeated wailing and calling out her name.

Neil had great difficulty in prising Adrian's two bloodied hands away from Shelia's left hand. He and Justin then carried him tenderly between them out on to the veranda where all three of them huddled together in the shade on the wooden floor, with their blood-stained arms wrapped around one another, and tried to give each other some comfort and to stem their river of tears. It was in this position that their mother, then shortly afterwards their father, found them a little while later. Between them, they helped their sons to take off their bloodied clothes, which Rosamund later washed in the kitchen sink, and to go round into the back garden where they were able to wash their bodies with buckets of cold water.

'Adrian, it must have been *Mau Mau* who came back and committed this butchery, no?' queried Rosamund who was in a complete state of shock and deeply saddened that their three sons had had to see the murdered bodies of Shelia, Romulus and Remus.

'I can only guess that the four *Mau Mau* who managed to escape after the last attack were in the group who have come back today and, knowing the presence of the two Alsatians, they must have brought those two large chucks of raw meat, thrown them to the dogs so that they would bite into them, and then killed the dogs with their spears, for those gashes on each dog were undoubtedly made by spears.'

'However', Adrian continued, 'all those lacerations on Shelia's body were made by a *panga* or more than one *panga*, depending on how many of those savages attacked her.'

'But why kill Shelia?' Rosamund screamed. 'She was a Kikuyu and I thought that most of the *Mau Mau* rebels are members of the Kikuyu tribe.'

'That is correct', replied Adrian. 'They were probably aiming to kill all of us whites or at least those who would be at home and, in addition, had decided to murder Shelia as punishment because she had remained our maid-servant, which they considered as treachery to the *Mau Mau* cause. In any event, tragedy has struck again with this loss of Shelia and the two dogs, but thank goodness the murderous bastards left before young Adrian then Neil and Justin arrived home!'

Later in the early evening, after the police had been contacted and had taken away the three dead bodies and the three boys were trying to gain some composure and to calm down, albeit with enormous difficulty, upstairs in their bedrooms, Adrian said emphatically to Rosamund in the living room, 'There is no way we can carry on living in this god-forsaken place!'

'What on earth do you mean?' asked Rosamund in a very surprised manner. 'This is our home, Adrian!'

'Well, we have had two bad *Mau Mau* attacks and who knows, if a third attack ensues, the *Mau Mau* will come back in a much greater number and they have neutralised our guard dogs, putting us in a weaker position, so the risk is too great that they will slaughter us and the boys as well. No, I am not prepared to take such an enormous and life-threatening risk. Tomorrow morning, I will drive first thing into Nyeri and speak to Edwin Rockbeare, the sole estate agent there, and ask him if he thinks he might be able to find a buyer for this farm as quickly as possible, without actually saying anything to potential buyers about these attacks on this property. I will also seek some advice as to what region in Kenya we can move to where we should have some safety from the *Mau Mau* threat.'

'All right, you do what you feel is right in the circumstances. We all love living here, even I have become used to the country and farming life and the boys have become well settled and have made some good friends. But after the tragedies we have just experienced I agree with you that we must do what is necessary to avoid any further risks and to ensure the safety of our family.'

***

Death appeared to be stalking Neil, Justin and little Adrian like a dark shadow, gradually transforming their days into a long, black and cold African night.

The three brothers did everything they could, but with very little success, to push to the back of their minds the horrific images of the slaughters of Ray, Shelia, Romulus and Remus. And they cherished sharing all their free time together and would go out into the small paddock, teasing the chickens, the rabbits and the goats. Then they would go for a long walk in the countryside, picking up stones and seeing who could throw his stone the farthest and collecting sticks of various lengths and inventing all sorts of games involving the use of the sticks.

One Saturday afternoon, they walked along a familiar dirt track and were approaching on the edge of a field a tall, wide and majestic flame tree with large, showy tulip-shaped, flame-red flowers in big clusters, which they had admired many times. They saw in the distance a teenage black boy, of about thirteen years of age, who they recognised as Jomo, the elder of two sons of a manservant who worked on the nearest farm to theirs. Whilst they always wore tee-shirts and caps to protect them from the scorching sun when they went out, Jomo only wore frayed and dirty shorts which barely covered his knees and his bare back glistened with the pearls of sweat caused by the hot, bright sun glaring down.

As they walked nearer, the brothers could not help but notice the very large insect swarm hanging down from the lowest branch of the majestic flame tree and Neil exclaimed, 'It looks to me like a swarm of hornets and it was certainly not there the last time we walked this way a few weekends ago. That swarm is huge and from what I have heard at school, hornets have a very nasty and painful sting, so we had better keep our distance and skirt around the tree by walking into the field, then regain the track much further along.'

As they started moving into the field, they realised that Jomo had also spotted the enormous, somewhat oval-shaped swarm, and that he had seen them as well. Suddenly, Jomo picked up a long and thick piece of branch lying in the field not very far from the tree. And without any warning, whilst glancing over at them, as if he wanted to impress them with his courage and audacity, he walked over to the tree, placed himself with his feet spread apart just below the swarm and swung the heavy piece of wood clumsily up at the swarm, hitting it two or three times in a purported attempt to dislodge it and make it fall from the branch.

The three brothers watched, as if transfixed and immobilised by a morbid fascination, as hundreds of hornets flew out of the swarm, instantaneously and with incredible velocity, and stung Jomo on his face, and on his bear arms, chest, legs and feet. He started screaming in agony and running back up the track, but hundreds more hornets poured out of the swarm and Jomo's screams were stifled to choking moans then ceased altogether as the horde of crazily enraged hornets surrounded his face, filled his ears, nostrils and mouth and suffocated and stung him to death, forming another, round swarm so that the three brothers could no longer see Jomo's head. At first, Jomo started running

around in circles like a headless chicken on the edge of the field, then his pace slowed, then he stopped running, his whole body twitched, trembled and became distorted in ghastly convulsions, his legs collapsed and he fell dead, in what seemed like slow motion, in the brown, sun-burned grass of the field.

Neil, Justin and Adrian looked at this macabre scene in absolute horror, disbelief and shock, without moving for a few minutes. Then they huddled together and wept silently and inconsolably, their bodies trembling in a paroxysm of pain and sadness, and they finally asked each other between choked sobs why they had to be unwilling witnesses to so many brutal and horrific deaths.

After a while, in a difficult attempt to regain some composure and calm their emotions and nerves, they looked over to where Jomo lay and saw that all the hornets had left his body and had flown somewhere else. They approached a little, not daring to go too near the stricken body, and saw that Jomo's head and entire body were reddened and horribly bloated from the many hundreds of sting and his face was so puffed up and distorted that it had become unrecognisable. They walked home as if in a daze, holding hands, and told their parents what they had seen and where Jomo's body lay. Their father drove up the dirt track in the Land Rover, recuperated the body, and delivered it to the ramshackle and run-down home of Jomo's distressed family.

The nightmares that the three brothers had already been suffering at night became ever worse. Rosamund contacted the doctor and he prescribed some medication to help ease their anguish and disturbed mental state.

Chapter 3

Sadness Without Father in Mombasa
Abandonment by Mother

Adrian announced the developments to Rosamund several weeks after the tragic death of Jomo.

'Edwin Rockbeare, the estate agent, has put announcements in all the local newspapers and in the Nairobi press that our homestead is for sale, and he has proposed, after making investigations through some contacts, that the safest place for us to go to live is Mombasa, for it is not thought that the *Mau Mau* gangs will reach as far east as Mombasa, which has, in any case, a large police contingent and a strong British Army presence.'

'Where is Mombasa and what type of town is it?' Rosamund asked.

'For God's sake, woman, do not show your ignorance of the geography of Kenya yet again!' Adrian shouted in a booming and angry voice and with a murderous look in his cold blue eyes. 'You ought to know that Mombasa is situated southeast of Nairobi on the Indian Ocean coast and is the second largest city in Kenya. As we are both Roman Catholics, it will no doubt interest you to learn that Mombasa has the status of a city because of the Holy Ghost Cathedral, built in the nineteenth century. Mombasa is a very old city, having been founded many centuries ago, and having been colonised successively by the Portuguese, the Sultans of Oman, and then the British. We will be able to rent a house and small garden at a reasonable cost, through the suggestions of Edwin Rockbeare'.

'The boys will be able to go to a good British school. And the city has plenty of good commercial establishments and shops and a pleasant, well developed social life for British colonialists like us, including a club for white people, which I gather is almost of the same standard and reputation as the Muthaiga Club in Nairobi, and which will undoubtedly be very pleasant.'

'All right, have your own way, as you always do. I must leave you to deal with all the arrangements and let us know when we will be leaving here and going to start a new chapter of our semblance of family life in Mombasa.' Rosamund put a strong emphasis on the word "semblance", as if she anticipated, prophetically, a complete breakdown of their couple.

With a bitter and wretched look, Rosamund turned on her heels and went into the living room. She stared at the new French windows, which had replaced the old ones shattered in the *Mau Mau* attack. Then she opened the

drinks cabinet and poured herself a generous glass of Scotch whisky in order to calm her nerves, dampen her rising sense of anger and control her overwhelming frustration at being tied up in a relationship with a husband she was increasingly feeling distanced from and was detesting more and more.

**

Six weeks later, the family boarded a train at Nairobi Railway Station, which was to take them to Mombasa. Whilst their farm had not yet been sold, Edwin Rockbeare had received several enquiries from potential purchasers and was very confident that he would soon be able to tell Adrian that the contract for sale had been concluded and signed by him under the power of attorney which Adrian had given him, that the Land Rover had also been sold to the new farm owners, and the net proceeds of sale had been wired by telegram to Adrian for deposit on his bank account.

Edwin had also managed to find a small but adequate house and garden for them to rent in Mombasa, so everything appeared to be going well. However, in appearance only, as Rosamund had great apprehensions. For reasons which she could not yet fathom, but as if she was having a morbid premonition, she became aware of a state of increasing anguish and a foreboding of disaster in the pit of her stomach.

The three brothers were very pleased to be on the train and were enjoying a boisterous and excited time, running up and down the corridor, shouting to each other loudly and generally making fools and nuisances of themselves, to the deep despair of Rosamund, who tried unsuccessfully to calm them down and gain some semblance of control over their spirited enthusiasm. Their father, true to form, basically ignored them and let them continue with their games and disturbances to other passengers, to the enormous embarrassment and fury of their mother, who was becoming ever more tired of her husband's awful attitudes and behaviour.

The train stopped at the station of a small town, some miles to the east of Nairobi. As Neil, Justin and Adrian were standing in the corridor, and Justin had easily pulled down a window, being already as tall as his elder brother, they all looked out at another train, which was standing stationary right beside theirs on the adjacent tracks, with a very small distance between the two trains. They saw that the carriages of the other train were not like theirs, but were open at each end, with wide sliding doors. There were British soldiers in uniform and armed with rifles standing guard at each opening and there were many ragged and exhausted looking black men standing or sitting in each carriage. They noticed that the men standing all wore iron shackles around their ankles and chains, which were attached to shackles around their wrists, and they guessed that all the black men sitting in seats also wore shackles and chains.

As the three boys stared uncomprehendingly at the shackled black men not very far from them, two of the men looked at each other, then rattled their

chains in blind fury and shouted obscenities and horrible threats at the boys, saying that they were going to slit their throats and the throats of all white children with *pangas* as soon as they could be free of their shackles and chains.

The three brothers recoiled in astonishment and terror, ran into the carriage where their parents were sitting and, in a great state of shock and distress, tried to tell them what had happened. Rosamund took all three boys in her expansive arms and tried to comfort them, whilst Adrian went into the corridor, saw the black men who were still agitated and shouting curses and threats and then stared as two soldiers bundled the men into the interior of their carriage.

Adrian came back and explained to Rosamund and the boys, who were still very disturbed and upset, that the other train must have been a military convoy taking *Mau Mau* prisoners to some army destination for internment. He pleaded with the boys to try to forget what the black men had said, but, after the atrocities perpetrated by *Mau Mau* warriors at their farm and the horrendous wounds caused by their spears and *pangas,* which the boys could not get out of their heads, it was just too much to ask to forget this latest incident. And all three brothers were destined to remain deeply shocked, disturbed and scarred by the hatred and barbaric, blood-curdling threats of these *Mau Mau* for a very long time to come.

***

The family arrived safely with no further incident several hours later at the railway station of Mombasa, after a long, slow and tiring train journey of over three hundred miles from Nairobi. The driver of a *matatu*, an old ramshackle type of minibus with six passenger seats, drove them to their new home situated in the small residential area, entirely populated by white colonial families, on the north side of the city overlooking the wide Tudor Creek estuary. Adrian had been told by Edwin Rockbeare that the Tudor Creek estuary was fed by the waters of the Mtsapuni and Tsalu rivers flowing down from the county of Kilifi. And there was a second estuary, the Port Reitz estuary, to the south, fed by the Mwachi and Shimba rivers flowing from the county of Kwale, with Mombasa Island, containing the old part of the city, situated between the two estuaries. But most of the white settlers tended to buy or rent homes on the north side of the Tudor Creek estuary.

The items of furniture, which they had decided to keep upon leaving the farm, had already arrived and had been placed in the house by the local estate agent in Mombasa, who welcomed them to the house, showed them around the rooms and gave them the keys. The house was neither small nor particularly large, with a cosy kitchen, small dining room and reasonably sized living room. It was a bungalow, with four bedrooms, so Rosamund decided, gruntingly excluding her husband from any choice in the matter, that little Adrian would have the bedroom next to hers. Neil and Justin would share the third, generously proportioned bedroom, and Adrian senior would occupy the last bedroom beside that of Neil and Justin and the farthest one from her own

bedroom, as she insisted that they had separate bedrooms in this new home in light of the increasingly deteriorating state of their marriage.

They were all pleasantly surprised and enchanted to see that the property had a lovely garden, with a well-kept green lawn, a small vegetable patch and a stunning view over Tudor Creek estuary, with a crescent-shaped sandy beach on the shore of the estuary which could surely be reached on foot. The three brothers chased each other gleefully around the lawn, then whispered to one another that it seemed life was improving and that the family would spend many happy years and pleasant times here after all the horrors and anguishing experiences they had encountered before. They felt very confident that this lovely and relaxing environment would entice their parents into overcoming their problems and improving their relationship again.

***

Adrian started working as an engineer at a boat-building firm based in the port of Mombasa, named Kilindini Port, the largest and most ancient maritime port in East Africa, which saw the arrival in April 1498 of Vasco da Gama, the Portuguese explorer, who stayed six days in Mombasa on his route to the East Indies, and which served as the base for ships of the Royal Navy of Zanzibar during the First World War and for ships and submarines of the Eastern Fleet of the British Fleet Air Arm during the Second World War.

After a couple of months, Adrian started returning home later and later in the evenings after work and disappearing for hours during the days and for entire nights at the weekends. Whilst the worried boys did not dare ask him any questions as to his whereabouts, each time Rosamund emitted any queries when they were alone he just replied that he had become an active member of the Mombasa Club, founded by British settlers in 1896 for social gatherings after work and frequented mainly by civil servants, railway employees and other British personnel living in Mombasa.

Despite the heavy atmosphere in the house and the increasing animosity and tension between their parents, the three boys settled down into their new life as contentedly as possible. They discovered several small black snakes in the back garden and were told by their father that they were undoubtedly black mambas and should be avoided, as the black mamba was one of the most venomous and dangerous snakes in Kenya, whose bite could kill a human being, despite its small size and unassuming appearance. The boys totally ignored their father's admonishment and Neil and Justin took great glee and pleasure in taking from the broom cupboard the two long-handled brooms, which their mother had bought at a local market, and chasing each black mamba they came across and crushing its head with the larger and heavier end of the broom. Young Adrian watched these encounters with great joy and admiration for his elder brothers' bravery and became upset and could not understand the reason when they flatly refused his entreaties to be able to hold

one of the brooms and deliver his own crushing blow to the head of a slithering black mamba as it slid stealthily across the lawn!

The three brothers spent as much time as they could down at the crescent-shaped sandy beach on the shore of the estuary, where they became acquainted with and played with other boys of their own ages. They discovered that the beach was situated on the lower part of the estuary, not many miles from the open sea. And that it was widely known that different types of sharks, including the man-eating great white shark, swam up the estuary as far as their beach and often travelled much further up, for which reason the authorities had placed thick and strong fisherman's nets, stretched out in an arc from the shore to some fifty yards out from the shore of their beach and of all the other beaches along the estuary, securely attached to the sea-bed by heavy concrete slabs dropped on the bottom and held at the surface of the water by large, round orange buoys at regular intervals, so that no shark could approach the shore and no swimmer was allowed to swim out beyond the security net.

However, one day when the children were playing with a ball on the beach, a tall and well-built white man, probably one of the colonials who lived nearby, sprinted down the beach and into the warm water, dived headlong into the waves and started swimming out in a strong, confident and stylish crawl. The three brothers, who were all good and enthusiastic swimmers, stopped playing with the ball and watched the man swimming with a feeling of great admiration and anticipation that when they were older they would all be able to swim as strongly and fast as him. Such admiration changed to astonishment when they saw that the man, on reaching the security net, did not stop but clambered without hesitation over the top of the net and carried on swimming towards the centre of the estuary. They continued to watch him as they could still see each arm coming up out of the water as he powered on with his strong crawl, but after several more seconds they were appalled to see that the man started flailing his arms, causing a flurry of white foam on the surface of the water. Then he screamed out in a heart-rending and chilling scream, disappeared below the surface, resurfaced again, thrashing his arms and pounding them on the water whilst screaming again in total agony. He dipped again below the surface, then reappeared as if he were a rag doll being flung about by some powerful force, screamed out very loud in a high-pitched scream one more time, then disappeared entirely and the surface of the water became calm again as if he had never been there. The three brothers, the other boys and all the persons on the beach who had witnessed the gory scene stood in silence, looking out to where the swimmer had been. Although severely shaken and in a state of shock, Neil tried to regain some composure and whispered to Justin and Adrian, 'I suggest that we do not mention to our parents what we have just seen, for they might forbid us from coming to the beach again for fear that it is a dangerous place and that one day a shark might manage to come over the security net and attack us in the water.'

***

A few weeks after witnessing the tragedy when the shark took the arrogant and stupid swimmer in the estuary, the three brothers became perturbed when they realised that they had not seen their father for several days. Finally, at about the same time that they had decided to broach the subject of their father's absence with their mother, Rosamund agitatedly asked them to come and sit with her in the living room. She sat on an armchair and her three sons sat on the settee opposite her, with Neil and Justin placing themselves protectively on either side of little Adrian and each taking one of his small hands in theirs. Their mother looked very tired and even worn out with a haggard look, dark and swollen bags under her eyes as if she was lacking sleep and had been weeping, and a dreadfully mournful expression in her eyes.

'My darling boys, you have no doubt noticed that your father has not been here in the house for several days now. I have been having a difficult time trying to pluck up the courage to tell you what the situation is. I feel terribly sad for the three of you, as I know that you all love your father, even though he can sometimes appear very cold, aloof and distant and does not often express a fatherly love towards you. Rather than beating about the bush, I think it is better if I tell you simply and directly what has happened. Ten days ago, your father informed me that he had received a telegram from his mother, your grandmother, in England, explaining some unhappy events that had hit their family and that, under the circumstances, he had decided to return to England by aeroplane from Nairobi airport and would be away for a certain amount of time. Four days later, while you were all away down at the beach, he left by taxi with two suitcases saying he would take a train from Mombasa to Nairobi railway station, then another taxi out to Nairobi airport.'

A short, poignant silence fell upon the room. The three boys looked at one another in a bewildered, confused state, all of them shocked that their father had left without even taking the trouble to say goodbye to them. Then little Adrian burst into tears and threw himself into the comforting arms of big brother Neil, who stroked the top of his head, kissed his hair very tenderly then caressed his cheek with a hand. Neil looked over at Justin and saw that his magnificent blue eyes were also welling with tears. As Neil was now ten years old and was a very intelligent, quick-minded and perspicacious young fellow, to whom his two younger brothers looked up with admiration, he forced himself to choke back his own tears, put on a brave and proud front and looked hard at his mother, without saying a word.

'Is our father going to come back to us one day, Mother?' little Adrian finally dared to ask Rosamund whilst trying to quell the tremor in his voice.

'Yes, I am confident that he is going to be away only for a temporary period to sort out the affairs of the family in England and that, as soon as his presence there is no longer needed, he will fly back home to be with us here again.'

However, the total lack of conviction in the sound of her voice, the fact that she only said "confident" and not "certain" and the doubtful look in her sad eyes was not lost upon her sons, who were far from stupid.

Later on, when the three boys were alone in the bedroom of Neil and Justin, they huddled together, wept in each other's arms, then agreed in desperation that they would just hope against hope that their father would someday show up again and return to live with them as before. However, each one of them harboured a very painful and distraught feeling that he had been rejected and abandoned by his father, tossed and turned on his mattress each night and rocked himself fitfully from side to side for a long time before sliding eventually into a wretched and superficial sleep with no restorative quality, so that each one started the day each morning in an already exhausted and miserable condition.

A heavy pall and deep shroud of sadness fell upon the household and this unhappy state continued for what seemed like almost ten months. During this period, the boys would ask their mother several times each week whether she had received any news from their father and she would shake her head miserably and promise them that she would tell them as soon as she did receive a telegram from him. Although the three brothers tried to live a semblance of a normal life, they felt wretchedly unhappy, anguished and worried about the future. They experienced difficulty in concentrating on anything and they suffered the mockery and bullying of other boys they knew, who all lived in normal, happy families with both their mother and father and who constantly ribbed them, with that great cruelty of which children can be so capable, that they were so worthless and had such little merit in the eyes of their father that he no longer wished to live with them and had turned his back on them and abandoned them forever, so that his disappearance was entirely their own fault!

All of a sudden one day, Rosamund told the boys that she had to speak to them and once again they assembled in the living room. Rosamund sitting in her armchair and the three boys sitting side by side on the settee with a hopeful, optimistic and almost gleeful look in their three sets of blue eyes as they stared at her in great expectancy.

'My loves, I have to say at the outset that this is going to be extremely difficult and painful for me to have to explain to you the latest development, which is not at all what I had expected to happen!'

Rosamund broke down completely, hid her face in a handkerchief as she burst into tears and hunched her shoulders over as if they were burdened by the heaviest and saddest of news.

The boys looked at one another in a state of blind panic. In one fell swoop, their mother had in that short sentence completely dashed their hope that their father was returning home!

'Mother,' exclaimed Neil with a distraught and uncomprehending tone in his voice, 'please do not cry! Can you manage to tell us quickly and simply what has happened? If it is bad news and father is not coming back, we will have to do our best to cope with it. However, we will continue to be here with you and will have the happiness of growing up in the company of and with the help and support of our beloved mother – and all three of us will also give you

our support and comfort!' Neil attempted to adopt a manly, adult and comforting tone of voice.

'My darling boy!' Rosamund burst out, whilst blowing her nose and choking back her tears and attempting without success to straighten back her slouching shoulders.

'The beautiful words that you have just said make it even harder for me to tell you the dreadful situation that I find myself in after reading your father's recent telegram. However, I have the sad duty to tell you. Your father has sent me a telegram informing me that he has left me, will continue to live in England and is ordering me to buy three one-way aeroplane tickets from Nairobi to Heathrow airport near London in England for the three of you, as soon as I receive the necessary money for the tickets which he is cabling to me. And then to put you all on a flight to Heathrow, where he will meet you in order to take you to his new English home to live with him.'

Neil, Justin and Adrian were completely flabbergasted and lost for words on hearing this. They stared at one another, stared at their mother and looked again at each other with eyes wide open like those of scared barn owls.

Eventually, Neil was the first to regain his wits and he said to his mother and his brothers, 'We were hoping that our father would come back here and we could all live together as a real and happy family and have a good future together like all normal families. We feared that he had rejected and abandoned us. Now we learn that he has not turned his back on his sons and wants us to go to live with him in England, but he wants to wrench us away from our mother, whom we love so deeply! How is this possible? Does he hate you so much and want to punish you that much by causing a split between you and your sons and taking us away from you? Whilst it is good news that our father does want to be with us, it is dreadful and appalling to know that he does not want us to be with our mother! He is putting you and us in an absolutely impossible position! It is natural that children should be with their mother and it is abnormal and even evil to tear them away from her!'

'I agree,' added Justin. 'Surely you can send him back a telegram, refusing to accept his order and telling him that the three of us are staying here with you? Whilst we have missed father dreadfully, we have got somewhat used to his absence and it seems to me that if we are having to choose between our father and our mother, we would prefer to continue living here with you.'

'I am terribly sorry', Rosamund replied with a heavy heart and a deep sigh, 'but neither I nor you have a choice in the matter. Your father also wrote in his telegram that if I refuse to obey his order he will cut off completely all financial support for me and you that he has been providing. And he will send horrible reports about me to everyone in powerful positions in the white, colonialist settlements everywhere in Kenya, telling them that I am a slut, as bad as a prostitute, and ruining my reputation so that I would be cast out of and rejected by all levels of society here and would not even be able to get any employment, with the result that I would have no financial means with which to support you, bring you up and ensure a good future for you, so that you too

would be shunned and spurned and looked down on with contempt by the members of British society here. It breaks my heart to have to let you go, but please believe me that I must take your father's cruel blackmail very seriously and must obey him and send you over to him for your own good and best interests. For your father's family has wealth and good fortune in Wales and England and he will be able to provide for you, ensure that you receive a good education and open doors for you so that you will each succeed in the adult world. Please do not argue with me about the matter, for I must do what I know will be best for your future.'

So, the painful decision was taken and the matter settled with great reluctance. If the atmosphere in the house had been sad and heavy over the past months, it now became unbearably unhappy, stifling and oppressive. Not only Rosamund but all her three sons spent sleepless nights, filled with nightmares and painful anxieties, and tried to get through each day like zombies, with dead hearts and lifeless demeanours. Rosamund told them one day that she had received the money from their father for the aeroplane tickets, had bought the tickets for a flight in one week's time and had decided that, as they were Roman Catholics, she wanted them all to be baptised at the Holy Ghost Cathedral in Mombasa before they left Africa. She fixed the date with Reverend Father Eric Ryan, one of the priests at the cathedral, and the baptism of her three sons took place during a Mass at which Father Ryan officiated on January 14th 1955 on the last Sunday just three days before they were to fly from Nairobi to London. When the three baptismal certificates were given to her shortly after the Mass, Rosamund gave all three of them to Neil as the eldest son and told him to look after the certificates carefully and to give them to their father when they were reunited with him in England.

The four of them arrived three days later at Nairobi airport by taxi from Nairobi railway station after the long, tiring and miserable train journey from Mombasa. After Rosamund checked in their three suitcases, she hugged and kissed each son, promised them all that she would maintain contact with them by regular telegrams, and wished them a safe aeroplane journey, saying she would pray to God, asking him to protect and watch over them. She bade a wretched and tearful goodbye to them, hoping that she would see her sons again one day but feeling deep down very grave doubts that it would become possible and a mournful foreboding as to what the future held in store for all of them. With heavy hearts, the three brothers followed a stewardess onto the aeroplane and took the seats which she showed them. They were taking a BOAC flight on a De Havilland Comet 1 jet airliner, the prototype of which had first flown in 1952. This aircraft had a capacity of forty passengers, was the first jet airliner to be developed and had entered into service on May 2nd 1952 on the London to Johannesburg route.

Later on, once they were airborne and sitting in three adjacent seats down near the back of the aircraft, Neil, ten years old, and Justin, eight years old, started exchanging reactions about the disaster that had struck them and conjectures on the ensuing events and possible lifestyle that awaited them once

they were living with their father in as yet unknown surroundings somewhere in England. They said that they felt very sorry for and commiserated with their mother and agreed that she had had no choice and had been obliged to let them go and send them to live with their father.

Little Adrian, six years old, said nothing, having heard the exchanges between his brothers, but his emotions were boiling and swirling, causing abominable pains deep in his heart, his head and his entire being. He could not and would not agree that their mother had had no choice.

He kept asking himself repeatedly, 'Why does one abandon a child if one loves that child? Why did our Mother abandon her three sons if she loved us?'

Adrian had been told by Shelia that the Swahili word for faith was *imani*. He now said to himself that he had lost his *imani* in his mother as she had betrayed the trust he and his two brothers had placed in her. He felt with a conviction that caused great mental and emotional agony, turmoil and anguish that his mother had rejected and abandoned him and his beloved brothers to a dreadful and extremely unhappy fate because she did not love them.

Chapter 4
Shock Rejection and Abandonment by Father

Heathrow airport west of London, formerly a Royal Air Force military base during World War II, became London's new civil airport in January 1946. At the outset, there was one passenger terminal, which was quite primitive but comfortable, equipped with floral-patterned armchairs, settees and small tables containing vases of fresh flowers.

Upon leaving the aircraft after its arrival at the terminal, the three young brothers were escorted by a stewardess to collect their three suitcases then along a corridor to the small arrival area, where about twenty people were waiting for the passengers having arrived on that flight. When the stewardess asked if they saw their father amongst them, Neil pointed to a tall, slim man and they all walked over to him, the stewardess spoke to the man then said goodbye to them and left them with their father.

In actual fact, Neil had almost hesitated before pointing him out, as his father had grown a moustache and bushy beard and he appeared slimmer than before and had a very weary look, but Neil could not mistake that aristocratic, proud attitude and confident stance and those large, piercing blue eyes. Their father barely bent down to greet them and did not attempt to give each son a fatherly hug and kiss but shook hands with each one and merely ruffled his hair, saying hello in a somewhat stiff, formal and embarrassed manner, causing an awkward and cold atmosphere to prevail when he should surely have been overjoyed to be reunited with his sons again after such a long separation. His starchy, aloof and distant approach, as if he barely knew them, was not lost on each of his highly sensitive sons.

Standing beside their father was a young lady, obviously several years younger than him, almost as tall as him, who had a very pretty face, a square jaw with a pointed, determined-looking chin, thick and curly dark brown hair cropped just above her shoulders and lovely, large brown eyes with a friendly and warm expression. She smiled down at the boys and they were all enchanted by that lovely, radiant smile which warmed up the atmosphere like a ray of sunshine.

'Boys, this is your Aunt Anita,' their father said to them with a tone in his voice and an expression in his bright blue eyes which were not convincing to say the least.

As they were walking out of the terminal towards a small car park, with their father and Anita ahead of them, he carrying two of the suitcases and she

carrying the third one, Neil slowed his pace, pulling an arm of Justin and of young Adrian so that they slowed down as well on either side of him. Then he whispered to them in a conspiratorial and all-knowing tone of voice, 'That lady is not our aunt at all!'

Both Justin and Adrian looked up at him with a query in their eyes, not understanding on what basis he could make such an emphatic statement.

'You have both got to be more observant!' Neil said, in a somewhat pedantic manner, as if he took himself for a precocious and wise teacher. 'Did you not see her diamond ring on the same finger on the left hand as our mother wears her diamond engagement ring and her gold wedding ring? Our mother told me once that the diamond ring was an engagement ring, meaning that the man who gives it to a woman has taken a firm engagement to marry her as soon as possible, and that when they marry he gives her the gold wedding ring.'

'Does that mean that our father has made an engagement towards this young woman to marry her sometime in the near future and that he will never go back to our mother?' asked Justin with a sad and panicky tone in his voice.

'I do not know, but we must keep our eyes and ears open and we will hopefully find out soon what is going on and what our father's intentions are,' Neil retorted whilst lowering his voice even below a whisper as their father turned round to see how far behind the three boys were lagging.

When they reached the airport car park, Adrian senior and Anita stopped beside a magnificent-looking, long, low-slung, sporty black car with a reasonably large boot, an elongated, sleek and sloping bonnet, and a silver metal grill at the front which was narrow at the top and flared out at the bottom, giving the car a very racy, sporty and distinctive look. The three boys dropped their jaws in amazement and wonder at the beautiful sight of this vehicle, the likes of which they had never seen before in Kenya.

Adrian smiled laconically and in a superior manner at their reaction, turned to them and said very proudly, not without a dash of outright haughty snobbishness in his tone, 'This exceptional car is an Allard PI Sports, manufactured by the Allard Motor Company in south-west London. The company was founded by Mister Sydney Allard in 1945 and only makes each car after receiving a firm order and the down payment of a first deposit of the purchase price from its future owner. Only a few hundred of the Allard PI Sports model have been sold and are on the roads in Britain, being very expensive and reserved mainly to members of the elite and select aristocratic circle in society!'

His three sons looked at him with baffled looks on their faces, for none of them, not even perspicacious and knowledgeable Neil, had ever heard of such a thing as an "elite and select aristocratic circle in society". However, they felt obliged from their father's words to conclude that he was a member of such a circle, whatever it was, that he was a rich man and that he was one of the few hundred proud owners who could afford to buy an Allard PI Sports model. After their father placed their three suitcases in the boot, they sat in the back of the car, Anita took the front passenger seat, and their father drove the car out of

the airport car park and along various roads for what seemed to be a fairly long time.

They arrived at the front entrance of a medium-sized building dating from the Victorian era. Adrian senior told his sons that they were going to stay for a short time at this hotel, called The Thames Hotel, a warm and convivial thirty-bedroomed hotel situated right on the River Thames in the town of Maidenhead, which was in the County of Surrey. Once inside the building, the boys discovered an interior with old-world charm and, after their suitcases had been taken upstairs by a porter, they were shown to two bedrooms side by side, one quite large, which was attributed to Neil, and the other even larger containing two single beds for Justin and young Adrian.

When they discovered a very spacious double bedroom, which was shared by their father and Anita on the same floor but a little further down the corridor from their bedrooms, they scampered back to Neil's bedroom, jumped onto his bed in great excitement and agreed among themselves in hushed voices and suppressed giggles that the fact that their father was sleeping in the same bed as Anita was the concrete proof that, as Neil had clearly and wisely observed earlier at the airport, this woman was most certainly not their aunt!

***

It was now early February 1955 and the three brothers had been in England for just over two weeks. One day, they were standing with Anita on the wide terrace of the hotel, all of them wearing warm clothes and thick winter coats which Anita had bought for them as the weather was very cold and the sky was charged with heavy, black and menacing clouds. They were enjoying looking at the boats going up and down the River Thames and anchored on both shores of the river and were admiring a bridge straddling the river, which had ten large arches and must have been built many years earlier in Victorian times to allow horses and carriages, as well as pedestrians, to cross over the river, and which now bore cars, lorries, trolleybuses, bicycles and pedestrians.

All of a sudden, little Adrian exclaimed in surprise that a very cold and wet fluff of white cotton wool had settled on his right cheek and he wondered where it had come from. As Anita, Neil and Justin looked at him, a blanket of such cold, wet and white cotton wool descended upon them from above, thinly and slowly at first then thickly and rapidly, then in droves after a few minutes. The boys were startled, could not understand what was happening and rushed inside to avoid their hair, faces and coats becoming completely covered in this cold, wet, white substance which was entirely unknown to them.

Once inside and seeing their bewildered expressions, Anita laughed out loud, brushed the remaining white fluffs from their hair and coats and told them, in her soft, pleasant voice that they were all beginning already to appreciate, 'That cold cotton wool is called "snow" and comes down from the clouds in winter when the weather becomes very cold and the cloud mass develops. I can understand that you have never seen it before, as you lived in

45

regions in Kenya, from what your father has told me, where the weather is generally warm and sunny and even during the rainy season the temperature never drops low enough to produce snow, except up at the top of Mount Kenya. Let us go out into the garden of the hotel and I will show you how to make balls of snow with your hands for snowball fights and to build snow men!'

During the following two days the boys hardly saw their father, who was absent for long hours and left them in the company of Anita. On the third day, Anita suggested to the boys to go for a trolleybus ride, which they accepted with great alacrity and glee, as they had never done that before. When they boarded the trolleybus at the stop nearest to the hotel, there were only a few white passengers and the boys were fascinated to see the new passengers, all of them white-skinned, who clambered onto the vehicle at each stop and they counted them, like they had counted their goats back in Kenya, as they chattered contentedly to each other, almost forgetting the presence of Anita in their excitement. Then, at one stop, a tall man with black skin boarded the trolleybus, causing the brothers to stop chattering and to look at one another in astonishment with gaping mouths.

Little Adrian pointed rudely at the black man and blurted out loudly and in a screeching, emotional voice and angry tone, 'What on earth is that man doing here? He is a black man, so he should be in the country from which we have just come! A black man should be in Africa, not here in England!'

A heavy silence fell over the vehicle, some of the white passengers just remained still but hung their heads down and others looked sheepishly over at the black man. At first, he seemed to buckle over somewhat, as if having just been hit in the solar plexus, then his expression changed into a harsh grimace and without saying a word he started walking angrily over to Adrian and raised his right arm and opened his hand as if preparing to give Adrian a hard slap on the cheek.

Anita intervened, placing herself between the man and Adrian, and she explained to the man in as soft and conciliatory a voice as she could that the three young boys were born in Kenya, had always lived there, so had obviously been used to seeing black people there, and had only just arrived in England a few weeks earlier, where they had only seen white people until this day, so must have associated black people with African countries and been very surprised to see a black man here in England.

She told the man that Adrian was only a six-year-old little boy and could not possibly have had any racist intent in his unfortunate remark and she asked the man to calm down and to excuse Adrian for his hurtful but innocent reaction. She told Adrian to apologise to the black man and said that Adrian would no doubt see other black people in this area and that it was entirely normal. So, Adrian very sheepishly and ashamedly said to the man that he was very sorry and the man then smiled to him and patted him on the head and reassured him that there was no harm done.

***

A few days later, after the boys had not seen their father for two days, he reappeared during the morning and went for a walk with them after lunch in the streets of Maidenhead and in a nearby park, whereas Anita excused herself, saying that she had a bad headache and would remain in her bedroom to rest. When they returned to the hotel later in the afternoon, Adrian told the boys to take their baths and said that they would all go down at six-thirty in the early evening to the hotel restaurant for supper. When the boys left their bedrooms five minutes before the appointed time, they walked along the corridor towards the bedroom of Anita and their father, intending to knock on the door and ask whether they were ready to go downstairs all together. As they approached the door, they were shocked to hear very clearly the raised and agitated voice of Anita who was screaming angrily at their father.

'What is the matter with you, Adrian? I just do not understand your behaviour. Over the past two months, you have disappeared several times during the day and, what is far worse, during the night as well! Where have you been and what have you been doing and with whom? I have smelt the perfume of a woman on you when you have returned here on two or three occasions. As you well know, I am expecting your baby, which my gynaecologist has told me should arrive sometime in June, so I am five months pregnant. It seems evident to me that you have been sleeping with another woman or perhaps several other women. How can you hurt me in this way after having told me so many times that you love me and want to envisage your future with me! I cannot stand your behaviour anymore and I am not staying here any longer. I am leaving you, Adrian, I will pack my bags and leave by taxi in the coming half-hour, and it is up to you to decide what to explain to your sons. They are your responsibility; I hardly know them, have nothing to do with them and have no responsibility at all for their well-being, as that is your job!'

The boys waited just outside the door, heard their father weakly plead with Anita and ask her to stay, and heard Anita shout back that she did not trust him anymore and was definitely going to leave within the coming half-hour. When total silence followed this tirade, except for the soft sobbing of Anita as she put her clothes into her suitcase, the three boys tip-toed back to Neil's bedroom, shut the door and huddled together on his bed. Crying in despair and trembling, they cursed their father for his self-centred and egotistical attitudes and comportment, causing this disaster by driving Anita away, just when all three of them were beginning to get used to her, appreciate her lovely and gentle manner and her pleasant behaviour towards them and were beginning to love her as a substitute mother.

They now felt that their father was destroying them emotionally and ruining their chances of happiness and they started to ask one another why he had made their mother send them from Kenya to England. For from the first day of their arrival in this new environment their father had not shown any love, affection or tenderness towards them but had been, on the contrary, cold, aloof and distant.

They stayed shut up in Neil's bedroom for roughly another hour, then a hotel employee knocked at the door and brought in two trolleys with food and drink, saying that their father was indisposed and otherwise occupied and had ordered some supper to be brought up to them. The three boys were in such a state of distress and sadness at the turn of events that they hardly ate anything and they were especially saddened and afflicted by the fact that Anita had left the hotel without coming to see them and say goodbye to them.

Another incident of violent gravity occurred four days later. Adrian told his sons that there was a small cinema in the town of Maidenhead and he was taking them to see the matinee presentation that afternoon of a new film called "Simba" which he knew would be of great interest to them.

Little Adrian stirred in his seat and exclaimed, '*Simba* is the Swahili word for lion. Are you taking us to see a film about lions in Africa?'

'Yes, in a manner of speaking,' his father replied, 'but I will not disclose any more details about the film and you will see for themselves.'

The three brothers certainly saw for themselves as soon as the film started. The first frame showed the gory and horrific scene of a white man lying stark naked on his back, with his body lacerated from head to feet with deep and bloody gashes undoubtedly caused by a *panga*. He was still alive and barely breathing whilst grimacing in dreadful pain and in the next frame a black man arrived on foot, saw the agonising white man, looked him in the eyes, saw his pathetic look pleading for mercy and help, smiled cruelly, swung a *panga* with great force and struck the man across the left part of his chest in the region of the heart. Then spat in the dying man's face and walked away with a carnivorous and hateful expression in his cold eyes and a triumphant and conquering look on his face.

Neil, Justin and Adrian all gasped in shocked astonishment, turned to one another and clasped each other's hands in search of mutual moral support. They all started to feel sick as the film continued to show graphic and very violent attacks by groups of black men, no doubt *Mau Mau* members, on white settler families and on some of their black servants in various parts of Kenya, in particular in the countryside in the overall Nyeri farming community.

After several scenes portraying dreadful and bloody attacks by *Mau Mau* warriors on both white settlers and black servants of white families, little Adrian began to cry and, when he could not stomach any more of the appalling violence being shown on the screen, he screamed out loud, 'Oh my God! Oh my God! I must get out of here! I cannot breathe. Let me get out of here!'

Both Neil and Justin rose out of their seats, turned to their father and told him that they were going back to the hotel with Adrian and the three brothers rushed out of the cinema and ran together back to the hotel and locked themselves in Neil's room in a state of utter shock, despair and despondency. Some two hours later, when the three brothers were all still lying stretched out on Neil's bed with red eyes from weeping and feeling very disgusted, depressed and emotionally exhausted, the door of the bedroom opened.

Their father walked in, shut the door noisily and said to them in a severe, critical and haughtily disapproving way, 'Why on earth did you all rush out of the cinema like that? The film was a portrayal of the life and struggles against the British colonial rule of Jomo Kenyatta, who founded the *Mau Mau* resistance movement and was given the etiquette "Simba" by those who consider that he is a lion, a great leader, and will succeed in overthrowing the British rule and obtaining an independent status for Kenya. As this film has only recently been made and the conflict between the *Mau Mau* and the British authorities in Kenya is still ongoing and part of current affairs, I thought that it would be interesting and instructive for you to take the opportunity of seeing the film as it is now showing in the Maidenhead cinema.'

'Father,' retorted Neil, sitting up on his bed and facing his father bravely with an angry and bitter sound in his voice, 'we experienced your lack of sensitivity or love towards our mother on many occasions back in Kenya. We have now seen your nastiness and lack of sensitivity in the bad way you have treated Anita, and we have just now had to put up again with an example of your lack of sensitivity towards your own sons! How could you expose us to the horrible experience of seeing murderous and brutal attacks by *Mau Mau* on other people in that awful film after what we went through and witnessed at first hand when we saw the blood-curdling cruelty and barbarous attitudes and behaviour of the *Mau Mau* when we lived in Kenya?! We heard Anita ask you what is the matter with you. It is now our turn to ask you what is the matter with you and what is it in your character and personality that makes you treat others with such lack of love and so much insensitivity and disdain?'

Adrian turned red in the face, seemingly affected by what his eldest son had just said, then he regained control, his sense of pride and superiority and his starchy education as a member of the British aristocracy and upper class appeared to take over, forbidding him from showing much emotional reaction to situations.

He looked at Neil and his other two sons with contempt, emitting a loud 'Humph!' Whilst tossing his head arrogantly upwards, he then turned on his heels and left the room, banging the door loudly with brutal strength.

***

Over the coming few weeks, the boys were left much to their own devices and had to make their own entertainment and find various distractions inside the hotel and in the surrounding garden, whenever the changeable and unreliable English weather would allow, in distinctive contrast to the clear, azure blue sky and warm, sunny scene on a daily basis back in Kenya.

However, after lunch with their father one day, when he seemed to be in a more cheerful and even agreeable mood, he asked them to assemble in the living room of the hotel, saying that he had a surprise for them. When they arrived in the room, feeling intrigued and wondering what this surprise could be, their father excused himself for a few minutes and disappeared from the

room. He came back a few minutes later, held the door open, stood aside and beamed with content when Anita walked into the room, looking somewhat apprehensive about the reception that the boys would give her. She need not have worried, for, after a few seconds of looking at each other, looking up queerly at their father, then staring at Anita in disbelief, then convincing themselves that this was not a vision but Anita in the flesh, all three brothers rushed forward with open arms, crying out in unison 'You have come back! You have come back!' and threw their arms around Anita, or as far as they could, as her stomach had expanded some more since her disappearance. Anita was almost thrown backwards by their enthusiastic charge and nearly fell over but managed to maintain her balance and she enveloped the three boys in her arms as best she could whilst bursting into joyous tears at this happy, enthusiastic and warm welcome.

After smiling contentedly and giving the boys and Anita a couple of minutes to embrace, kiss and talk excitedly among themselves, Adrian made a croaking sound, as if clearing his throat, and clapped his hands together like a headmaster at a school calling the pupils to attention at an assembly.

When he had gained their attention, he said with a detectable note of pride and satisfaction in his voice, 'Boys, when Anita left she told me she would keep in casual contact by telephone. We have met up a few times, discussed a number of important issues, worked through a few problems and differences and we have now decided that we will give our relationship another try and live together again, which I hope is good news for you as well, as Anita will be giving birth in June to your half-brother or half-sister. We do not know yet whether the baby is a boy or a girl, so we will all have to be patient until the time of the birth to discover its sex'.

'I have some more happy news for you. I have managed to take out a rental lease on a lovely, individual furnished house with a spacious garden in a residential quarter of the town of Caterham, which is not all that far from here. As we are now in mid-March, and the house is empty after the departure of the last tenants, I have been able to arrange with the house owner, through the estate agent, that we will move into the house and take possession on April 1st 1955!'

Neil whooped with glee, Justin and little Adrian jumped up and down with joy then threw themselves into their father's arms, ran back to Anita and swarmed her with kisses on both cheeks as she bent down, then Adrian declared that they were all going out for supper at a restaurant in Maidenhead to celebrate this happy turn of events. On leaving the hotel to climb into the majestic Allard car, the three brothers hugged each other and Neil declared in a hushed voice that, after all the sad, tragic occurrences, traumas and unhappiness that they had endured over the past years, he was sure they had a very happy future ahead of them on the horizon, with the upcoming move into the house, followed by the arrival in about three months of their baby half-brother or half-sister.

The house, which had a brick exterior painted white, was called "Paddock Gates" and was situated on a pleasant residential street lined by several large, very comfortable individual houses in an affluent suburb of the enchanting town of Caterham. It had a huge kitchen, separate dining room, a lovely, large sitting room and five bedrooms. As Adrian and Anita took the largest bedroom and reserved the one next to it for the soon-to-arrive baby, Neil, Justin and young Adrian were delighted to be attributed a bedroom each, a luxurious promotion. The whole house was very tastefully and comfortably furnished and the three boys loved especially to bounce up and down on the two large sofas and the three armchairs in the living room and bury themselves in the warm and absorbing comfort of the outsize cushions.

They were equally enchanted by the very spacious garden, which was almost an acre in size. There was a large and wide stone terrace leading from the French-windows of the living room to an enormous green grass lawn, bordered on two sides by flower beds, one of which was consecrated to several varieties of roses, which would produce a wonderful array of colours in the coming summer months. Along one side of the house, leading from the gravel driveway at the front, was a long path made of flagstones in a crazy-paving pattern and the three boys soon got used to playing hopscotch and various other imaginative games up and down the flagstones. The other element which the boys and Anita came to appreciate very rapidly was the delightful wooden summer house situated on the edge of the lawn lower down the garden. It contained several deckchairs and they soon got into the habit of bringing them out and sitting on them as soon as any welcome rays of warm sunshine appeared in the spring sky.

They all settled into what promised to be a pleasant, slow, relaxing lifestyle in this lovely house with its large, enchanting and welcoming garden and the first three weeks were delightful. As they neared the end of April and Anita's expectant stomach became larger and rounder, whenever they were all seated in the living room Anita would settle in the middle of the largest settee, the three brothers would sit on either side of her or on the floor at her feet and in turn they would stroke and caress her expanding tummy and would laugh gleefully each time any of them felt the baby moving and turning.

One afternoon at teatime, whilst Anita was chatting to the boys and telling them stories, she placed her empty tea-cup and saucer on the top of the bump of her stomach and started whirling her hands in circles by way of illustration of a scene in a story. All of a sudden, her baby gave an energetic kick and knocked the teacup and saucer, which crashed to the floor and the cup broke into several pieces. The three boys laughed loudly and excitedly, clapping their hands in glee at this amusing scene. Anita also laughed happily and said that it was fortunate that she had drunk her tea and the cup was empty when baby decided to stretch his or her legs!

However, this idyllic setting and new, happy way of life soon became disturbed and Neil, Justin and Adrian started to feel perturbed and nervous, for their father rapidly became grumpy, discontented and unpleasant and he started bickering and quarrelling with Anita over all kinds of subjects, some of them somewhat petty and lacking in importance, giving the boys the impression that he deliberately provoked such arguments and verbal fights with Anita as if he were seeking to drive a wedge between them.

Further, he started disappearing for two or three days and nights at a time, as he had done earlier when they were in Maidenhead. Each time he returned, he did not give any explanation as to the reasons for his absences and the already strained atmosphere in the house became more and more heavy, tense and unpleasant. Poor Anita lost her happy demeanour and joyful smiles and laughs, became withdrawn, sullen and pensive, starting to suffer great fatigue from anxious, sleepless and restless nights when Adrian was away somewhere, no doubt, she thought, in the arms of a woman. And over the coming days she spent less time playing with, talking to and entertaining the boys, who became confused, deeply saddened and mentally and emotionally destabilised.

By mid-May, Adrian's absences stretched to four days and nights at a time and the situation became intolerable for Anita. She confronted Adrian and was severely shocked when he adamantly refused to apologise for his behaviour, showing no remorse whatsoever, and did not make any promises to reform and stay at home and stop disappearing for periods of days and nights. She concluded with a chilling and depressing finality that he did not love her after all and did not have any desire or intention to make any engagement or commitment towards her and her unborn baby.

When he concurred silently with her, merely with a hard, cold look in his steely blue eyes, that they did not have any future together, she rounded on him in fury and bitter anguish and exclaimed, 'You are nothing but a selfish, cold-hearted bastard. When I first met you, about eighteen months ago, you were a patient ill in a London hospital and I was a very young nurse. When I was assigned to take care of you, on the orders of the hospital doctor, you set about to seduce me and I was taken in by your good looks, your Welsh charm and that very special combination of black hair and bright blue eyes, as well as your impressive natural class and aristocratic bearing. What a damned and naive fool I have been!'

'After I became pregnant, your interest in me started to wane and since I naturally became less interested in having sex with you due to my condition, you have treated me with utter contempt, have pursued other women with your seductive abilities and insatiable appetite, have shown that you have no real love for me or for your child that I am carrying, and have no sense of gentlemanly behaviour or of living up to your responsibilities.'

'As I told you the last time that I left you, your boys are your sons, they are not mine, and it is your responsibility, not mine, to take care of their well-being and their future happiness. I am going to leave but this is the last time that I leave you, there is no future in our relationship, and I will never come back to

you. You are now thirty-seven years old, while I celebrated my twenty-first birthday with you this past mid-February, in between your disappearances and your reappearances. With your pathetic and unacceptable attitudes, you already appear so much older, but I am still very young and I have a whole life to live and much to achieve in the future, both for myself and for my child. I am going back to my mother, I will give birth to the baby in a few weeks' time, and I will let you know through a competent solicitor in due course to which bank account you must pay a certain amount of money for me and for the maintenance of our child. I will say goodbye to the boys and I do not want you to be around when I do!'

Anita asked the boys to come to the living room and their last farewells were excruciatingly tearful and heart breaking. She asked them to forgive her for going away permanently but explained that their father was rendering her life impossible through his behaviour; she saw that he did not love her and she could have no future with him. She said she hoped that they could continue living with their father in this lovely house and she promised that she would let them have news through their father in the months to come as to how the birth went and how she and their half-brother or half-sister were faring. She added just before saying a tearful final goodbye that she hoped very much to be able to come back to this house that she had liked so much to present the baby to them and their father in roughly six months after the birth.

***

After the departure of Anita, which was final and definitive this time, life became empty, dull and bereft of hope, purpose or any future happiness for the three brothers, all of whom fell into deep depressions caused by a grave and desperate sense of having lost their natural mother then a second, potentially adoptive mother and of being caught in a dreadful and miserable prison with this father who only thought of his own immediate pleasures and enjoyment and had no feelings of love or concern for or responsibility towards other people. Firstly their mother Rosamund who he had left back in Kenya, secondly Anita, who was adorable but had been treated so badly and despicably by him, thirdly Anita's unborn baby who was after all his own child as well, and fourthly themselves, his own sons, who had difficulty in recognising themselves as such, due to his aloof and cold attitudes towards them and his lack of love and warmth in his dealings with them.

Instead of showing love, personal care and concern for his three sons and attempting to help them to overcome their depressed state by spending more time with them, sharing games and activities with them and demonstrating a certain degree of fatherly love and affection towards them, Adrian compounded and aggravated the human and emotional distance between him and the boys by engaging the services of a live-in governess who slept in the room originally reserved for Anita's baby and whose mandate was to cater for all the usual material needs of his sons on a daily basis.

This manoeuvre enabled Adrian, who did not have a professional job and seemed to be living on income from the family fortune, to spend many hours of each day away from the house and many evenings and nights in the company and open arms of attractive women that he managed to meet in various ways and to seduce with the ability and ease of which he continued to remain very confident. He also brought women home to his bedroom on several occasions. One night little Adrian had to get out of bed in the middle of the night and go to the bathroom to release an urgent bodily need. As he approached the bathroom door he heard muffled moans, groans and sighs as well as noises of squeaky bed springs coming from his father's bedroom and it was immediately obvious that he and a female companion were also releasing their own urgent bodily needs. Young Adrian rushed into the bathroom, locked the door and slumped miserably down on the floor between the sink and the toilet and wept bitterly with a heaving chest for a long moment, as the image of his father in bed with some strange woman threw his mind violently back to all those wretched nights back in Kenya when he had had to endure the appalling and heart-breaking scenes of his mother having sex with different strange men in the family home.

***

One day, near the end of June 1955, at the time when Neil, Justin and Adrian had been surmising to one another that Anita had given birth to her baby and wondering whether they had a half-brother or a half-sister, their father said that he wanted to speak with them in the living room. The boys felt sure that he was going to announce to them that the baby had arrived and that Anita was going to visit them here at the house with the baby so that they could meet their half-brother or half-sister, so they all ambled into the living room with a barely disguised sense of joyous anticipation.

When their father spoke in his usual coldly detached, pedantic and superior manner, he did not say a word about Anita or the baby but announced simply to them that he was taking them up to the village of Dickleborough in the County of Norfolk, some way north of London, to spend a summer holiday at the home of his eldest sister, their Aunt Clotilda, as he had already mentioned to them some while earlier that he would do. He reminded them that he had already told them that he was the youngest of four children and had three elder sisters, their Aunts Clotilda, Patricia and Celestina in that descending order.

On July 1st 1955, after the governess had packed a suitcase for each of the three brothers and had said goodbye to them and their father after breakfast, as she was told by him to stay in the house and ensure that all remained in good safe condition while they were away, Adrian drove them in the beloved Allard during a journey lasting several hours until they arrived a little before supper time in the small Norfolk village called Dickleborough and drove into the driveway of a somewhat large, old and rather ramshackled house. They were greeted by a lady who appeared several years older than their father, was somewhat shorter than him, possessed a lean face and body, with icy blue eyes

and a nose very similar to those of their father, and a somewhat brusque, business-like and no nonsense manner. At first, the three brothers were slightly daunted and frightened by Aunt Clotilda, but they warmed to her when she hugged each one and gave each one a kiss on both cheeks, welcomed them to her humble home and then introduced them to her only son, their Cousin James, who was one year older than Neil but much taller and larger, with a strange look in his eyes and a very odd, disarticulated way of moving his head and his limbs. Upon seeing the brothers' disconcerted and alarmed reaction to James, Aunt Clotilda calmed them down and explained that James had been totally normal at birth, just like each of them, but had contracted a dreadful illness called meningitis when he was three, which had been hard and long to treat and had left poor James with irreversible lesions and damage in his brain and had affected his bodily functions and movements. During the evening, the boys also made the acquaintance of their Uncle Henry, the husband of Aunt Clotilda, when he returned home from work. He appeared to be a hard, unsmiling, unfeeling and unpleasant character, who hardly said a word to the boys or their father, and all three brothers found him obnoxious and took an instant dislike to him. The house possessed four spacious bedrooms, the largest being occupied by Uncle Henry and Aunt Clotilda and the one next door being that of James, whom Aunt Clotilda had to visit two or three times each night when he came agitated, fretful and upset. Aunt Clotilda gave the third bedroom to the three brothers, as it had a large double bed, in which she suggested Justin and Adrian could sleep, and she had put a camp bed next to it, which she attributed to Neil as the eldest boy. She showed their father to the fourth bedroom, which had a pleasant view over the garden and which he knew well, as he had slept there before on visits to see his beloved and cherished eldest sister.

After a leisurely start to the next morning, with a lie-in followed by a copious cooked breakfast prepared and served by Aunt Clotilda, the three boys felt charged up, full of energy and ready for a day packed with new adventures. Their father suggested that they walked around the village, saying he would show them some of the spots that he knew well in this community with its old-world charm and that after a late lunch he would take them in the Allard to meet his mother, their paternal grandmother, and then their Aunt Patricia, who both lived in the vicinity.

When they set off in the Allard, Adrian drove up the main street of the village at a respectably slow speed and, as they were approaching the outskirts, he turned left and accelerated like a formula one racing driver along a straight road for half a mile, causing the boys to jump with joy on their seats. When the road turned to the right in a sharp but long bend, he seemed to accelerate some more, screeched the tires as the car roared through the bend, making all his sons scream in delight, then a mere fifty yards out of the bend he braked suddenly and veered to the left, roaring the engine again as the car entered a gravel driveway, swerved on the gravel several times as he accelerated again and finally braked harshly and turned off the engine. Neil, Justin and little

Adrian tumbled out of the car, somewhat shaken with their heads spinning but totally delighted and laughing loudly at the prowess of their father and the powerful performance of this exceptional car that they so loved.

The boys looked at the long, cob, whitewashed front wall of the three-hundred-year-old cottage, with its three windows and black front door, and when they looked up they admired the expanse of thick thatch on the roof and the weathervane in the shape of a cockerel.

Nobody came to open the unlocked front door, but as Adrian came through it, followed by the three boys, they heard a deep and gruff female voice say, 'I know that it is you, Adrian, for you always make that ridiculous and noisy performance of swerving into my driveway and screeching your tires every time that you come here in that fancy sports car of yours.'

As they entered the beautifully furnished and comfortable living room, the boys saw a somewhat large, plump and imperious-looking elderly lady, dressed in black, sitting on a large arm-chair to one side of an open hearth, in which a log fire was merrily crackling and giving off a welcome warmth and orange and yellow tongues of flame, despite it being early July.

When they lived in Kenya, the boys had seen black and white photographs of Queen Victoria in her later life and the vision of this lady before them threw them back to the images of the queen who was very fat and was dressed in black and had a severe, haughty, regal expression. Adrian greeted his mother with a somewhat cold and distant attitude, an offhand manner, and a fleeting peck on the cheek devoid of filial affection. He then introduced the boys to their grandmother and she spoke to them for a few seconds in her deep and gruff tone of voice and intimidated them with her haughty, aloof and aristocratic manner and her stony-faced, severe facial expression, bereft of any warmth or of any smile in their direction.

They sat down timidly on the large sofa and merely listened while their father exchanged some superficial words with his mother, who may not have been their grandmother at all as far as they were concerned, as she did not show any interest in them and did not encourage them to speak, as if practising the adage from the Victorian era "small children should be seen and not heard". The boys all stood up instantaneously and skipped out of the house with great relief, with a mere movement of a hand and a quick 'Goodbye Grandmother!' in her direction, as soon as their father told them that it was time to leave.

When they were back in the car, Adrian drove silently and at a disappointingly sedate pace, with a sombre facial expression, did not mention their grandmother at all, giving the boys the distinct impression that he was not on very good terms with his mother. He merely told them after a mile or so that they were approaching the home of their Aunt Patricia. They arrived in front of a light pink bungalow. Adrian rang the doorbell and a blue-eyed, tall, very slim lady, a few years older than her brother but appearing even older, opened the door, greeted him in a truly sisterly fashion, showing her pleasure at seeing him, and kissed each of the boys on the cheek in a somewhat awkward and timid way but with a genuine warmth, which struck them positively in contrast

with their grandmother who had not seemed to want to lower herself to hugging, kissing or touching them in any way as if they were poor urchins plagued by leprosy.

In the living room, Aunt Patricia offered Adrian a cup of tea and gave a fruit juice and some ginger biscuits to each of her nephews, an act of kindness and generosity which impressed them very much as their miserly and dragon-like grandmother had not even offered them a glass of water!

Whilst they sat drinking and eating, the boys were enchanted by Aunt Patricia's pair of small, white Sealyham dogs, who brushed up against their legs, lay on their backs asking to be caressed and showed all manner of interest in the boys and love and affection for them. After they were refreshed, Aunt Patricia led them into the kitchen and they all melted with gleeful emotion when they saw the four Sealyham puppies. She told them that her now elderly male and female dogs had had several litters over the years, this was the most recent one and she would be giving the puppies away to animal lovers in the district. The boys excitedly pleaded with their father to let them have one of the puppies, saying forcefully that they definitely came into the definition of animal lovers and they promised to look after the puppy with great care back at the lovely house and garden in Caterham. He refused flatly and sternly, causing Neil to give a knowing wink to his brothers and make a mock scowl with his eyes and cheeks behind his father's back as if to say that their father took after their battle-axe of a grandmother with a similar lack of sense of generosity and kindness and what a pity it was that he did not take after his sister Patricia.

Finally, Aunt Patricia led them out into the garden and showed them her ten chickens in their coop and her five delightful and charming black and white goats in their pen at the bottom of the garden. As they watched the chickens clucking and pecking at their feed, played with the goats and stroked their lovely coats, the three brothers reminded themselves of their own chickens and goats from which they had derived so much pleasure back in Kenya. Their father joked that their aunt almost preferred the company of animals to that of human beings and she agreed with that assessment, saying that humans were complicated and could behave in most strange, mysterious, treacherous and nasty ways whereas animals were always straight, true and faithful.

On their way back to Aunt Clotilda's house in the Allard, the three boys chatted excitedly among themselves after the lovely visit to see Aunt Patricia and they told their father how much they had liked her and her animals and would appreciate to be able to return there with him. Strangely, he did not react, drove with a poker face and Neil in particular noted in the back of his mind that he did not promise that he would take them to visit Aunt Patricia again, making Neil reflect with sadness upon Aunt Patricia's auspicious words "humans could behave in most strange, mysterious, treacherous and nasty ways".

Two mornings later, their father said that he had got up early and had been chatting with their aunt and Neil asked him what they were going to do during that third day of the holiday. Adrian glanced at Aunt Clotilda, looked up at the

ceiling then at the wall and replied, with a detached, cold expression in his eyes and a slightly embarrassed look on his face, 'As I have been explaining to your aunt, I am having to drive back down to London today as I must deal with an urgent business matter that has suddenly cropped up. I will come back here as soon as I can finish the business, which I imagine should be achieved in four or five days, and we will then be able to enjoy a lovely holiday together. In the meantime, Aunt Clotilda will ensure that you have a pleasant stay.'

His three sons choked and became red in the face, staring in astonishment at their father, then at Aunt Clotilda then at one another and feeling totally shocked and baffled by this sudden change. They had understood from him that he would be with them from the first day throughout the duration of the holiday, although he had not said for how many weeks the holiday would last before going back home to Paddock Gates.

However, they had long become accustomed to and had suffered from their father's erratic and unpredictable behaviour, as well as his deceitful ways and lies. And they had known countless disappointments and had been badly hurt on so many occasions due to his decisions, so they knew that there was no point in protesting or arguing and they just had to accept this as yet another disappointment, betrayal and extremely hurtful act on the part of their father.

A little while later, they all suffered very painful emotional pangs again when their father opened the door of the Allard and sat in the driving seat without stooping to hug or kiss any of them and simply drove off whilst waving casually out of the open window and bearing a satisfied, smug and crooked smile as if he were most pleased to turn his back on and be rid of his three sons.

Two weeks passed without any sign of Adrian and not even one telephone call from him. Aunt Clotilda did her utmost to entertain the boys and on several days went for long walks in the countryside and along a nearby river with them together with James, who moved with a somewhat uncoordinated gait but loved walking and enjoyed the company of the boys. They in turn started to appreciate being with James, found that he could play some simple games with them and they were moved by the many signs of affection that he showed towards them.

Then, on July 21st, the boys became very excited when they heard the familiar and lovely purring sound of the Allard's engine in the mid-morning and they rushed joyfully out of the house into the driveway to welcome back their father. However, as he clambered out of the car they stopped abruptly in their tracks and their faces dropped in shock as a young, beautiful, buxom, blond woman stepped out of the passenger seat, came round the back of the car and took their father's hand. She did not appear to be one day older than Anita and had truly lovely features and laughing grey-blue eyes and long false eye-lashes, giving her the appearance of a film-star.

'Hello, boys,' Adrian said in a rather cold, supercilious, detached and unfeeling manner, giving no sign of affection, not even a pat on the head, to any of his sons. 'This is Melinda, who is a business partner working with me on the project that has been occupying me and is still taking up most of my

time. As we have to drive to Norwich for an important meeting followed by lunch with some people, we thought it would be nice to pop in for a half-hour and see how you all are.'

'Nice? Only nice? Just a half-hour?' Neil shouted at his father with temerity, not able to contain his anger and disgust. 'Is that all you feel for us? And why is that woman holding your hand if she is only a business partner? I am entirely fed up to hear all your lies! We have had to put up with your constant lies, deceit and betrayal over all these years. I cannot bear it any longer!'

With that, Neil turned on his heels and bolted past Aunt Clotilda as she came out of the house and he ran up the stairs and into the bedroom he was sharing with his two brothers. A few seconds later, Justin and little Adrian burst into the room, slamming the door, and the three boys collapsed on Neil's bed in a flood of anguished tears. When Aunt Clotilda came in a little while later and pleaded with them to come down to say goodbye to their father, who was having to leave with the lady, all three boys refused to see him and asked Aunt Clotilda to try and understand how badly their father had hurt them, deceived them and made them suffer by pretending that they were having a holiday only to abandon them here and enjoy a good time running after pretty women.

They asked Aunt Clotilda to tell their father that he would have to prove that he cared for and loved his sons by coming back to Dickleborough on his own, without any woman, by the end of that week and spending some weeks with them on a real holiday and then taking them back to their house in Caterham. She promised that she would give him the message, she returned downstairs and a mere five minutes later the boys heard the sound of the Allard car as it left the property.

The three brothers waited anxiously until the end of the week and their aunt reassured them that she had given their message to their father before he had left the house. When the middle of the following week arrived at the beginning of August without any sign of or news from their father, they were overwhelmed by an extreme state of anxiety and became desperate. When they were all seated around the dining room table just before lunch, they asked Aunt Clotilda what was happening and if she knew in how many days their father was coming back to be with them and to enjoy a true holiday with them. Their aunt replied that she was very aggrieved and sad and did not quite know how to break the bad news to them.

When Neil, assuming the leading role as the representative of the three boys, shouted in a very nervous and trembling voice that they all wanted to know what the situation was and in how much time their father would be coming back, Aunt Clotilda broke down, wept wretchedly for a minute, with her chest heaving, dried her eyes with both hands and, plucking up as much courage as she could muster, she told the boys in such a soft murmur that they had to lean in closely to her to hear the words, 'My dearest nephews, it pains me terribly to have to tell you that your father is not coming back.'

Neil, Justin and Adrian recoiled in total shock, stared in disbelief at their aunt and at each other, then Neil retorted with a shaking voice, trying to choke back his tears, 'What do you mean he is not coming back? Do you mean he cannot come back right now because he is ill or has had a car accident or some other type of accident?'

Neil just could not contemplate the possibility that their father had died.

'No, my dear,' his aunt replied wearily, leaning her head on one hand, 'your father is not ill, he has not had an accident and he is in perfectly good health. The terrible situation is that he called me by telephone yesterday evening, saying that he just cannot cope with bringing you up or even spending much time with you, has great difficulties just coping with life in general. And he has asked me to accept to keep you here and bring you up as part of our family in this house. I can understand that his behaviour must appear incomprehensible to the three of you and it is causing many complications for our household and I will have to analyse many elements with your Uncle Henry and see what we can do. At any rate, you can continue to live here for a little bit longer while we search for a solution. I am dreadfully sorry but that is all I can say at this instant.'

She adopted a deliberately brisk, business-like manner in finishing the sentence in an attempt to disguise her emotional turmoil, in order to avoid breaking down again and to prevent her three nephews from retorting with further queries or remarks.

The three brothers were appalled and flabbergasted. Each one of them felt punch-drunk as if having been hit hard in the face by a clenched fist. They all arose groggily and unsurely from their chairs, as if mentally stunned by what they had heard, then excused themselves, saying that they had no appetite to eat anything, and they walked slowly, silently and sadly up the stairs, shut themselves in their bedroom and collapsed together on Neil's bed. They all broke down as if smashed into little pieces and they wailed heartbrokenly at their dreadful misfortune and unhappy destiny in a torrent of tears.

After a while, little Adrian, between trying to dry his eyes and pouring out more heart-felt tears, said feebly and miserably, 'Why is it that we have parents who do not love or want us? Firstly, our mother showed that she did not love us by sending us over to our father, and now we discover that he does not love us either and has abandoned us, as he does not want to be with us. What is wrong with us? Is there something so wrong and abnormal with us that our parents do not love us?'

Neil and Justin commiserated with their younger brother, hugging him and rubbing him tenderly on the back with their hands, but they did not even attempt to give an answer to his pertinent questions, for it was utterly impossible to answer such poignant, difficult and painful queries.

Chapter 5
Misery and Desperation in Orphanages

The ensuing three days seemed endless and cheerless, with a heavy atmosphere and acute tension hanging over the house. The three brothers hardly saw any sign of Uncle Henry. And they felt so down-hearted and were suffering so much from what their aunt had told them that they hardly felt in the mood to play any games amongst themselves or with James, who sensed that something had gone very awry but could not understood what had caused the miserable atmosphere in the household and no one talked to him or gave him any explanations.

After lunch on the fourth day, Aunt Clotilda asked her nephews to remain at the table, led James out into the garden where she told him to play quietly with some games on the lawn then she came back, sat down and looked at the boys with an ashen and sombre expression on her face and extreme sadness in her eyes.

She spoke to the three brothers so slowly, so softly and so hesitatingly that it seemed each word cost her an anguished and emotional effort.

'I am terribly sorry, dear boys, but it is impossible for us to keep you here any longer. As you have seen, due to James' state of health I have to give him an inordinate amount of attention and it is very time-consuming and mentally, emotionally and physically exhausting for my system. I just could not cope with all the work of being a mother to the three of you as well as James.'

'Also, your Uncle Henry is away at work each day and he has told me that he does not agree to adopt you as he does not earn much money and our financial situation would not allow us to manage if we took you on as we can barely manage right now catering for the needs of James and paying all the expenses of running the household as it is.'

'Uncle Henry took some time off work the other day and drove over to Norwich, the capital city of the county of Norfolk, to speak with the officials in charge of catering for parentless children, who are called orphans, and he has arranged with them that you will go to the children's home called Garfield House in the small town of East Dereham, which is about fifteen miles west of Norwich. He has agreed with the manager of this orphanage that he will drive you there in our car after breakfast tomorrow morning. I will help each of you to pack your suitcase during this afternoon and once you arrive at Garfield House they will attend to all your needs and will provide you with any further

clothes that you will need as summer ends and the fresher autumn and winter months will arrive.'

Aunt Clotilda said the last sentences so emphatically and with such finality that the three brothers sensed immediately that there was no point in arguing and pleading with her to be able to remain there with her and that they were obliged to accept this abominably cruel fate of being carted off to a strange and unknown destination in an orphanage in a small town called East Dereham. Without saying a word, but with dark and deathly expressions in the eyes as if they were condemned prisoners on their way to be hanged at the gallows, the boys left the table, climbed the stairs and threw themselves once again across Neil's bed and lamented their awful destiny. Neil remarked how ironical, bizarre and unjust it seemed that their aunt had said orphans were children without parents but they did have parents, who were both alive! Justin added that he supposed that if your parents simply did not want you, you were deemed to be parentless and therefore orphans. Little Adrian recalled with a sudden flash in his mind and behind his eyes the bad premonitory feeling that he had had during the flight from Kenya to London that their mother had treacherously rejected and abandoned them to a dreadful and extremely unhappy fate.

'I hate our mother!' Adrian screamed piercingly as he wept bitterly, clenched his fists and shook them in anger and desperation. 'None of this would have happened if she had refused to obey our father's orders, had given us her love and had kept us with her. We would have had a happy life living with her in Mombasa. It is all her fault that we are now wretched parentless orphans being carted off to a horrible orphanage in this goddam country!'

'It is our father that I detest!' snarled Neil with a violence in the tone of his voice that shook Justin and Adrian. 'We could have had a happy life living at Paddock Gates with him, lovely Anita and our half-brother or half-sister, but he treated Anita so badly that he messed everything up and has now turned his back on us and entirely abandoned us, the selfish, unloving bastard!'

Justin was the calmest and had the most placid, well-balanced and easy-going temperament of the three youngsters.

He dried his tears, looked tenderly and sadly at his beloved brothers and merely said, 'I do not hate our mother or our father. I feel terribly sad and sorry for both of them and for us. I am certain that mother misses us and feels very lonely without us back in Kenya. As for father, I suppose he must have his own reasons with his way of life why he cannot cope with bringing us up and there seems no point in us trying to understand his decision.'

Such a wise statement from such a young lad impressed his brothers profoundly, left them speechless and put an end to the conversation.

**

In the mid-morning of the following day, August 6th 1955, Uncle Henry bundled their three suitcases into the boot of his car and drove them without

saying a word, as if highly embarrassed and even feeling guilty, for what seemed an eternity until they reached the outskirts of East Dereham and pulled into the driveway of Garfield House, a rather small, grey coloured and drab looking manor house built in the Victorian era.

The manager and his wife greeted them cheerlessly and without a smile, helped them take their suitcases up to a fairly large but dark, drab and colourless bedroom containing three single metal-framed beds, similar to those seen in army barracks, accompanied them downstairs again and showed them around the miserable looking, old-fashioned living room, communal dining room and kitchen. Uncle Henry then shook hands stiffly and awkwardly with each of the boys, wished them good luck during their stay in this home and said that their aunt would be in touch with them before very long. He seemed in a rush and very relieved to get away from this lugubrious orphanage housing young children, loaded down by and crushed under layers of unhappiness for various reasons and from varying backgrounds, as he opened the car door, sat in the driving seat, turned on the engine and sped away as quickly as he could without even a glance back towards his three nephews whom he had just abandoned and marooned in this hellhole.

The brothers soon discovered that there were twenty young children in the home, whereas the maximum capacity was in fact for only fifteen, so some children were packed three or four to a bedroom, which should have contained two at the most. They also saw rapidly that there was a very unpleasant, depressing and violent atmosphere in the building, as all the children were unhappy, nervous wrecks and on edge constantly and suffered from emotional insecurity and mental instability due to rejection and abandonment by their families or the unfortunate deaths of both their parents.

To make matters worse, the manager and his wife were cold, distant, strict disciplinarians, seemed devoid of any sense of humour or fun, never smiled to the young orphans, did not tolerate any fooling around or unruly behaviour among the children and used their hands and even a leather strap to slap disobedient boys and girls on the palm of the hand or on the backside, depending on what they judged to be the severity of the misconduct.

Neil, Justin and Adrian were extremely miserable and unhappy from the outset and had the impression that they were under the supervision of wardens in an old-fashioned prison rather than in the care of social workers doing their best to ensure their well-being and welfare. There reigned in the home an atmosphere of a lack of human warmth and an attitude and behaviour by the manager and his wife which were borderline on mistreatment of the poor, defenceless and wretchedly unhappy young inmates.

All three brothers found it very difficult to integrate into the home and make friends with any of the other children. As Neil and Adrian had bottled up a lot of anguish and anger inside themselves over the awful plight which had befallen them and felt a high degree of frustration and pent-up violent emotions, both of them got into arguments, scraps and more serious fights with other boys on several occasions, felt the full force of the manager's leather

strap on their bottoms more than once by way of punishment and were soon branded by the manager and his wife as trouble-makers to be supervised very closely.

Only Justin remained as cool, calm and collected as he could under the circumstances, and on each occasion that he was provoked by any boy looking for a fight he daunted the boy with a withering look of contempt in his magnetic blue eyes, turned his back and simply walked away. The manager and his wife soon gave Justin the etiquette "the wise one" and after the first ten days, the other boys in the home came to respect him and left him alone. Small, six-year-old Adrian was bullied and taunted on several occasions behind closed doors by a gang of three ten-year-old boys. He did not dare tell Neil and Justin, for he did not want the bullies to gang up on them, so he suffered in silence.

Three weeks after the arrival of the three brothers at the orphanage, during which time their mental and emotional state of unhappiness, sadness, despondency and despair became worse and aggravated with each week, the manager told them that Aunt Clotilda was coming to visit them the next day, which helped to cheer them up slightly but not very much, as she had decided together with their uncle to send them to this dreadful and miserable children's home.

They felt that they had been rejected, betrayed and abandoned not only by their mother and father but by their aunt and uncle as well and they had unavoidable feelings of wariness and suspicion as to the motivations of the visit of their aunt. When she arrived in the early afternoon the following day, she did at least hug and kiss each one of them, asked them how they were faring and bearing up and showed a degree of sympathy and commiseration with them over their sad plight.

The manager asked her to accompany him to his office, they remained behind closed doors for about twenty minutes, he then came out and asked the three brothers to join them in his office.

'Boys, as I have just explained to your aunt this home is only a short-term children's home for orphaned children up to and not beyond eleven years of age. I have seen from your birth certificates and baptismal certificates which your uncle showed me when you arrived that you, Neil, had your eleventh birthday this June, you, Justin, became nine years of age this July and you Adrian will have your seventh birthday in about ten days' time. The other consideration, perhaps of greater importance, is that we normally have one orphan at a time from each family, on a few occasions we have had two from the same family but your case is the first in the history of this home when we have had three orphaned children from the same family. As my wife and I feel that the three of you should not be separated and should be allowed to remain together, but it is difficult for us to keep you here, I have been in contact with the central authorities for children's care in Norwich and it has been decided with them that you will be transferred in about ten days from now to a much better adapted long-term orphanage in Overstrand, a village on the north coast

of the county of Norfolk, which will be able to cater for all your needs during the years to come. A special bus will drive you up to that home.'

The three boys looked at one another and the same thought transpired from the look in each one's blue eyes, which were welling up with anguished and desperate tears. All of them were painfully struck by the manager's phrases "long-term orphanage" and "during the years to come". Was there to be no escape for them from this living hell? Were they going to be obliged to endure this mental and emotional torture in another harsh, impersonal and loveless orphanage for so many long years to come until each one became an adult and could finally break the shackles of the prisoner status? Was there no hope for them that any member of their large and supposedly wealthy family would take them under their wing and provide them with a loving, happy, stable and secure family environment? Their sense of hopelessness and utter despair deepened when their aunt said in a brusque, conclusive manner not to be argued against that she agreed with the manager that there was no other choice and a transfer to the long-term orphanage in Overstrand appeared to be the sole solution.

***

The Walton-Mornick brothers were not the only children being transferred from Garfield House to the children's home in Overstrand. Together with them on the bus on September 7th 1955 were three other children, one boy and two girls, none of whom were related to each other. The driver, a round-faced and somewhat over-weight man in his fifties, was very affable with a kindly attitude towards and concern for these unfortunate orphans and he spoke to them and told them jokes to cheer them up and make them laugh during the entire trip up from East Dereham to Overstrand.

He told them that the orphanage was called The Grange and could cater for up to twenty-five children and he wished them the very best of good luck in their stay at the home. He said he hoped very much that each of them would have the good fortune of being adopted at some point in time by kind and loving people who would give them a new home and a happy environment in which to live and grow up. As adoption by strangers external to one's family was a notion which was completely unknown and baffling to the children, they asked him questions excitedly about the state of adoption by third parties and felt somewhat encouraged by the time that they arrived at the children's home that such good fortune might possibly become a reality for them one day. However, their optimism became quickly dampened, as Neil, Justin and Adrian wanted desperately to grow up together and they feared very much that no couple of adults in their right minds would accept to adopt three brothers together.

The Grange was a much grander mansion house than Garfield House. It had been built in the Edwardian architectural style, had a very large gravel driveway leading up to a circular space enabling several vehicles to be parked near the front door, possessed a charming looking small forest containing

several species of trees over to the left side and a huge, beautifully kept green lawn and several colourful flower beds on the back side of the house. When Neil, Justin and Adrian saw the garden, they were wracked with sad, nostalgic memories of the lovely garden that they had so enjoyed at Paddock Gates.

The manager and his wife were called Mr and Mrs Watson and the welcome they gave the children contrasted with that given by the manager and his wife at Garfield House, as they appeared a little warmer, less starchy and somewhat more sensitive about the sad fate that had befallen these unfortunate urchins. However, this was an orphanage, just like the first home, and the three brothers sensed straightaway that there was also a blatant lack of loving atmosphere in this house and, after the experience at the first children's home, they knew that they could not have too many expectations on the emotional front and that this place was also a jungle where each child had to fend for himself or herself and had to do his or her best to survive in the environment where no parents were on hand to give love, affection, kind attention, guidance and close consideration to all their mental, emotional and bodily needs.

The house had a very large entrance hall and a magnificent, wide, wooden staircase leading up to the first floor containing some of the bedrooms and bathrooms, whilst a narrower white-painted staircase led up from the first to the second floor where a few more bedrooms and bathrooms were situated and were occupied by a few older boys aged between fifteen and eighteen. On the first floor, Neil was given a small but pleasant bedroom by himself and Justin and Adrian had to share an adjacent bedroom containing two single beds. As soon as they had unpacked their suitcases and arranged their clothes in the cupboard and chest of drawers, Justin and Adrian rushed into Neil's bedroom next door and the three brothers reassumed their beloved habit of diving onto Neil's bed and huddling together. The love they felt for one another and the close bond between them were so strong that they did not have any need to talk and were merely contented to lie there together and feel each other's brotherly warmth, tenderness and moral support.

After a moment's silence, Neil ruffled little Adrian's hair, wrapped one arm over his shoulder, kissed him on the cheek and said, 'Today is September 7th 1955, baby brother. It is your seventh birthday! Many happy returns of the day, if "happy" is the right word under these circumstances!'

'Oh my God!' Adrian exclaimed. 'This is one birthday I will never, ever forget. I have been thrown into a beastly long-term orphanage on my seventh birthday! How will I ever forget such a miserable birthday? However, this year has also been miserable for you two as well on your birthdays, for none of us has received any card, telegram or gift or any wishes at all from either our mother or our father for our birthdays this year. Nor will we in the years to come, for we no longer have a mother or a father!'

With that deep sentiment of rejection, abandonment and loss overwhelming him yet again, Adrian burst into tears and threw himself into the arms of Neil and Justin and all three brothers broke down and wept bitterly together for quite a long time.

After six weeks, the three boys were still attempting, not without difficulty, to manage to settle down into the mundane routine and life devoid of any loving atmosphere in this orphanage together with all the other children. And were becoming used to participating in class studies, activities and sports at the local primary school in the village of Overstrand side by side with all the other schoolchildren who were not orphans but had their own parents and a normal family life.

An incident happened suddenly one Saturday, which perturbed their routine and disturbed the three brothers immensely.

They were playing together in the games room and heard the front door bell ring. As they continued playing without taking any notice of who had arrived at the house, they were shocked when Mr Watson came into the room, told them that Aunt Clotilda was there and asked them to follow him to his office. As they came through the door, their aunt arose from a chair and said hello to them and asked them how they were faring with a rather sad and guilty look on her face. She stood awkwardly, did not attempt to kiss or hug the boys and they did not move forward to greet her, but simply stared at her as if she was some strange creature from a planet in outer space. She broke the silent and difficult atmosphere by picking up a large carrier bag and distributing a few small and clumsily wrapped toys to each boy.

Neil angrily said to her, 'What are you doing here, Aunt Clotilda? What are these toys? We do not want to receive toys from our family, we want and need to receive love and affection, we want and need to be given a true home with a real family atmosphere. We have been abandoned by our mother, then by our father, then by you and Uncle Henry, who carted us off to a first horrible orphanage and then we were brought to this awful orphanage. Please take these toys back, go home and leave us alone as we are trying our best to cope with our unhappy situation with the lack of any family members to love us and take care of us.'

Little Adrian, although somewhat daunted and intimidated by the harsh and brutal outburst of big brother Neil, turned to him and queried sheepishly, as he gazed longingly at the toys, 'Neil, Aunt Clotilda has come all this way to see us. Do you not think it is possible for us to accept the toys which she has brought us?'

'No way!' retorted Neil, raising his voice in an even angrier manner. 'We must not accept any toys from her, for she is only trying to assuage her guilty conscience at having abandoned us by bringing these toys and trying to foist them on us, as if she is attempting to buy our forgiveness!'

As Aunt Clotilda went very red in the face and showed a very pained and upset facial expression, before she could say anything Justin intervened and simply said in a calm but resolute way in a very poised manner for one so young, 'Neil, you are being very unfair towards our aunt. We cannot blame her for our unhappy destiny and for ending up in this place. The guilty ones are our

mother and father. They are the ones who abandoned us, not Aunt Clotilda, who has her own problems and difficulties to cope with, as she has to bring up poor handicapped James. Personally, I think that we should accept the toys Aunt Clotilda has offered us as a way of showing our gratitude for her visit and out of respect for her.'

Neil almost rounded on his brother and was on the verge of adopting the proud and overbearing attitude of the older brother wanting to put him in his place. Then he stared intensely for several seconds into Justin's lovely blue eyes with their intelligent, mature depth, and he checked himself as if feeling admonished by the reasonableness of his younger brother whom he loved so much.

In attempting to control his own angry emotions he placed a hand on Justin's shoulder and replied affectionately in as light-heartened a tone of voice that he could muster, 'All right, wise one, I recognise that you are the most sensible and well-balanced of the three of us. I agree that there is no harm in accepting the toys that Aunt Clotilda has brought us.'

After this deflation of a very tense and difficult beginning to their aunt's visit, the three boys took the toys which she gave them with great alacrity and enthusiasm and the rest of the visit went very well and Aunt Clotilda stayed with them for as long as she could before she said that she had to leave in order to return home to her chores and her duties towards James.

Two weeks later, Mr Watson told the three brothers to come to his office and, once inside, they were very surprised to see Uncle Henry standing there, as well as Mr and Mrs Watson. Without even asking them how they were, their uncle said in a somewhat distant, perfunctory and cold-hearted way, 'After her recent visit to see you, your aunt was very upset and affected by the idea of having to leave you to your fate in this orphanage. After a lot of soul-searching, she told me that, whilst there is no way we could harbour all three of you, she was prepared to have Justin and give him a family life in our home. Because from what she can see, he is the calmest, least emotional, most sensible and reasonable of you all and would be the easiest to bring up. Whereas you, Neil and Adrian, appear to be the most highly-strung and emotionally unstable and disturbed ones and would be very difficult for her to cope with, especially as she already has the problems of managing the delicate health situation of poor James. She asked me naturally if I would agree that we take on Justin and I have given my consent. We contacted the authorities and Mr Watson here, who are very pleased about this development, and your aunt has asked me to drive up here today to collect Justin and take him to live with us in Dickleborough. So, Justin, I will wait here while Mrs Watson will help you to pack your suitcase with your clothes, toys and any other personal belongings.'

There was a heavy silence in the room as no one moved, then the three brothers looked at one another with shocked expressions.

Little Adrian shattered the silence by screaming at the top of his voice, with tears pouring down his cheeks and his whole face and body trembling, 'No! No! You cannot take Justin away! We are three brothers, we have always been

together. We belong together. We must stay together. You cannot take him away!'

Adrian flung himself against Justin, who was so much taller than him, threw his little arms around his waist and pressed his small face against his belly and spurted out as he sobbed bitterly, 'I love you, Justin. I love you so much. Please do not leave Neil and me. Please let us stay together, I beg you!'

Uncle Henry just stood there with no reaction, completely at a loss as to what to do. Mr and Mrs Watson were very moved by this touching display of brotherly love and as tears welled in Mrs Watson's glistening eyes, her husband discreetly handed her a handkerchief.

Justin was in a turmoil and he stroked Adrian's head with one hand and pressed his other hand affectionately against the small of Adrian's back and rubbed the hand up and down his back as he said softly between his own tears, 'I love you too, little brother. I love you very much. I love both you and Neil very deeply.'

Neil was weeping as he turned and wrapped his arms around Justin and Adrian. The three of them stood locked in a tearful, heart-wrenching brotherly embrace for what seemed like several minutes.

Eventually, Neil moved a pace away, placed a hand on each brother's shoulder and gave each of them an immensely tender and affectionate look with his blue eyes slightly reddened from so much weeping as he said in a croaky, emotional voice, 'This is the worst day of our lives, the day when we are being separated; through all our past happy moments and our dreadfully unhappy and turbulent times, we have always had the joy of being together side by side, like three gallant musketeers! It is a horrible thought that Justin is to be taken away from us, but you and I, Adrian, have to accept this awful separation for the sake of Justin. We must put him first, for he at least is being given the opportunity to have a proper home and be brought up in a normal family environment with security, stability and, we must hope, love, affection and the possibility for a much better future. This is terribly hard and living without seeing Justin every day will be excruciatingly difficult for us, but we can only hope that we will be allowed to get together with him for a day or so every now and then at weekends and during school holidays. So, Justin, I hate having to say this but you must go with Mrs Watson, pack your suitcase and we will wait here to say our goodbyes as soon as you are ready to leave.'

Whilst they were waiting for Justin to return with Mrs Watson, Neil sat on a chair with his head bowed and covered by both hands as he fought hard to retain his tears. And little Adrian paced up and down the room like a desperate, crazed, lost wild animal, chewing his fingernails and gnawing at the knuckles on both hands with such force that his teeth broke the skin on his right hand and he spent several minutes sucking up the blood which started seeping on to the back of his hand.

When Justin and Mrs Watson reappeared and Uncle Henry nodded a silent, embarrassed farewell to nobody in particular and walked out with Justin's suitcase to put it in the boot of his car, Neil, Justin and Adrian hugged one

another again and said, in a sad and tearful goodbye, that they prayed to be able to be reunited before very long.

As Mr and Mrs Watson escorted Justin through the open front door of The Grange towards the waiting car, Adrian impulsively rushed after them and hurled himself at Justin's disappearing back, wrapped his arms around his midriff, pressed his head against the small of his back and emitted a piercing, anguished wail then pleaded with Justin between sobs not to go but to come back into the house.

Before Justin could turn around, Neil intervened and grabbed Adrian by both shoulders, pulled him off Justin energetically and ordered him to let Justin go as he dragged his little brother back into the hallway and shut the front door. Adrian flailed at Neil with both clenched fists, freeing himself frantically from his grasp, and ran up the stairs, crashed into the door of his bedroom as he turned the knob, slammed the door shut once inside and flung himself onto his bed, burying his head under his pillow in a flood of tears as he rocked his body from side to side in a fit of absolute despair and wretchedness.

From that day onwards, Adrian's attitudes and behaviour changed radically. During each day, he was sullen, withdrawn and never smiled to any of the other inmates at the orphanage or to any of the other children at the local primary school. Mr and Mrs Watson and the teachers at school could only guess from the miserable look on his face and the painful expression in his eyes the depth of his mental anguish and emotional suffering at the loss of his beloved brother. In his bed each night he sobbed continuously for a long time and rocked his body from side to side frenetically for what seemed like hours, until he was so exhausted that he finally fell into a fitful sleep. But was haunted by dreadful nightmares and horrible images of his dear brother Justin being hacked to death by *Mau Mau pangas*, causing an unbearable and inconsolable feeling that he would never see Justin again.

To make matters worse, Adrian lost his appetite, refused to eat any breakfast and only accepted to eat very small amounts at lunch and suppertime. Whereas he had always been rather chubby, he began to lose weight and became very skinny rapidly, his face took on a gaunt appearance and the look in his once cheerful blue eyes became dimmed, expressionless and lifeless, causing Mr and Mrs Watson and the teachers at school to become very alarmed.

After a few weeks of observing Adrian's condition deteriorating dramatically, Mr Watson asked the local doctor attributed to the orphanage, as he had a qualification in child psychiatry, to see Adrian and undertake a thorough examination. The doctor concluded that Adrian was in a state of shock, moroseness and deep depression caused by the traumatic separation from Justin and was so wretchedly unhappy and convinced that he would never see his brother again that he was losing his interest in life. And the doctor feared that he might capitulate and resign himself to a slow death if nothing was done very quickly to reverse the tragic situation. He said that the best treatment that he could prescribe was to have Justin brought back to the

orphanage and reunited with his little brother for a while. During which time he would see Adrian regularly for psychiatric sessions and endeavour to help him understand that the best way for him to demonstrate his deep love for Justin was to accept that it was in Justin's best interest to be with their uncle and aunt and live in a normal and stable family environment and to set Justin free and allow him to leave the orphanage a final time and return to his new home in Dickleborough.

The doctor and Mr Watson also spoke at length with Neil and they soon realised that he, now aged eleven and four years older than Adrian, had rapidly acquired an impressive maturity and a realistic outlook, which he said he had learned from his brother Justin, for whom he had much love and a tremendous admiration due to his calm, wise and reasonable disposition.

He told them that whilst he had been terribly sad at Justin's departure, he had resigned himself to this twist of fate and their separation, as he knew instinctively inside himself that it was for Justin's good and that he should not do anything to obstruct Justin's chances of living a better and happier life. He agreed with their plan to have Justin brought back temporarily to the orphanage and was certain that intelligent and wise Justin would quickly understand the reason. He promised to cooperate with the efforts of the doctor to prevail upon little Adrian to accept what was in Justin's best interests and to help Adrian to be cured of his melancholy and deep depression. At the end of their discussion, Neil took the opportunity, with a malicious twinkle in his eyes and an angry edge in his voice, to tell Mr Watson and the doctor in no uncertain terms that the fact he was being realistic about his fate did not mean that he was content, for, on the contrary, he was very unhappy in the orphanage, detested the environment and the other kids there, hated the local primary school and the other kids there and hated everybody in general!

The plan worked, to their great relief; Aunt Clotilda brought Justin back with his suitcase, Neil and Adrian were overcome with joy to be reunited with him, the doctor's treatment had positive results, as Adrian responded well over several psychiatric sessions as well as to prescribed medication, and later on Uncle Henry was able to take Justin away from the orphanage, after very emotional and moving hugs and loving gestures between the three brothers but without any frightful tantrums from Adrian, just in time for Justin to participate in the celebrations of Christmas 1955 together with Cousin James in the family home in Dickleborough.

For Neil and Adrian, however, their first Christmas at the orphanage was an immensely sad, pathetic and very detestable event, for it was the first time in their young lives that they had to endure a Christmas without any other members of their family being present to share it with them, in particular Justin, and they procured no joy or satisfaction whatsoever from the obligatory but unwanted company of all the helpers and the other orphans in the house.

As Neil and Adrian were Roman Catholics, and one of the female helpers at the orphanage named Mrs Drisedale was also a catholic and regularly attended mass at the local Catholic church in Overstrand, with the agreement of

Mr and Mrs Watson she arranged with the parish priest and an enthusiastic catechist that this latter lady should include Neil and Adrian in her catechism group and she gave them their instruction in preparation for receiving their first Holy Communion.

As they made good progress and learned all the contents of their catechism with satisfactory results, despite some difficulties to concentrate, Neil and Adrian received their first Holy Communion together with twenty other children in the Overstrand parish at a specially organised mass on the last Sunday of April 1956. Little was young Adrian to know that his regular attendances at Sunday masses and other periodic celebrations at the catholic parish church in Overstrand, accompanied by Mrs Drisedale, were to have overwhelming and life-changing repercussions for him in the coming few years.

***

Life at The Grange did not become more pleasant or easy for Neil and Adrian, for they were both very damaged psychologically and emotionally by the strong sentiment of betrayal, rejection and abandonment caused by the comportment of their mother and their father and the feeling that they were worthless and undeserving of love in the eyes of their parents. They both had great difficulty in integrating into the life at the orphanage. Especially as the nervous tension and underlying current of potential violence between all the poor children who had landed there was very acute. And each of the inmates had their own problems and were unbalanced, unstable and traumatised by the different personal experiences that they had had to endure leading up to the misfortune of being abandoned for whatever reason by their parents and their families in general to the fate of surviving as best they could in the cold, impersonal and unaffectionate atmosphere which reigned in the orphanage. Poor little Adrian became the victim of bullying and harassment on a regular basis by several teenage boys.

Neil developed rapidly a rebellious attitude and antagonism against all forms of authority and he did not manage to pass his eleven-plus exams, which it was obligatory to succeed, under the prevailing educational system at all the primary schools in the country, in order to be able to attend a grammar school, which allowed the ensuing possibility to accede later on to one of the country's universities.

Due to this failure, Neil would be reduced after leaving the primary school to attending the local secondary school, which afforded fewer career openings in later years than an attendance at the grammar school. Mr and Mrs Watson were disappointed for Neil that he failed the eleven-plus exams, but they were not in actual fact very surprised by this failure, as the records showed that no orphaned child who had lived at the orphanage and attended the Overstrand primary school had ever passed the eleven-plus exams since The Grange had been established.

One Saturday afternoon in late autumn 1956, a few months after Neil had had his twelfth birthday and Adrian his eighth birthday, Adrian declined an invitation by some other boys of his age to participate in a game of Cowboys and Indians in the grounds of the orphanage and went in search of Neil, who seemed to have disappeared. Adrian had not seen him since lunchtime, was missing him and hoped that Neil would accept to play a game with him, as Adrian hero-worshipped his eldest brother and loved spending as much time in his company as possible.

In his search, Adrian looked in vain in the games room and certain other areas on the ground floor, in the bedrooms and bathrooms on the first floor. Then his attention was suddenly caught by the white staircase which led up to the top floor, forbidden territory for a youngster like him as it was the preserved domain where the much older boys between fifteen and eighteen years old had their bedrooms and bathrooms. Adrian became distracted away from his search for Neil, who he was certain would not have gone up to the older boys' floor, and although he knew that he should not go up there his curiosity got the better of him and, after looking from left to right and back again to verify that no one else was there and he was all alone, he found himself venturing up those alluring stairs and tip-toeing silently and excitedly along the carpeted landing of the hallowed ground belonging to the senior boys. As he moved past a few closed doors and came abreast with another closed door he trembled and nearly panicked as he heard muffled sounds, quite soft but very much like stifled human grunts and screams, coming from the other side of the door.

It was well known among all the inmates in the house that there were no keys in the key-holes of any of the bedrooms or bathrooms, in order to avoid the possibility of any of the orphans locking themselves inside, whether by accident or deliberately. Adrian crouched down and put his right eye against the keyhole of the door whence came the strange sounds. He recoiled in total shock and bewilderment, not believing what he saw. Struggling to regain his composure and needing to verify that what he had seen was unfortunately real and not a mere figment of his imagination, he moved forward again slowly and cautiously and placed his right eye once more against the keyhole.

In the narrow vision afforded by the small, vertical key-hole, Adrian saw the reddened face of big brother Neil pressed down on the counterpane at the bottom end of a bed, turned towards the door, with a white handkerchief tied tightly between his open lips and knotted behind his head, thus gagging his mouth and tongue and stifling the terrified and painful sounds he attempted to emit. Large drops of sweat and tears dripped down his face onto the counterpane, both his nostrils flared and deflated like those of a raging bull as he struggled to breathe through his nose and both eyes opened then shut in rapidly successive blinks. Adrian was able to detect each time the eyes were open the appalled, revolted and horribly painful look in those normally beautiful blue eyes, which were now dimmed, blood-shot, bloated and reddened from many tears and much cruel suffering.

Adrian almost fainted, slid down onto his knees, shook his head then bowed it low, cupped his eyes in both hands and rocked back and forth as he started to cry silently for a few seconds. Then, as incomprehension followed by a fierce determination and forceful rage started to well up in his little chest, he seized himself, stopped crying abruptly and dried away the tears with the back of each hand. Something or someone was inflicting terrible and painful torment on his beloved brother the other side of that door and, although he was gripped with fear and apprehension, he told himself that he had to find out what was the cause of his brother's predicament and awful suffering.

Staying down on both knees, Adrian made the sign of the Cross, closed his eyes and prayed silently but fervently to God, asking Him to give him courage and help him to save Neil from whatever torment and pain he was enduring. Then, he stood up with difficulty, almost falling down as his knees weakened, knocked together and nearly buckled as terror overwhelmed his small frame. He stared at the door, looked at the door-knob, took a nervous shallow breath, almost fell back in fear but heard again his brother's stifled screams, took his courage in both hands, took another very deep and long breath, then turned the door-knob slowly and silently and pushed the door open very cautiously as wide as he could, without daring to step into the bedroom but remaining trembling on the door-step.

The scene before Adrian was so appallingly shocking that he stood transfixed with gaping mouth and bulging eyes. Neil was kneeling, stark naked, with his head pressed down on the counterpane, both arms held behind his back and his two hands immobilised in the grip of Stuart Benson, a sixteen year old boy who Adrian instantly recognised, who was also naked and was standing on the other side of the bed facing Adrian, with his protuberance jutting out fully erect.

Since arriving at the orphanage, Adrian had learned from other boys that the male protuberance was called the penis. Behind Neil a second naked boy was kneeling between his spread-eagled legs, had both his hands firmly on Neil's buttocks and rocked the lower part of his body back and forth as his long and fat penis thrust rapidly in and out of Neil's backside. Adrian recognised Daniel Turnbull, a tall and muscular seventeen-year old bully, who was the leader of a small gang of older boys who terrorised several of the younger boys and girls on a regular basis.

Adrian was amazed to see a third naked boy, sixteen-year old Simon Braithwaite, standing by the bed just behind Daniel holding his erect penis in his right hand and pushing the foreskin forwards and backwards in a vigorous motion, a movement which appeared to give him much pleasure by the look on his face and the expression in his eyes. Adrian was puzzled by this gesture and did not understand what Simon was really doing, as nobody in the care home had yet mentioned to Adrian anything about the practice of masturbation. He knew well that Stuart and Simon were members of Daniel's gang of bullyboys and he had seen them beating up one or two other younger inmates at the

orphanage, but he was totally shocked and horrified to see what the three of them were doing to his eldest brother.

As soon as the three boys saw Adrian standing in the doorway, Stuart and Simon stared at Daniel with quizzical expressions and he turned his head to look fully at Adrian.

Whilst continuing to pump his penis in and out of Neil's backside, he growled at Adrian with a snarling curl of his lips like an enraged wolf and whispered menacingly, 'What are you doing here, you little runt? You know very well that kids of your age are forbidden from coming up to this floor. Turn on your heels right now and get back downstairs to play with the other small sissies. Your big brother has a juicy, tender, tight arsehole and I bet that your arsehole is even more enticing. Keep your mouth shut and do not ever breathe a word to anyone about what you have seen here, otherwise we will bring you up here and bugger you just like your brother. Then we will kill you and cut up your body into small pieces, chuck them in a large black plastic bag and throw the bag out with all the other black bags in the garbage collected each week by lorry. Mark my words, we will bugger you then slaughter you if you ever squeak a word, so keep this matter completely secret. Now, get out of here, you little worm, and close the door quietly behind you!'

Adrian did as he was told, shinned down the staircase so fast that he very nearly fell down half of the stairs, then he rushed to his bedroom, pushed the door shut and threw himself onto his bed. He lay prostrate for a few minutes, then his whole body started to shake and tremble uncontrollably as the delayed shock of what he had seen, the violence of the act of Daniel brutally violating his beloved brother and the ghastly words and threats to which he himself had been subjected by Daniel overwhelmed him and cast him into a state of deep dejection and utter despair.

He projected his mind painfully back to those various occasions at night in Kenya when he had observed a man penetrating his mother with his penis, but he knew that they penetrated her vagina, for he had seen his mother entirely naked several times and had even taken baths with her and had noted the positions of her vagina and what Daniel had just called the arsehole. It appeared normal and natural in hindsight that those men's penises had penetrated her vagina, as he had seen for himself the amount of pleasure that they had given to his mother and the fact that she had consented willingly to the act.

On the contrary, Daniel's penetration of Neil's arsehole appeared to Adrian's logic, even as a small eight-year old child, to be very abnormal and wrong as Adrian had seen the expression of disgust, loathing, pain and suffering on Neil's face and in his eyes as he was being penetrated. There was no trace of consent or pleasure at all and Adrian concluded sadly and angrily that Neil had been the victim of a very bad, cruel and sadistic sexual attack, which Daniel had called "buggering", a term that little Adrian had never heard before then.

On several occasions over the coming days and weeks when Adrian could be alone with Neil, he attempted to broach the matter, but Neil became embarrassed, fidgety and tearful and begged Adrian to drop the subject. When Adrian could not prevent himself from asking Neil if he had been subjected to the act of buggering by Daniel or any other boy on more than that one occasion, Neil became angry and almost violent, risking to lose control of himself and to strike Adrian with his fists. But as he loved his little brother very dearly he wrapped his arms around him, hugged him tenderly for several seconds then implored him in a soft voice to avoid talking about that subject ever again, as it was unbearable and had to be buried at the back of Adrian's mind as if it had never happened. Adrian nodded silently and he kept his promise and never did raise the matter again, but he continued to carry inside him a deep sadness and a bitter regret that he could do nothing to prevent the suffering being endured by his beloved brother and could not call his other brother Justin for help. As he had to keep the secret and he had not in any case had any contact at all with Justin or his aunt and uncle since they had taken Justin away from the orphanage for the last time. Both he and Neil missed Justin dreadfully and the lack of any contact with him deepened their feeling of abandonment and rejection and heart-rending unhappiness caused by their dreadfully miserable and wretched fate.

Neil became progressively more and more withdrawn and taciturn and his demeanour took a more sullen and aggressive turn towards everybody at the orphanage. Whilst he attempted to control his temper and pent-up anger, it was to no avail and he became involved in a greater number of fights with other boys as time went on, except with the famous trio of bully boys led by Daniel Turnbull. He never breathed a word to anybody about the exactions he was being subjected to but to Adrian it felt instinctively evident that his poor eldest brother was continuing to be sexually abused by the trio on occasions.

At several times over the ensuing months, when Neil and Adrian were alone, Neil repeated to Adrian with desperate exasperation in his voice and welling tears in his sad eyes, 'I want to get out of here! I must get away from this damned place! I will find a way to get away from here! I hate this awful life and I cannot stand it anymore!'

Mr and Mrs Watson could not help but note the degrading change in Neil's disposition and attitudes and they became very worried about his psychological and emotional state. On several occasions, they tried to talk to him and asked him if anything was amiss and if he wanted to speak to them about any specific personal problems that he might have, but Neil just clammed up and refused to communicate any information to them. It was impossible for them to know that any of the boys in the orphanage were subjecting any others to any sexual abuse. For all the victims were sworn to silence and secrecy by way of dreadful threats and menaces and Mr and Mrs Watson in their naivety never even guessed that such heinous practices were being perpetrated inside the home.

After some reflection and being very sad to see how unhappy Neil was, they offered to adopt him as their son, but Neil refused their offer flatly, saying

that he wanted to put an end to the existence of life connected in any way with the orphanage. That evening he told his little brother about the offer of adoption he had received and the answer word for word that he had given to Mr and Mrs Watson.

In the next summer, all the children at the orphanage were taken by coach one Saturday afternoon down to the beach at Overstrand and as it was a pleasant, sunny and warm day, they played gleefully on the long stretch of golden sand. Under the supervision of the staff, they were able to swim in the sea whilst keeping in their depth, as the North Sea currents could be strong and treacherous and the risk of being carried out to sea were not to be under-estimated.

All of a sudden, one of the girls jumped up and down frantically, pointed out to sea with an outstretched arm and screamed at the top of her voice, 'Alert! Alert! I can see a boy way out there in the sea flaying his arms about! He will drown if nobody goes out to save him!'

One of the members of staff, who was already in his swimming trunks splashing around at the edge of the sea with some younger boys and girls, started to swim out and being very fit and a strong swimmer he soon reached the boy and brought him back to the shore. The boy was in a bad way and had been very close to drowning. The staff member laid him gently on his back and carried out the life-saving exercises and mouth-to-mouth resuscitation that he had learned some years back in courses at the St John's Ambulance Service.

Everyone came running over to see what was happening and Adrian was horrified to see that the boy lying on the sand, coughing and spluttering and regaining his breath, was his beloved brother Neil. The staff arranged for an ambulance to come and Neil was transported to Cromer Hospital and was kept in bed under observation overnight and the following day the doctor gave his authorisation for Neil to be discharged from hospital and taken back to The Grange. Mr and Mrs Watson, as well as Adrian, could not prevent themselves from wondering intuitively and sadly whether Neil had swam all that way out to sea on his own with the deliberate intention of putting an end to his life by drowning but had panicked at the last moment as he was sinking beneath the waves and could not go through with it.

Yet again, Neil simply clammed shut, would not say a word about the incident and just shouted at them that they should forget that it had ever happened. This possible attempted suicide by his beloved brother haunted little Adrian for many days and brought on horrible and scary nightmares during many nights.

In October 1958, four months after his fourteenth birthday, Neil rushed over to Adrian one morning waving a sheet of paper and harbouring a grin on his face, the first time that Adrian had seen his brother smile for a very long time. 'I have got it, little brother!' Neil exclaimed excitedly. 'I have got it!'

'What have you got?' queried Adrian, with a puzzled look on his face.

'This piece of paper is the letter of my admission to the Royal Navy shore training ship HMS GANGES to train to become a sailor!' Neil replied with a strong trace of pride and satisfaction in his glowing blue eyes and radiant smile.

Adrian stood there for several seconds in a shocked and dazed state tinged with fear that he would soon be losing his bigger brother whom he loved and cherished so much and whose comforting presence was so important to him.

'I do not understand,' he managed finally to whisper with a nervous and feeble voice.

'This is my escape route, my way to get away from this hellhole, little brother. As I could not stand living here, I simply asked one of my teachers at school if he knew of any way for a boy of my age who is very unhappy in this orphanage to obtain freedom from this life and start a fresh life with some activity or training somewhere else. He carried out some research and came back with the answer that I could apply for admission to start a training at HMS GANGES to become a sailor in the Royal Navy. He said that it is a shore training ship based at Shotley Gate on the east coast opposite Harwich, to enter boys normally have to be fifteen years of age but he was sure that if my unhappy plight was explained to them they would accept to take me now as I am already fourteen years old. At my request, he talked about it with Mr and Mrs Watson, who accepted to do everything they could to help. They assisted me in obtaining the necessary forms and making the application and Mr Watson drove me down there discreetly one day for an interview and a visit around the training facilities. I was told to wait some time while my application was being analysed, and I have just received this letter accepting to admit me and telling me that I will start at the training ship in early January! I have showed it to Mr and Mrs Watson, who are very pleased for me, and they said they would leave it to me to show you the letter and explain the situation to you.'

After he had absorbed this incredible and unexpected news, Adrian burst into tears. Then flung himself into Neil's arms and hugged him tightly for several long seconds before telling him that he was going to miss him dreadfully but he understood how miserable and desperate Neil had been and was very happy for him now as he had the prospect of a better life.

'There is one thing that I must tell you,' Neil said as he kept his right arm affectionately wrapped around Adrian's shoulder. 'I have never mentioned to anybody, not to Mr and Mrs Watson, not to any of my teachers at school, nor to any of the persons who interviewed me at HMS GANGES, the horrible things that that bully boy Daniel and his ghastly cronies have done to me, as I am sure they would not believe me. Those boys would deny everything and I could not provide proof that they were lying, so I would be refused by HMS GANGES who could accuse me of being a mischievous liar and troublemaker, and I fear that Daniel and his gang would take it out on you and subject you to those awful abuses if I spoke out. So, please let us keep this dark secret just between the two of us, do not say anything about the matter to anyone at all and do your best to keep out of the way of those brutal bullies.'

After Christmas and New Year, Mr and Mrs Watson organised a pleasant tea party with all the children to celebrate Neil's departure from the orphanage and to wish him all the best in his new life. A car arrived on the morning of January 8th 1959 and, after prolonged hugs and kisses and tearful farewells between the two brothers, Neil opened the back door of the car, gave his little brother one last loving gaze, settled in the back seat and was driven away from The Grange, never to return, hoping that he was going to a better place and a chance to find some happiness and peace of mind.

However, he left with a heavy and sad heart at having to leave Adrian behind and he wept during most of the journey as he wished bitterly that he could have been able to take young Adrian with him.

Chapter 6
Difficult Adoption and Painful Experiences During Upbringing

Within a couple of days after Neil's departure, Adrian's mental, psychological and emotional state deteriorated dramatically. He seemed to withdraw into a shell, spent most of his time outside school on his own away from the other children at the orphanage, started to rock himself and fling his body frantically from side to side in his bed every night again, had enormous difficulty to settle into sleep and began to wet his bed and suffer again the horrific and terrifying nightmares that had not pursued him for some time.

He had now lost his mother, his father, both his beloved brothers and he missed them dreadfully. He could not prevent his mind from thinking continuously about the ease with which his mother had rejected, betrayed and abandoned him and his two brothers. And the cold, unloving detachment of his father and the way in which he too had rejected, betrayed and abandoned them and caused them to be thrown into the two awful orphanages and then to be separated from one another.

He felt intuitively deep down inside himself, without anyone ever having told him, that the first and fundamental role of a mother and a father was to love, cherish and protect each of their children and that the failure to do so was a heinous betrayal. The pain and suffering which the rejection, betrayal and abandonment by his parents and the loss of his two brothers caused Adrian to endure was excruciating and permanent and wracked every fibre of his frail being.

Then a recurring, forceful and convincing thought began to invade Adrian's mind and haunted him so much that it became a strong evidence to his damaged psyche. He could not prevent himself from repeating to himself that if his mother then his father had rejected, betrayed and abandoned him it was entirely his fault. It was because something was very wrong with him as a human being. He had been born with a deformity, had an ugly face and body and did not possess any physical traits or any traits of character that attracted love or deserved to be loved. And it was normal that his parents had no love or consideration for him and in actual fact hated him, because he was a pathetic and ugly being from every point of view, was not worthy of any love or esteem and was devoid of any value and was completely worthless. Despite his miserable efforts, he could not shake off this conviction that he was worth

nothing at all and the smallest insect grovelling on the ground was worth much more than him.

Adrian started to feel very guilty about being such a worthless and valueless baby then a small boy that he had caused his parents so much pain and frustration that they were not able to love him or consider him positively but were obliged to turn their backs on him and were forced to reject and abandon him. He repeated continuously to himself, "it is all my fault, I am the guilty one, I am totally worthless". This stark evidence became so engrained deep inside his being that wherever he went he started to see in his mind and in his eyes a grey, sombre and sinister vortex, shaped like a swirling tornado, which turned in circles at very high speed then sped down into a deep, long black hole which became a narrow tunnel into which his worthless and pathetic body was hurled and dragged down into the darkest and deepest recesses of the bowels of the earth and swallowed up in the black void. Having become convinced of his lack of value and of his guilt for having caused his parents to do to him what they forcibly had to do, Adrian started to feel that he had no right to continue living. And over the coming weeks and months, he began to harbour convictions that the only issue for him was to commit suicide but he was terrified at the thought and just could not think what method of annihilation of his valueless and pathetic being would be the swiftest and least painful.

***

Was it destiny? Was it sheer good luck? Were destiny and good luck of the same importance and to be equated to each other? Mrs Drisedale at The Grange had continued to take little and miserably unhappy Adrian with her to Sunday Mass each week at the Catholic church in Overstrand. After Mass one Sunday, a short, slim lady aged in her mid-sixties, with grey hair and glasses perched on her elegant but slightly twisted nose and impeccably dressed in a green cardigan and purple skirt, walked up to Mrs Drisedale, placed a hand gently on her left elbow, drew her aside, leaving Adrian standing awkwardly on his own, and engaged in a conversation with her.

Then she walked over to Adrian with Mrs Drisedale, who introduced her to him.

'Adrian, my dear, this lady is Mrs Maureen Packman. She lives in a bungalow near the cliffs here in Overstrand and has been an active member of this parish and also of the catholic parish in Cromer for some years and over time she has tried to help orphaned children in any way that she can. She has taken an interest in you and would like to get to know you, as she has been told that you are an orphan living at The Grange.'

With his nihilistic attitude about himself, Adrian just looked blankly at the lady without any expression or reaction in his lifeless blue eyes. How could she take any interest in him, for he was less worthy than a small worm and was devoid of any value? He stood still as rigid as a marble statue for a few more

seconds then clasped his hands together in front of him, lowered his head and eyes and stared at the ground, into which he felt he was going to be swallowed.

The lady bent down, took one of his hands in hers, placed her other hand under his chin and raised his head up gently so that his eyes were looking into hers, which were brown flecked with green and had an engaging, kind and warm expression. She said a few words to him, told him she was looking forward to seeing him at church the following Sunday, said goodbye to him and Mrs Drisedale and walked away to find her car.

For several Sundays, the lady approached Mrs Drisedale and Adrian after Mass and talked quietly to them for a few minutes. Then one Sunday, she asked them whether it would be allowed at the orphanage for the two of them to come to her bungalow the following Saturday afternoon for tea and cake or biscuits. She gave Mrs Drisedale her telephone number and told her that she could come to The Grange in her little blue Austin A30 car to fetch them and would drive them back to the orphanage later in the afternoon. Mr and Mrs Watson were delighted at this development and readily gave their approval, so Mrs Drisedale telephoned Mrs Packman and she arrived at the gravel driveway exactly at the agreed time on Saturday. Mrs Drisedale sat beside Mrs Packman at the front and Adrian luxuriated in the fact that he had for himself the entire back seat of the little car, which he thought from the outside resembled the round shell of a snail, so he said to himself that he was riding in "the little blue snail on wheels".

The bungalow was small, its outer walls were painted white and the front door and windows were painted blue, giving the house a fresh seaside atmosphere, which was very appropriate as the reasonably large garden led to the cliffs and the view of the North Sea was spectacular.

The garden was neat and well kept, with several flowerbeds bearing the remnants of a few flowers which had survived the winter and other precocious yellow, white and pink early spring flowers. The large lawn still had dull yellowish grass from the winter and it would be weeks yet before any scarification could be undertaken and fertiliser spread over the lawn to encourage the growth of the new grass which would become a lovely green carpet over the ensuing months leading to the Norfolk summer.

Mrs Packman led them through the tiny hall into the cosy lounge with the walls covered in a light and soft green wallpaper, providing a soothing and restful atmosphere. After inviting them to sit on the comfortable beige sofa, she disappeared into the kitchen and soon reappeared carrying a large tray loaded with a teapot, milk jug, cups and saucers for her and Mrs Drisedale, a tall glass of lemonade for Adrian and plates piled with chocolate biscuits, ginger biscuits and cupcakes. She sat down on a large armchair opposite the sofa and was a charming and delightful hostess as she entertained them with pleasant conversation during the next two hours. She drove them back to The Grange, wished them a lovely evening, saying she looked forward to seeing them at Mass the following day, and drove away in her amusing little blue snail on wheels.

The ritual of afternoon tea at Mrs Packman's white and blue bungalow became a fixture each Saturday afternoon over the following weeks. At first, Adrian was very sullen, hardly said a word, never smiled and did not show any sign of enjoying these outings, except that he gulped down the lemonade with relish and gobbled down several ginger biscuits with great greed and enthusiasm. These sessions at the cliff-side bungalow instilled in Adrian a life-long love of ginger biscuits!

It was not long before both Mrs Drisedale and Adrian divulged to Mrs Packman that he had before him near end of June that summer the gruelling and daunting task of taking the 11-plus exams. Whilst Adrian could not bring himself to mention it, for it would evoke such sad and wretched memories of all the suffering his eldest brother had endured, Mrs Drisedale told Mrs Packman that Neil had failed the exams. She also mentioned that no child who had lived at The Grange had ever managed to pass the 11-plus exams since the establishment of the orphanage in the village. Mrs Packman looked at them silently for a few moments then they saw a bright twinkle in her expressive eyes and a mischievous grin on her pretty face slightly lined with wrinkles.

'Well, we shall have to try to do something about that, shan't we?' she said softly but with determination and enthusiasm as she clapped her hands together.

Mrs Drisedale and Adrian looked at one another with puzzled expressions and Adrian said nothing but merely scowled and shrugged his shoulders.

After a moment's silence, Mrs Drisedale asked Mrs Packman what she meant by her remark. 'I am willing to help Adrian to prepare himself for the 11-plus exams. If you do not mind, I can collect Adrian by himself without you each Saturday afternoon. He can bring his little satchel with his books, papers and materials here to the bungalow. And after he has drunk his lemonade and devoured his beloved ginger biscuits, to give him sustenance and fortitude, we can sit down at the dining-room table and work together so that I can school him and help him to prepare himself satisfactorily and in time to pass the 11-plus exams with what we hope will be flying colours!'

This generous and unusual proposal was put by Mrs Drisedale to Mr and Mrs Watson. They discussed the matter with Mrs Packman and, after they had given their consent, she was as good as her word and, saying that there was no time to lose, started to help Adrian with the learning and preparation for the exams as from the following Saturday afternoon. She had had several experiences with orphaned children over the past few years and was fully aware of the dreadful traumas, deep unhappiness, insecurity and mental and emotional instability which these sad children suffered and the long-term detrimental consequences caused by the loss of parents through death or by parental rejection and abandonment, lack of love and consideration and the miserable life in an orphanage cut off from family ties and connections.

She was able to understand little Adrian's total lack of self-esteem, his irrational feeling of worthlessness, his distrust of other people, his inability to smile and socialise and his great inability to concentrate on subjects for more

than a minute or so. She felt very sorry for his brother Neil that he had had no help or support from someone like her to bolster and encourage him, had consequentially not been able to pass his 11-plus exams and was being deprived of the possibility of attending a grammar school and obtaining a good and higher education at a university or another educational establishment which would provide bigger chances of a better future. She felt guilty inside herself that she had not been there to help Neil but she could not have done so as she had been spending all her available time and some of her financial savings providing assistance and support to two other orphaned children in other parts of Norfolk and had succeeded in finding adoptive parents for one boy. Unfortunately, she could not find any adoptive parents for the other boy, as his was a very grave and extreme case of psychological and emotional derangement and very deep depression, almost a lost cause in reality. He had had to be admitted into a mental hospital at some point in time and would undoubtedly spend many years interned in that institution.

Mrs Packman felt gratified that she had met Adrian and had taken him under her wing. She was determined to do the very best that she could to provide assistance and moral support to unhappy and unstable Adrian. Her sessions with him were far from easy at the beginning, for he was a rough diamond, very raw, sore and over-sensitive, devoured by unhappiness and suffering, shrivelled up and withdrawn into his shell by so much lack of love with what seemed an impossibility to respond to her kindness, small attentions and gentle consideration.

She had to work hard to peel away deep layer upon layer in him of anger, despair, hatred and distrust of any person's affections because of a contempt for himself and anxiety about others, very raw susceptibility, great negativism and a huge visceral fear of being rejected and hurt again. However, she somehow detected some good potential in him and soon decided to pick him up at the orphanage just after lunch, earlier than at the beginning, and to prolong their sessions together by returning him back to The Grange much later in the afternoon. The greatest obstacle, which caused their progress to be slower than she had hoped, was his great difficulty to concentrate and the deep sadness, hurt state and negativity which inhabited his being. On several occasions she felt frustrated and mentally exhausted at the end of their afternoon together, but she said to herself that she had to persevere and that, if she felt exhausted, how much more mentally and emotionally drained must poor Adrian have felt!

Her perseverance and dedication to the difficult task paid off, for that summer Adrian just scraped by with the minimal marks but he succeeded in passing the 11-plus exams. He became the first inhabitant at that orphanage ever to have passed the 11-plus exams!

He could not believe it when, on that Friday afternoon near end of June, the headmaster of the little Overstrand primary school lined up six wooden chairs in front of all the teachers and pupils at the school, called out the names in alphabetical order of their surnames of five children who had passed the exams

that time, inviting them to stand on the chairs, and then called out his name, the surname of Walton-Mornick being almost at the end of the alphabet!

He felt abashed, confused and embarrassed. Due to his deep-seated inner feeling of being unworthy, useless and without any value, he just stood still, trembling slightly, whilst everyone looked at him, and when the headmaster called his name again and some fellow pupils starting pushing him from behind towards his chair, he felt so self-conscious, nervous and lacking in confidence that he stumbled, nearly fainted and fell flat on his face. His humiliation seemed complete, but the headmaster lifted him under the arms, helped him to steady himself and stand up on the chair, and when all the teachers and pupils present in the classroom clapped their hands in applause and shouted a hearty bravo to the six successful pupils, including himself, he became completely overwhelmed with emotion, burst into tears and clasped both hands over his eyes and stayed like that for what seemed an eternity. His bowed head and hunched shoulders were rocking up and down, until he felt the kind arms of the headmaster wrap themselves around him and heard his voice congratulating him and telling him that his achievement was a very big one, would be most important for his future and would provide encouragement to other orphans at The Grange.

On the next day, Saturday afternoon, Mr and Mrs Watson organised a special tea party in the large dining room at The Grange for all the inmates in order to congratulate Adrian for his personal success and for creating history for the orphanage.

In the morning, Mr Watson had telephoned Mrs Packman inviting her to the tea party and, as she came into the crowded dining room at four in the afternoon she asked in her soft and enchanting voice, 'Where is he? Where is Adrian?'

As all the other children stopped chattering among themselves and stood aside to let him pass, young Adrian advanced very slowly and sheepishly and stood in front of Mrs Packman. She stretched out her right hand, shook his right hand strenuously and uttered a hearty congratulation and said that Adrian should feel very proud of himself. He replied with an almost inaudible word of thanks and Mrs Packman proceeded to move among the children, talking to many of them and placing a gentle and kind hand on the heads of several boys and girls, who lapped up her unexpected and welcome attention with immense glee.

Adrian could suddenly feel the circling vortex swirling fast inside his head and he felt that he was about to be hurled down by it through a long, narrow, winding black tunnel and buried in the deep and dark bowels of the earth. He felt cruelly disappointed and upset that Mrs Packman had only shaken his hand and had not taken him in her arms, had not hugged him and had not given him a loving kiss on the cheek or any other sign of affection. His need for one sign of warm love was enormous, after having received cold, practical and technical assistance from her. At the first opportunity, he saw that Mrs Packman was enjoying herself being surrounded by and chatting with several other children.

And Mr and Mrs Watson were busy with other staff members bringing in more fruit juices, cupcakes and biscuits. He started slowly walking sideways weaving his way between some children, like a crab slinking surreptitiously between rocks in a seawater pool on the beach, until he had left the dining-room and reached the bottom of the staircase. Then he silently climbed the stairs, tiptoed to the door of his bedroom, turned the door knob very slowly and, once he was in the room and had safely closed the door behind him without hearing any voice calling after him, he threw himself on the bed and buried his head on the pillow as he burst into tears and his chest started heaving as his pent-up pain overwhelmed him.

After a moment he called out in an anguished and desperate whisper, 'Where are you mother? Where are you father? Where are you Neil and Justin? I miss you all so dreadfully much. Why has our family been destroyed? Why is it that we cannot all be together again? I need to see your faces, gaze into your eyes, feel your arms around me and bask in the warmth of your love. I feel so unloved, rejected, abandoned and horribly lonely!'

Adrian searched deep inside himself for answers to all his questions, but he could find none; he could not understand this awful destiny, all he could see in his mind was a black void, a sense of nothingness and an overpowering conviction that he was nothing. His heart ached, his head nearly exploded with the heavy weight of depression and he continued to lie on the pillow as he sobbed in fits and starts until he felt so weary that he finally started to fall asleep. However, his whole night was disturbed by dreadful nightmares and great pangs of guilt, which submerged him, as he told himself forcefully over and over again that it was he who had caused the break-up of his family and the ensuing unhappiness of each of its members. Yes, he was the guilty one and would have to be punished severely in this life by a painful and lonely existence devoid of any love.

***

Adrian was convinced in his tiny and troubled mind that Mrs Packman had no interest in him at all and that she had only helped him to prepare for the 11-plus exams out of a selfish motivation for her own vanity, personal satisfaction and glory if and when he succeeded.

Consequently, on Sunday the day after the tea party, as he and Mrs Drisedale came out of the Overstrand church after Mass, he was utterly dumfounded and confused when Mrs Packman walked up to them, greeted them courteously with a pleasant smile and asked Adrian whether he would like to go with her on the following Friday, if Mr and Mrs Watson agreed, as the school summer holidays had started, to the Golf Club in Cromer, just a few miles along the coast from Overstrand, and start receiving lessons on how to play golf from the professional instructor at the club, for which she was more than happy to pay, being a keen golfer herself.

'In actual fact, it is called the Royal Cromer Golf Club,' Mrs Packman explained to Mrs Drisedale and Adrian. 'It was created in the latter part of the nineteenth century and quickly attained royal status in 1888 through the patronage of the then Prince of Wales, who later became King Edward VII, as he was one of the club's founding members. The club has entertained ever since members of the royalty, rich, famous and aristocratic people and over the past six decades it has been graced by the presence of princes, princesses, prime ministers and literary maestros such as Alfred Lord Tennyson and Oscar Wilde. I have been a member since I moved up to Overstrand from Amersham in Buckinghamshire, which is on the west side of London, after the death of my husband a few years ago. All of its present members, including myself, are very proud to be associated with the Royal Cromer Golf Club!'

She looked at Mrs Drisedale then down at Adrian with a proud and satisfied look on her face and in her eyes. Adrian looked blankly back up at her, with no enthusiasm in his facial expression and indeed with a look in his sad blue eyes of total apathy, lack of interest and lack of comprehension or concentration. He appeared not to care at all about what she had just told them, then lowered his eyes and his head, shrugged his shoulders and started to turn away from the two ladies.

Mrs Packman, not wishing to be put off or to appear offended by his rough rudeness, retained her calm composure and simply added, 'My dear Adrian, it may not appear to you at this moment that the game of golf is interesting or has any purpose, but I am confident that once you have had a few lessons and some practice you will start enjoying the game and understanding its benefits. If Mrs Drisedale will kindly ask Mr and Mrs Watson for their permission, and if they give it, will you at least come with me to the club on Friday, as the forecast is for fine weather, meet Mr Bernard Dobbins the pro, as we call him, and allow him to introduce you to the rudiments of the game of golf and give you your first lesson?'

'All right then,' murmured Adrian, with a begrudging pout and a distinct lack of gratitude for this generosity. 'I will give it a try, if you insist.'

As Mr and Mrs Watson were once more impressed and delighted by Mrs Packman's kind and generous gesture towards Adrian and immediately signalled their approval, Mrs Packman arrived at The Grange shortly after lunch on Friday and drove Adrian in the little blue snail on wheels, which was at least something that seemed to give him a minimum of pleasure, to the Royal Cromer Golf Club. When they arrived at the clubhouse, Mr Bernard Dobbins was there waiting for them at the precise time of the appointment which Mrs Packman had arranged by telephone.

She told Adrian that she was leaving him in the capable hands of the pro and would see him later back at the same spot, as she was going to play with three lady friends a nine-hole game of golf, rather than the full eighteen holes, which had become too tiring for her at her age.

Mr Dobbins carried a golf bag containing a few iron clubs the suitable size and length for a ten-year old boy. When they arrived at the first part of the

practice area, he explained to Adrian, before commencing with the first lesson, 'This golf course is situated about half-way between the town of Cromer and the village of Overstrand, was created along the Cromer range of undulating rugged cliffs and stands some three hundred and twenty feet above the sandy beaches down below. The town of Cromer, where I live, is dramatically poised on a high bluff, is a seaside resort and boasts a long Victorian pier jutting out to sea with the famous Pavilion Theatre standing proudly at its end. This golf course is what one calls a cliff top course with spectacular coastline views and it has all the features of a coastal course with a wealth of sandy hills, grassy valleys, abundant yellow gorse bushes and a sizeable quantity of bracken. The entire course is a mighty test at times due to strong winds, which blow in from the North Sea. After this first lesson, we can take a little walk and you will see in particular the lovely view from the fourteenth hole looking straight towards the charming white lighthouse.'

As Adrian's sole reaction was a look and an attitude which indicated that he could not care less and had not been concentrating, Mr Dobbins thought to himself that it was not going to be easy with this little lad, but he proceeded to demonstrate how to hold a club correctly and so on.

At the end of that first one-hour lesson, Mr Dobbins' fears were realised, as his young pupil had shown no enthusiasm whatsoever, remained stiff and wooden in his stance and overall attitude, and demonstrated very little aptitude for the noble game of golf. The feature which disturbed Mr Dobbins the most was the great and most unusual difficulty on Adrian's part to concentrate on each of Mr Dobbins' explanations and instructions, on the direction ahead of him along the grassy course indicated by the pro, and on the ball itself when he attempted to swing the club, causing him to miss the ball entirely and on several occasions to strike the ground with the club and gouge out a large divet, which Mr Dobbins did his best to press back into the ground with his golf shoe.

However, Mr Dobbins had been told by Mrs Packman that Adrian was a very disturbed and unhappy orphan living at The Grange, so he felt sympathy and some degree of pity for Adrian's sad plight. As they walked back to the club-house after having gone as far as the fourteenth hole and looked along the fairway towards the white lighthouse, Mr Dobbins playfully ruffled Adrian's jet black hair with his hand, then placed his hand around his shoulder and said gently to him, lying between his teeth, 'You know, Adrian, that was not bad at all for a first lesson. Golf is a difficult game to learn and master and it requires much patience, perseverance and practice to get the hang of it and play well. I am sure that you will make good and rapid progress after a few lessons'.

Mrs Packman arranged for Adrian to have two more lessons with Mr Dobbins during the following week. After the second ruefully disastrous lesson, with hardly any progress at all being achieved by Adrian, as he and Mrs Packman were ensconced in deep, comfortable green leather armchairs in the members' lounge at the club-house consuming refreshments, she leaned over towards him and murmured almost inaudibly, 'Tell me, Adrian, have you had

any contact with your brother Justin since he left The Grange to live with your uncle and aunt in Dickleborough?'

Adrian recoiled in shock, as if he had been slapped on the face, then stared at her for a short while and shook his head miserably as large, round tears welled up in his eyes then rolled fast down his cheeks, like raindrops cascading down a tree trunk in a tropical forest.

He shuddered and, as he tried to control the tremors in his body and voice, he croaked, barely able to emit the words, 'No, I have had no contact at all with him or any other members of my awful family.'

'That is exactly what I suspected. Well, I have had some contact and I thought that you might like to know how he is faring. I obtained your uncle and aunt's address and telephone number from Mr Watson, I called, spoke with your aunt then with her permission drove over to their house and met them and Justin. After having met him twice, he confided to me that he thought that he might have a vocation to become a catholic priest but did not know how he could go about things to obtain the suitable training. It so happens that, together with Brigadier Edward Gwynn, a retired army officer who has been a good friend of mine for many years, I have paid the fees for lodging and training for another boy who has just graduated from the seminary called Buckden Towers and will soon be ordained a catholic priest.'

'Let me give you a piece of history – and do try hard to concentrate on what I am telling you, my dear boy. Buckden Towers is situated in the town of Buckden in the county of Cambridgeshire, a little south-west of the county of Norfolk. The place has a very rich history, spanning over nine hundred years, if you can imagine that great length of time. It was formerly known as Buckden Palace, when it was a wooden palace in the twelfth century used for housing the Bishops of Lincoln. It was replaced around 1475 by a large brick and stone building with a tall brick tower, then the Victorian house now present on the site was built around 1870. Having a great love for history, I have studied a substantial amount of the history of Buckden Towers and can tell you that some very important people in British history have stayed there during the past centuries, including King Henry III in 1248, King Edward I in 1291, King Richard III in 1483, King Henry VIII and his wife Catherine Howard in 1541, and King James I in 1619. Do not look so bored and please replace that vacuous look in your eyes by a more lively expression showing that you are managing to maintain some concentration on the subject!'

'The Claretian Missionaries were given the site of Buckden Towers in 1956 by the Bishop of Northampton. It is now used as a Junior Seminary providing preliminary training to boys aged from eleven to eighteen years aspiring to become priests or brothers in the order of Claretian Missionaries. I know that you will be eleven years old on your next birthday on September 7th, in two months' time. As your brother Justin has just turned thirteen a few days ago in early July, Brigadier Gwynn and I have managed to arrange for Justin's admission to the Junior Seminary at Buckden Towers. He will start there as a full-time boarder when the new scholastic year commences in early September,

allowing him to receive a normal scholastic education at the same time that he undergoes the preliminary training on his road to become a priest, if such be God's will and he really does have a vocation. As your uncle and aunt made it clear to us that they could not afford to pay the fees for Justin at Buckden Towers, Brigadier Gwynn and I have accepted to share the payment of his fees between us for as long as is necessary.'

Adrian felt mentally and emotionally exhausted, for the enormous effort to sit up straight, concentrate on and assimilate all these facts had drained his energy. He stopped looking at Mrs Packman, slumped back in the armchair, covered his face and eyes with both hands and remained immobile for a couple of minutes.

Just as Mrs Packman was starting to wonder whether he might have fallen asleep, he uncovered his eyes very slowly, clenched his fists and pressed them on the side of both cheeks, placed his elbows on each knee as he leaned forward slightly and said in a wretchedly sad, low whisper, 'Thank you for giving me this news about my brother Justin and thank you also for helping him to create a better future for himself. But, when will I be able to see him again? I love him so much and I miss him dreadfully, just as I do my eldest brother Neil! I just do not understand why we cannot be together again. We are three brothers, we need to be together, we want and need to grow up together!'

The anxiety and desperation in his voice and the suffering and pleading expression in his eyes as he started weeping again were heart-rending and Mrs Packman was sorely tempted to spring forward and wrap her arms around this poor, dreadfully unhappy young orphan. But she could not, for the stuffy and severe Victorian education she had received from her parents and at her schools so many years ago had inculcated in her the harsh and rigid rule that you must not show your emotions and you have to show a "stiff upper lip". So, she merely stretched out her left hand, stroked the back of Adrian's right fist still pressed against his cheek, took out a silk embroidered handkerchief from her handbag and dabbed his eyes as she caught his large falling tear-drops, then said to him as his glistening, doe-like blue eyes penetrated her heart, 'I cannot tell you when you will be able to see your brothers again. I do not know the answer to that difficult question. But I can promise that I will do my best to found out how they are both faring on a regular basis and let you have the news.'

***

Back at the orphanage, the summer holidays rolled on in a slow, lazy and mundane fashion. The staff did their best to entertain the poor orphans by organising games on the large lawn and in the neighbouring copse among the trees and one or two outings to the Overstrand beach and even a coach trip to a small seaside town and its beach down south in the direction of Great Yarmouth. Adrian could not derive any joy or pleasure from any of the activities with the other inmates, and he could not establish any closeness or

friendships with any of the other children, as he was miserably and unavoidably enclosed in his own world of anguish.

He missed his brothers so achingly and suffered such overwhelmingly painful pangs of guilt, due to feeling horribly convinced that he had caused the break-up of his family and the rejection and abandonment of his brothers and himself by their mother then their father, that he rocked his body frenetically and violently from side to side in bed at night, had the most awful nightmares and felt continuously the swirling vortex hurtling him inexorably down through an ever-narrowing black tunnel into the deep bowels of the earth and into chaos and oblivion.

Further, his irrational but forceful condemnation and hatred of himself as being utterly useless, worthless and without any value in the eyes of himself or other people caused him to become progressively more mentally, emotionally and psychologically unbalanced and distorted, as well as sullenly and mournfully withdrawn from normality. To make matters worse, he continued to be insulted, mocked and bullied by some of the older boys.

He had two more golf lessons with Mr Dobbins, then he told Mrs Packman that he did not want to continue with the lessons, as it was hopeless because he could not concentrate, he could not play golf and derived no pleasure from playing the game. He felt unworthy of such attention and generosity and it was a waste of Mr Dobbins' time and Mrs Packman's money as he was useless. As he looked so thoroughly miserable as he said this, but appeared bizarrely convinced by what he was saying, she felt very sad but decided not to argue with him or try to persuade him to persist with the lessons. She merely accepted his abjectly negative and backward decision, whilst feeling silently deep inside herself that this was a particularly unhappy and severely damaged young orphan, one of the worst cases she had ever encountered.

A few days later, Mrs Packman arrived at The Grange in her cute little blue snail on wheels and asked to speak with Mr and Mrs Watson in their office. They came out a while later, found Adrian sitting alone on a rock beside the lawn staring in a strange, distracted and detached way at a flower bed and asked him to join them all in the office. He was astonished, somewhat apprehensive and even fearful when he was told that Mrs Packman was inviting him to join her, her daughter and her son-in-law on a week's holiday in a hotel near the seaside town of Hunstanton on the north-east coast of Norfolk not very far from The Wash. As his evaluation of and confidence in himself were at zero level, he trembled to think what Mrs Packman's daughter and son-in-law would think of him and he felt sure that they would dislike him intensely and would have nothing but contempt for him.

Mr Watson said that this trip would take place in the last but one week before Adrian was to commence in early September his last year as a pupil at the local primary school in Overstrand before going to the grammar school in Cromer. He was happy for Adrian to benefit from this unexpected and generous break and he wished him a very pleasant week with Mrs Packman,

her daughter and son-in-law and asked Mrs Watson to help Adrian select his clothes and pack his little suitcase for the escapade when the time came.

In the morning on the appointed Saturday, with their two suitcases installed in the small boot of the little blue snail on wheels, as Adrian sat in the front passenger seat and Mrs Packman drove out of Overstrand and turned right onto the main road in the direction of Cromer, she said in a cheerful and bubbly tone of voice, 'We are going to stay at the Heacham Manor Hotel on the Hunstanton road. Heacham Manor is situated between the pretty village of Heacham, which is renowned for its gorgeous fields of lavender, and the Victorian seaside town of Hunstanton, a perfect location to enjoy the outstanding beauty of the North Norfolk Coast with charming unspoilt beaches, quaint old villages and coastal walks. For example, it is forty-five miles from Cromer to Hunstanton along the coastal footpath. My husband and I stayed on three occasions at this hotel during some summer holidays and we stayed there the last time just a few months before he died suddenly and tragically of a massive heart attack.'

Adrian was looking sideways at Mrs Packman, doing his very best to concentrate and to retain her words. As she said the last phrase, mentioning the death of her husband, he saw the expression in her eyes cloud over, her face hardened and he felt certain that she was making a huge effort to fight back tears. She fell silent for the rest of the journey, which suited Adrian well as he realised with a sense of guilt and shame that his power of concentration was pathetically limited and he would not want to have to admit to her that he could not recall much detail of what she had told him.

After what seemed to him a rather long time, they turned off the main road, drove a short distance in narrow lanes just outside the village of Heacham, then swerved into a wide driveway and Mrs Packman parked the car in a space near the back entrance of a long, imposing and impressive building. After a member of staff took their suitcases from the boot and carried them into the vast reception area of the hotel, Adrian followed Mrs Packman into the building, where they were met by the hotel manager, who greeted Mrs Packman with flattering words in an effusive manner like a long lost friend. He then turned to Adrian, addressing him as "young master" as he wished him a warm welcome and a very pleasant stay. Adrian felt very small, daunted and sheepish as he looked up at this tall man, and he then went red in the face like a beetroot as the shock hit him that this man, with his great height, piercing blue eyes and handsome features, reminded him of his own father!

The manager feigned not to notice the redness in his face and the embarrassed and aggrieved expression in his eyes.

He placed a hand gently on the top of his head then on his shoulder as he led them from the welcoming reception hall into a large, comfortable lounge and said to Adrian, 'Young master, Heacham Manor is a charming sixteenth century Carrstone building steeped in history, with this lovely lounge, a spacious dining room with a superb rounded, luminous conservatory and a bar leading onto a flag-stoned terrace overlooking the beautiful gardens. They include an ancient mulberry tree dating back four hundred years, a vine

trellised arbour, three ponds, several secret sitting areas, and the terrace provides a perfect place to sit, relax and enjoy the Norfolk sea air and watch the sunset over the Wash.'

'I am sure that you will derive much pleasure from exploring all the aspects of our gardens during this coming week, but do please be very careful not to trip over and fall into one of the ponds if you are by chance walking around on your own! Now, if you will both follow me upstairs I will show you to your bedrooms, where your suitcases have already been taken.'

Whilst Mrs Packman was attributed a large single bedroom on the second floor with a beautiful view over the spacious gardens and the blue sea in the distance, Adrian felt contented with his much smaller single room lower down on the first floor, which allowed a view over the gardens but did not permit him to have a glance at the sea. The room was pleasantly furnished, the mattress felt firm and comfortable as he bounced up and down several times on the bed, and he felt that this was luxury compared with his very small, pokey and depressing bedroom and his bed with its lumpy, uncomfortable mattress back at the orphanage!

When he re-joined Mrs Packman downstairs in the lounge, she told him that her daughter Margaret and her husband Keith would not be arriving until sometime in the afternoon, as they had to drive up from Pinner, an area near London where they lived, which required a car drive of several hours on the poor and circuitous network of roads between the London area and the north of Norfolk. She suggested that they ate a light lunch in the dining room then enjoyed a rest on deckchairs on the lawn, as it was luckily a cloudless day with a clear blue sky and welcome warm sunshine. She agreed with the manager that he would come out to tell them as soon as Keith and Margaret arrived.

It was almost three o'clock in the afternoon when the hotel manager came out onto the lawn and he had to shake Mrs Packman on the shoulder, as she was fast asleep and snoring in a gentle rhythm and emitting an almost musical sound, which the manager felt sad to have to interrupt.

As Adrian was nowhere in sight, he started to search the garden and found him lying on his stomach beside one of the circular ponds with his face almost touching the surface of the water and a hand in the water and his fingers moving back and forth in slow motion, as if trying to tickle or even catch any of the goldfish and other species of colourful fish which might swim within the reach of his hand.

The manager smiled in complicity, knelt down and told him that some of the yellow, orange, red and green medium-sized fishes were Nile perch which were several years old and had lived all their lives in this pond.

Adrian pulled a face of displeasure, emitted a loud groan and was very loathe to leave his new-found paradise when the manager told him that Mrs Packman's daughter and son-in-law had arrived and were sitting in the lounge. He felt terrified to have to meet them and depressed by his overwhelming conviction that they would judge him as being ugly to look at, utterly uninteresting, not meriting any affection and not even worth knowing.

In the lounge, Mrs Packman introduced Adrian to them and he was struck to see how much Margaret resembled her mother physically, even being as short as her, except that she did not wear glasses and she was slightly plump whereas her mother was slim. Margaret looked down at him slightly severely, without smiling and with almost expressionless green-brown eyes, which he realised differentiated her from her mother, whose eyes were much more expressive and so much warmer. He did not know how old Margaret was, but as Mr Watson had once told him and some of the other orphaned children that his wife was forty years old, Adrian guessed that the woman now standing before him must have also been about that age.

As his gaze turned to the man, Adrian looked up at a medium-sized and rather thin man who appeared to him to be very old, even ancient, with deep wrinkles and two or three scars on his face. He wore round glasses with thin metal frames, giving him a rather intellectual and professorial look, and he appeared somewhat reserved, unassuming and modest in his manner, quite the opposite of Adrian's father with his self-confident, arrogant and rather pushy, cocky way of holding himself. This man looked down at Adrian for a few seconds then smiled in a timid but pleasant way and Adrian detected a warm, sensitive and kind expression in his brown eyes as the man said a few words to him with a soft, gentle and lyrical tone of voice. Although Adrian had felt very tensed up, highly nervous, inadequate and anxious about this encounter, he started to feel slightly more at ease in the presence of this man than that of his wife, who seemed to be a little starchy, prickly, severe and judgemental. But, he could not prevent himself from thinking that from his elderly appearance the man could easily have passed for her father rather than her husband.

Keith and Margaret had a double room up on the second floor on the same side of the building as Mrs Packman's room with a lovely view over the gardens and the sea. Each morning they had breakfast in their room and did not join Mrs Packman and Adrian until late morning. Adrian sensed somehow that Margaret did not seem to have a very easy or smooth relationship with her mother and he wondered whether she did not in actual fact want to spend too much time in her mother's company each day. They all sat down to lunch together on most days at the same table near the window looking out over the terrace and the luscious green lawn.

However, they did venture out on one or two excursions in Keith and Margaret's car and Adrian was intrigued and amused to discover that they had the same make of car as Mrs Packman but theirs was a little green, round-backed snail on wheels.

As the weather remained clement on most days and the summer sun blessed them with its shining light and welcome warmth, they drove down on several afternoons to the town of Hunstanton, parked the little green snail on wheels in the public car park nearest to the beach, walked down to the beach and hired deck-chairs for a couple of hours. The most outstanding features as one looked back up from the beach to one side were the tall cliffs which had the appearance of a layered cake, with honey-brown rock in a two-thirds layer from

the beach level, then a one-third white chalk layer, topped with a green layer of grass meadows.

The seafront at Hunstanton retained the air of a Victorian seaside resort, having been purpose-built in 1846 as a bathing resort. Mrs Packman explained to Adrian that there were two sides to Hunstanton, the only west facing seaside resort on the east coast of England. Firstly, the elegant Victorian town with its Esplanade Gardens and its rather sedate air of days gone by, and, secondly, Old Hunstanton with its village feel and atmosphere, its large sandy beach, pony rides, other amusements and many rock pools spread out down into the sea, all backed by the honey brown and white striped cliffs.

Whilst Mrs Packman, Keith and Margaret sat and rested contentedly on their deck chairs, Adrian amused himself by searching for small crabs in the shallow salty rock pools, picking among seashells and observing lugworms casting their coils, when he was not dipping up and down between the waves in the sea and improving his crawl, back stroke and breast stroke. Which, one afternoon, suddenly brought back vivid, sentimentally nostalgic and painful memories of when he was taught to swim by his father in the Indian Ocean and in the swimming pool at the Muthaiga Club in Nairobi and was swimming with his older brothers, who had already become strong and efficient swimmers at a very young age.

All of a sudden and without any warning, he felt a painful constriction and pang in his throat, chest and heart like a vice-like grip squeezing his body, as he thought yet again just how much he missed his father, his mother and his two beloved brothers. His arms and legs became immediately very heavy, blocked, useless and motionless as if he were paralysed, his entire body felt like a two-ton rock and sunk rapidly beneath the waves deep into the sea. He swallowed a large quantity of salty water and when he finally managed to push himself up to the surface after a huge effort before very nearly drowning, he spluttered, coughed, spit out water and gasped for air as his head rose above the level of the waves.

He felt so exhausted and panic-stricken that he was obliged to lie flat on his back with both arms and legs spread-eagled for several minutes before he found some composure and the strength to swim back to the shore.

While floating on the surface of the sea, he was reminded vividly of the occasion when Neil almost drowned off the Overstrand beach. He started thinking that it would be better for himself if he actually drowned off this Hunstanton beach. For he was so wretchedly unhappy, inconsolable and devoured by depression and a sense of hopelessness after the break-up of his family and his separation from his brothers and an overwhelming sense of guilt as his tortured mind repeatedly blamed him for all the problems in his family, the breakdown of his parents' marriage and their rejection and abandonment of their three sons.

During supper in the dining room on the last evening of the week's holiday, Mrs Packman said all of a sudden in a chirpy voice and with a cheerful smile, 'It will be Adrian's eleventh birthday in a few days' time on September 7th, and

I realise Margaret that your birthday will be only six days after his on September 13th! What a lovely coincidence that you are both September babes, born under the sign of Virgo with birthdays so close to one another!'

Margaret's only reactions to this revealing exclamation by her mother were to say 'Humph!' under her breath and to pout, as if she felt that any fact pertaining to this boy was of no interest to her, since the boy was totalling lacking any interesting features and was worthless.

This was Adrian's immediate and unavoidable interpretation of her reaction and he wanted to slide under the table and be swallowed up under the floor and into the ground, so enormous and deep was his feeling that he was utterly useless and without value and could not be of any interest to anyone.

Keith stared disapprovingly at his wife then looked at Mrs Packman and Adrian with a greatly embarrassed expression and a reddening colour on his face. He opened his mouth and almost blurted out that he wished Adrian a happy birthday, but he suddenly checked himself, as if thinking that it felt incongruous, inappropriate and somewhat cruel to say happy birthday to this obviously unhappy and wretchedly miserable orphan, and he closed his mouth again and remained silent.

On the last morning of their stay, after all the bags had been put into the boots of the green and blue snails on wheels, Margaret gave a rapid peck on the cheek to her mother in a slightly frosty, distant manner, without much apparent filial affection. Then she said goodbye to Adrian whilst barely looking at him and cursorily wished them both a safe and pleasant drive back to Overstrand.

For his part, Keith shook hands with his mother-in-law, thanked her sincerely for a very pleasant week's holiday, and then also shook Adrian's hand and ruffled his hair playfully and gently as he said goodbye to him with a reserved but warm smile. In his overpowering and all-consuming need for some love, consideration and affection, Adrian almost threw himself into the arms of this elderly, kind and paternal figure, but he restrained himself with great difficulty and merely stood still and hoped that it would not be noticed as he choked back his tears and felt a stinging soreness in his reddening eyes.

Keith drove the little green snail on wheels out of the driveway and turned south to pass through Hunstanton on their way back down to Pinner, whilst Mrs Packman drove the little blue snail on wheels eastwards along the coastal road back to Cromer then onwards to Overstrand. After a moment of silence, as Mrs Packman concentrated on her driving, Adrian took his courage in both hands and asked her how old her daughter was going to be on her upcoming birthday on September 13th. Mrs Packman turned to look at him, with a bemused expression that he was curious about Margaret's age, and she told him that her daughter was going to celebrate her forty-first birthday.

Adrian smiled to himself, being pleased that he had guessed her age pretty accurately. He was dying to ask how old Keith was, but he did not dare to do so, as he was sure that Keith was very ancient so raising the subject of his age might appear as a lack of respect towards him. So he simply clammed up and they remained silent for the rest of the journey until Mrs Packman deposited

Adrian back at the orphanage, waving goodbye and saying she looked forward to seeing him at Sunday mass the following day at the Overstrand church, as she turned the little blue snail on wheels back down the driveway.

***

During the next two months, Adrian could not banish from his mind, warped by desperate unhappiness, emotional disturbance and loneliness, the deep feeling that washed over him continuously that Keith and Margaret had disliked him intensely, had no interest whatsoever in him and had felt with disdain and contempt that he was pathetic, useless and worth nothing, thereby increasing his already established complex of inferiority.

He continued to rock his whole body frenetically and brutally from side to side in bed each night. To suffer fretful and sleepless nights and to endure the same appalling and terrifying nightmare recurring incessantly of the swirling vortex hurling him down a long black and narrow tunnel and burying him deep in the bowels of the earth where nobody would ever find him again. He was weighed down in his entire being by the heavy, extremely painful and frightful feelings of rejection, abandonment and cruel lack of love by both his parents. And by the acute pains in his heart, chest, throat and head caused by his separation from his two beloved brothers, the lack of their presence and his overwhelming fear that he would never see Neil and Justin again.

Just as bad, if not worse mentally, emotionally and psychologically, was the enormous feeling of guilt and relentless conviction that he had caused the awful tragedies that had beset and exploded his family unit. A guilt which pursued him with ever increasing and crushing power, causing deep and ravaging damage in his entire conscious mind and senses but also in his sub-conscious being. So that he started to judge himself as being fundamentally bad and diabolical and to hate himself with such devastating and nihilistic effect and consequences that he did not want to live with himself, in fact did not want to live in this world at all and started seriously and continuously to contemplate suicide.

However, somewhere deep inside his pathetic little frame a tiny voice, almost inaudible and barely perceptible but constantly nagging, told him cruelly with persistence that suicide was not the right road and was not in fact an option. And that as punishment for his demolishment of his family's happiness he was obliged to continue living and to endure and face up to all the suffering, pain and wretched sadness which he carried like an immensely heavy and overbearing weight on his frail, childlike shoulders and back, causing his shoulders to sag and become rounded.

Two weeks before Christmas 1959, Mr Watson told Adrian on Wednesday evening that Mrs Packman had telephoned him, asking if she could come to the orphanage on Saturday morning to speak with him, Mrs Watson and Adrian, and that he wanted Adrian to be at his office at ten o'clock that Saturday. When he knocked on the door of the office on the appointed day and hour, trembling

and full of anxiety and negative apprehensions about what was going to happen, Mrs Watson opened the door and ushered him in with a flourish. Mrs Packman rose from a chair to greet him with a large smile and Mr Watson beamed at him whilst remaining seated behind his large and wide desk.

'Adrian, my dear boy, Mrs Packman has some very good news for you!' exclaimed Mr Watson with a proud and grand air, motioning to Adrian with an outstretched arm to sit in the last unoccupied chair in the office, as Mrs Packman sat down again in her chair so as to be at the same level as young Adrian. As soon as Adrian had hesitatingly sat in the designated chair, Mrs Packman looked at Mr Watson, then Mrs Watson and finally Adrian as she said in a calm voice but barely disguising her excitement, 'Adrian, you and I have known each other for some time now. I will not beat about the bush and will tell you directly in a straightforward way that my daughter Margaret and her husband Keith, whom you will recall you met during our summer holiday at the hotel near Hunstanton, have accepted to adopt you!'

Adrian slumped back in his chair as if he had received a violent blow on the head. After his initial shock and confusion, he could not prevent himself from asking himself silently whether this was good news. He almost panicked, struggled to regain a small measure of control, then simply stared in astonishment and bewilderment at Mr Watson, Mrs Watson then Mrs Packman without uttering a word.

'I understand fully that this must come as a huge surprise,' Mrs Packman said in as gentle a voice as possible. 'As I have invited Margaret and Keith to spend a week's holiday with me in a fine hotel in Norfolk each summer over the past few years, enabling them to get away from the big city of London for a few days, I decided this summer to invite you as well so that they could meet you, as I had tried very hard in my searches to find a young married couple to adopt you but had not succeeded. So I wondered whether my daughter and her husband, although he is much older, might accept to have you living with them in their home, to adopt and raise you. Since that week together this summer, I have had many and long discussions with the couple, especially Margaret. I will not hide from you that at first it was somewhat difficult, as she raised understandable arguments and objections causing her and Keith to hesitate and tend to think that the adoption of a miserably unhappy eleven-year old orphan was not a project that they could take on and handle with success. However, after many more talks and much soul-searching they have finally accepted to adopt you, for which I am very happy and grateful.'

Whilst Mr and Mrs Watson nodded their heads in agreement and approval and all three of them looked at Adrian to see his reaction, rather expecting him to jump up for joy, all he did was to lower his head, sag his shoulders even more and then remain motionless for a few minutes without uttering a word. As a palpable tension reigned, Mrs Packman decided the best thing was for her to continue her explanations and she spoke again directly to Adrian.

'Keith has worked as a middle-ranking manager in a large bank in the heart of the City of London for several years, an activity which he has always hated

but endured as he must earn his living. As he will celebrate his sixtieth birthday in a few weeks' time in mid-January, he decided some months ago in agreement with Margaret to take his retirement in January and he gave his notice to his employer to such effect. Whilst they have been living in Pinner in the suburbs of London, both of them have dreamed for some time of spending their retirement in a typical old thatched cottage in the countryside down in the County of Devon in the southwest of the country. They started searching for a cottage months ago and have succeeded in buying a very small, two-bedroomed thatched cottage with a fairly large garden in a tiny hamlet not very far from the town of Cullompton. As soon as they agreed to adopt you, we set in motion the procedure for applying to the Norfolk County Council at its headquarters in Norwich for their official approval allowing Keith and Margaret to adopt you in accordance with the prevailing adoption laws. As the legal and administrative measures leading to your adoption might take a few months, but there is no reason to think, from what officials in Norwich have told me, that it will not be approved by the competent authorities, it has been agreed that Keith and Margaret will sell their present house in Pinner and will move down to their cottage in Devon in early February. I have put up for sale my bungalow here in Overstrand and, as soon as the authorities issue the legal documents approving your adoption, I will come here to collect you on a date which we will agree with Mr and Mrs Watson and will drive you down to the cottage in Devon, during a pleasant trip which will take us two days with a stopover at a hotel for the night. I will rent a flat in a seaside town down there not too far from where you will be living, so we will be able to see one another very frequently. You will see, you will embark on an exciting new adventure and all will be very well in your new life with Keith and Margaret, not forgetting myself, naturally! So, having said all that, I will leave you in peace now and I look forward with great pleasure to seeing you at church tomorrow morning, my dear boy.'

The last thing that Adrian felt was a state of peace and his mind was boiling in an utter chaos of turmoil, anguish and desperation. As soon as he was freed from Mr Watson's office, he flew up the stairs three at a time, almost knocked his bedroom door off its hinges as he thrust open the door with great violence, then slammed the door shut with a loud bang and threw himself onto his bed in his usual pathetic way when he was disturbed and upset.

He curled his legs up to his chest, wrapped his arms around his knees, lowered his chin onto his knees and stayed in the tight foetal position for quite some time with his eyes screwed shut and a deep frown on his face. Suddenly, he burst into tears and could not prevent his chest from heaving violently as he wept and wailed in utmost misery and feared that his heart would break from his intense feeling of unhappiness, inadequacy, painful confusion and furious frustration. He turned over several times in his mind all the words that Mrs Packman had said and concluded vehemently and miserably that they only confirmed what he already felt deep down. Namely that Mrs Packman's daughter and son-in-law had disliked him, had considered him ugly to look at,

uninteresting to talk to, inept company, unworthy of love and totally worthless and they had not at all desired to adopt him. But had only accepted begrudgingly to do so because of the persistence, badgering and persuasion exercised by Mrs Packman, who he thought angrily was not really interested in him but in her own satisfaction and personal glory as a church-going do-gooder. His tears rolled down his face, onto his curled-up knees then onto the bedspread as he wept bitterly, almost suffocating from pains in his throat and chest. Thinking firstly of his father and mother, wishing in deep despair that they could have loved him and cherished him. Then secondly of Neil and Justin, whom he adored and missed more and more as time wore on. With his child's logic and his mind damaged and warped by so much unhappiness, he felt desperately certain that this adoption, which would take him down to the other end of the country in some strange place called Devon, would take him still further from his beloved brothers and separate him even more from them and that because of this adoption he would never see his two brothers ever again. This was the most heart-breaking thought of all and he just could not conceive how he would be able to survive in this life without any contact with his elder brothers who meant the world to him. At the same time, he knew he was powerless and could do nothing to prevent the adoption and concluded agonisingly, with his overwhelming guilt complex, that he was being condemned to a fate worse than death for his heinous crime of causing the destruction of his family unit.

As the days passed by, Adrian could not and would not enter into the joyful spirit of Christmas, for he felt no joy whatsoever in the prospect of the upcoming adoption and was becoming increasingly submerged by a horrible state of depression. He continued to attend the classes in his last year at the local Overstrand primary school without any enthusiasm and in a sombre, negative and apathetic state. He found it increasingly difficult to make any friends among the other schoolchildren who came from united, loving and normal families and became a loner as the other children mocked him, bullied him and ostracised him for his unsociable and withdrawn attitudes and behaviour, the reasons for which were completely beyond their comprehension.

It was three weeks before Easter 1960 when Mr Watson and Mrs Packman announced to Adrian that the legal documents approving his adoption had been issued by the authorities and that Mrs Packman would drive him away from The Grange and from Overstrand in fourteen days' time so that they would be able to spend Easter with Keith and Margaret following their two day drive down to Devon.

On the day before his departure, which was a Friday, the staff organised a tea party in the late afternoon in the dining-room with all of the orphans in honour of Adrian and they all wished him good luck and as much happiness as possible in his new life. A few of the children, some younger than Adrian and some of his own age or even older, told him that he was very fortunate to be adopted. And they envied him for being able to leave the orphanage and start a

fresh life elsewhere with a couple who would love him and take good care of him in a family environment.

In his nihilistic and depressed state of mind, Adrian did not furnish any replies to their remarks but, deep inside himself, questioned whether the couple who were adopting him would in actual fact provide him with any or much love, affection and tenderness, which had been lacking so terribly in his life for so long and which he needed and yearned for tremendously but was rather sceptical about receiving from this couple who were so much older than his own parents and the parents of most children of his age.

In mid-morning the following day, Mrs Packman drove up the gravel driveway of The Grange in the little blue snail on wheels which Adrian liked so much. All the staff and the children said good-bye to Adrian, and Mrs Watson placed his one suitcase containing all his clothes and other personal effects and a plastic bag containing some toys and books on the back seat of the car, as the boot was full of Mrs Packman's suitcases. Adrian settled into the passenger seat at the front, Mrs Packman hooted the squeaky horn several times and waved cheerfully out of her open window to everyone. Whereas Adrian just sat still like a lifeless dummy, in a state of confusion and gripping apprehension as to where they were heading as they set off on a journey into a new life and a fresh set of hopefully positive adventures. After they had left the village of Overstrand and turned onto a main road, Mrs Packman said to Adrian in an enthusiastic manner, 'We are now on a road which will take us due south until we will reach a town called Newbury, which is in the County of Berkshire, where we will spend the night in a charming old hotel that I know and appreciate, having stayed there twice before. Newbury is a very ancient market town which was founded by a Norman knight after the invasion of England by the Norman King named William the Conqueror who won the battle of Hastings in the year 1066 when the English monarch King Harold was killed by a Norman arrow which pierced his eye. I love history and hope that you will also enjoy learning all the history of this wonderful island of ours when you will start history classes at a grammar school in Devon as from this coming September.'

Adrian did not respond and simply stared ahead of him, but the cogs in the wheels of his mind started turning rapidly. He could not prevent himself from nearly panicking as he thought with feverish apprehension that he hated the prospect of having to commence grammar school in September, for, with his total lack of confidence in himself and of any esteem for his capabilities, he was sure he would be a miserable failure at the upper school and would be mocked, bullied and despised by all the other pupils.

Being entirely unaware of the mental torture seizing Adrian's tormented and fragile psyche, Mrs Packman continued chatting in a happy voice. 'Newbury has a magnificent and famous racecourse for horse races which was built in the early 1900s. My daughter Margaret and I love watching horse races and we have been to the Newbury racecourse a couple of times over these past few years. On the second occasion, we had the good fortune to see our new

monarch Queen Elisabeth the Second and her husband Prince Philip, the Duke of Edinburgh, who were in the royal stand together with a group of other members of the royal family. Queen Elisabeth was crowned only seven years ago in 1953, when you were only five years old and still living in Kenya from what I have been told, after the sad and unexpected death of her father King George the Sixth. She was in actual fact visiting Kenya in February 1952 when she learned the news of her father's death and had to return rapidly back to England. She was crowned queen in Westminster Abbey in London in June 1953, a heavy burden which was placed on her shoulders at a very young age, as she was only twenty-five years old. However, she is turning out to be a wonderful and much loved queen and I pray that she will remain our monarch for many years to come.'

As she said this, Mrs Packman made a sideways glance at Adrian, with a proud glint in her eyes and a mischievous smile on her face, as if intent on and satisfied in giving this formerly orphaned and soon to be adopted young wretch a smattering of instruction in matters of general knowledge.

Both Mrs Packman and Adrian felt very weary when they arrived in the early evening at the hotel in Newbury, after several hours of driving on roads which were not always in very good condition and had been quite bumpy in several places. As they had only stopped for a light lunch at midday in a small town, they were both hungry and were able to sit down to a proper and pleasant supper in the charming dining room of the hotel and then relax afterwards in the deep and comfortable armchairs in the formal sitting room and admire the many rows of books, most of them leather-bound, lined up like tidy, upright soldiers on each of the long shelves in the tall, majestic bookcase which occupied one entire wall of the large room.

A while later, Adrian was given the luxury of a hot bath in a huge, Victorian period bath standing on curved metal legs and graced by two large and decorative bronze taps. As the baths at the orphanage had been small, cramped and very basic, Adrian profited fully from ducking under the water, holding his breath, crawling along the bottom of the long bath then coming up noisily to grab a new intake of air into his lungs before ducking under again, and joyfully turning the taps on and off every few seconds, especially the tap emitting the very hot water. He luxuriated in the bath for as long as possible, until he heard the voice of Mrs Packman telling him it was time to get out of the bath, dry himself down with the enormous, soft, first-class quality towel and prepare himself for bed and a good night's sleep, as the next leg of their journey down to Devon next day would also be very long and just as tiring.

However, even though he was very tired after the long and weary journey, Adrian found it impossible to sink into a deep sleep and was pursued for several hours by his usual fiendish and frightful nightmares. He wept for quite a long time while images of his father, mother and two brothers flashed intermittently before his eyes, as he rocked and thrashed his body fretfully from side to side and called out to his parents and to Neil and Justin and told them how much he missed them and how bad and guilty he felt that he had caused

the breakdown of the family and their separation. He was dreadfully worried that once he lived down in Devon with the couple who were adopting him he would never see any of them ever again.

In the morning, as they were sitting in the little blue snail on wheels after breakfast and Mrs Packman drove away from the hotel and out of Newbury and then turned right onto a new main road, she told Adrian that they were heading south-west, would drive down towards a town called Taunton in the County of Somerset, then after driving through Taunton they would carry on in a south-westerly direction until they reached the town of Wellington. She then proceeded, proud of her knowledge, to give Adrian another history lesson by explaining that a very famous British political and military figure of the nineteenth century, Arthur Wellesley, was made a Duke after he had won some battles and, as he had to be named the duke of some place, while he was abroad on a military campaign his brother chose for him the name of the Somerset town of Wellington so that he would be called the first Duke of Wellington because of the similarity of the name of the town to Wellesley the name of their family. The first Duke of Wellington then became even more renowned after he defeated the French emperor Napoleon at the Battle of Waterloo in 1815. As a tribute to the Duke of Wellington for this resounding and historical victory, a monument called the Wellington Monument was constructed on a hillside not far from the town of Wellington between 1817 and 1820. Mrs Packman said that the monument is in fact a triangular stone column, built from local sandstone, is pointed at the top like one of the bayonets used by the soldiers in the Duke's army, stands an impressive 170 feet tall and can be seen from many miles away in all directions. She told Adrian to look out for the monument up on the hill to their left as they drove through the small town of Wellington.

After they had passed through Wellington in the early afternoon and both had seen the monument standing proud and tall up on the hillside, Mrs Packman explained that they were nearing the end of their journey and should reach Keith and Margaret's small Devon cottage in about two and a half hours if all continued to go well and her beloved little car did not have the misfortune to break down. They had made several short stops on the way down from Newbury in order to rest the car and avoid the risk of the engine over-heating.

'We will cross the boundary from Somerset into the County of Devon and after a while we will arrive at a small market town called Cullompton. Then we will leave Cullompton on a smaller road in an easterly direction. I hope that I will be able to follow Margaret's instructions without getting us lost as we will drive in the countryside for a few miles, go past a very large mansion called Bradfield House, then past a farm on the left and into a tiny hamlet called Stenhill, where I must turn left and we should see their cottage called Stenhill Cottage on the right hand side as we drive down a lane which leads to another farm. After we arrive at the cottage and have eaten some supper, I will leave you, Keith and Margaret and will drive back to Cullompton, where I will spend the night at a hotel called the Manor House in the high street. Margaret has recommended it to me and, knowing how much I love history, she told me that

part of the hotel's building dates from 1600 and another part was added on in 1718 and the building has an impressive and pleasant looking half-timbered front and four gables under the roof. I will sleep there and drive up to the cottage in the morning, as Margaret said that their cottage is very small and only has two bedrooms, so she cannot sadly accommodate me. After a few nights at the hotel, celebrating Easter with the three of you and seeing that you are settled in at the cottage, I will drive over to a seaside town called Sidmouth down at the coast, where one of my contacts has been able to rent a small flat for me. It will not take too much time for me to drive up to Stenhill to visit you all or for you to drive down to Sidmouth to see me every now and then.'

They must have been about halfway between Wellington and Cullompton when Mrs Packman heard a soft noise resembling sniffling to her left. So she glanced furtively at Adrian whilst trying to keep her eyes looking at the road ahead and she was saddened to see a pained expression on his face and tears rolling down his cheeks, as he attempted but failed to stifle another sniffle.

'What is the matter, my dear boy? Is something troubling you?'

'I cannot stop myself from thinking about my two brothers,' Adrian replied as he choked and coughed and wiped away tears with the back of each hand. 'You are taking me down to another part of the country, far away from them, and I fear that I may never see them again. I am so unhappy without my brothers! I do not even know how they are and what is happening in the life of each of them! I feel so miserable and alone being separated from my brothers!'

After a moment's embarrassed and tense silence, Mrs Packman said gently to Adrian, 'I had decided not to say anything to you about your brothers because I was afraid that it would upset you too much at this stage. However, seeing the unhappy state that you are in, I think it will not hurt and will in fact be best if I tell you the latest news that I have gleaned as to how they are faring. Your uncle and aunt were naturally informed by Mr Watson that you are being adopted by Keith and Margaret and I am taking you down to Devon to live with them.'

'Mr Watson had hoped that either your uncle or your aunt or both of them together could drive Justin over to the orphanage to see you just before you left, but it was unfortunately not possible, as he has to stay at Buckden Towers during the whole of this week, as it is Holy Week. All the novitiates at the seminary are obliged to participate in all the church ceremonies and commemorations and will not be released for their holidays until sometime next week. Margaret absolutely wanted me to drive you down to the cottage this week so that we can spend this Easter weekend together and participate together in the Easter celebrations at the Catholic Church in their new parish of Cullompton. Although Justin could not come to see you, Mr Watson had then hoped that your uncle and aunt, or at least your aunt as she is your father's sister, would drive over to The Grange to visit you and say goodbye to you, but there was no reaction to his invitation. I was very sorry to see that they did not make the effort to come. Please forgive me for saying this, but your father's family do appear to be strange people with some attitudes and behaviour which

are somewhat difficult to understand. However, having said that I realise that I must be careful in my remarks, for we must remember that your uncle and aunt did accept to take on Justin and to bring him up, although I have been given to believe that they are not formally and legally adopting him, in the way that Keith and Margaret are adopting you.'

Mrs Packman glanced over at Adrian again and saw that he had a black and sombre expression and had lowered his chin onto his chest and was still sobbing and was muttering to himself under his breath. She could imagine that he was cursing the bad fate which had befallen him with parents and certain family members who did not love or cherish him and had rejected, abandoned and betrayed him. She felt a pang of sadness in her heart as she felt truly sorry for him. Then she remembered that she had not yet given him any news of Neil.

'I was able recently to speak by telephone with my contact at the Royal Navy to ask him how Neil is faring. After making his enquiries, he rang me back to tell me that Neil is doing very well at the junior training ship HMS GANGES, both in the classes, where he is learning many scholastic subjects as well as those pertaining to naval activities, and in the sports events, where he does very well at athletics and is by far the best swimmer of all the naval cadets. As you know, he will be sixteen years old this June and I have been told that if he succeeds well at HMS GANGES and passes all the exams in two years' time, he will be able to be transferred to a senior training ship, but I have not yet been told where that will be in the country.'

Adrian thanked Mrs Packman for the news but fell silent and did not want to talk any more. However, he was smiling to himself at the news that big brother Neil was the best swimmer of all the cadets, and he thought to himself that this was only normal and natural, as he reminisced back to those long gone days watching proudly as Neil swam almost as well as their father in the strong waves of the Indian Ocean at Diani Beach, or in the swimming pool at the Muthaiga Club in Nairobi, or later on in the waters of the estuary near their house in Mombasa. He almost giggled to himself as he imagined that the shark, which had taken the imprudent man in the estuary, would not have been able to catch his big brother Neil, for he would have swum so much faster than that damn shark!

After some time, they arrived in the small town of Cullompton and, as they drove into the market square in the high street, they saw the imposing half-timbered front and the four gables of the Manor House hotel. Mrs Packman told Adrian to stay in the car while she walked over to a couple of people standing and chatting by the roadside and asked them the right direction to drive to Stenhill. She then turned the car round and drove a short way back in the direction from whence they had come, then veered to the right and took a smaller road which the couple had told them led to Stenhill then the small town of Uffculme.

As they drove along what seemed like a very minor country road they saw suddenly on their left, about two miles out of Cullompton, two large and tall

stone pillars supporting two huge wrought-iron gates and a very long sandy coloured gravel driveway leading up to an enormous, imposing and very impressive building. Mrs Packman smiled and squealed in an excited voice,

'That must be Bradfield House. Margaret told me over the telephone to look out for it on our left and said it is situated about halfway between Cullompton and Uffculme. She has managed to learn from some local people that the house was originally built in the latter part of the 12th century, during the reign of King Richard I, and in the 13th century during the reign of King Henry III, then was enlarged in the Tudor style during the reign of King Henry VIII and his daughter Queen Elisabeth the First stopped here with her retinue and slept in the house on her journey down to visit the Duchy of Cornwall in the latter part of the 16th century. It was later substantially enlarged in about 1860 during the reign of Queen Victoria and is now one of the largest manor houses in the County of Devon. It is surrounded by hundreds of acres of parkland in which stand many majestic and very old cedar trees. It has apparently remained the property since the 13th century of the same aristocratic family, named Walrond, a well-known family in Devon whose different members own other mansions in various parts of the county. That is all Margaret has been able to tell me so far, but I am looking forward with great interest to learn much more about the history of this important manor house, which is just down the road from where you will be living.'

By the time she had stopped talking, they had left the Bradfield estate behind them and were climbing up a small hill, then on the flat they saw the house and the outbuildings of a fairly large farm on the left. Mrs Packman drove on another hundred feet or so until they arrived at an expanse of grass in the middle of the road, with a signpost erected in the middle, pointing to the right where a road branched off and to the left where a lane started winding down, whilst the road they were on, leading to Uffculme, continued straight ahead.

As they looked slightly ahead and to the right, they saw a small gaggle of four houses huddled together, each with its own garden containing a vegetable patch and some flowerbeds producing a lovely array of colours with various spring flowers.

As large black letters painted on the upright of the white signpost read "STENHILL", Mrs Packman sighed with content and turned left down the lane. On the corner immediately on the left hand side, they saw a brick house and slightly lower down on the right hand side they saw the thatched roof of a small white washed cottage. They passed the wooden pedestrian gate, saw the black painted front door and two black painted windows on either side, continued on for a few more feet then turned right into a wide but short driveway without a gate and parked in front of the old wooden garage. They looked at one another and smiled as they saw the little green snail on wheels nestled in the garage, which did not have any door.

As they walked towards the kitchen, which was new and had obviously been recently built onto the old cottage, the door opened, Margaret came out

and greeted them, giving her mother a perfunctory peck on the cheek and bestowing a vague nod on Adrian, without leaning down to kiss him on the cheek or even to shake his hand. Adrian was struck by her distant manner and asked himself in a confused manner whether this was the normal definition of a warm welcome by a future adoptive mother.

Once inside the house, Keith greeted them in the kitchen in a pleasant but somewhat timid and reserved way and led them through the very small dining room with a low ceiling into the sitting room. This room was somewhat larger than the dining room but also had a low ceiling and three large wooden beams which spread from the inner wall to the outer wall in which there was a wooden front door and two square windows, one giving onto the small front garden and the other in the side wall from which there was a very pleasant view of the main garden which was substantial in size. As soon as one came into the sitting room from the dining room, one could not help but see first of all the very large open fireplace, adorned by a massive solid oak beam and wide hearth, in the left hand corner of the room.

As Adrian felt extremely nervous and had a suddenly urgent need, Margaret showed him the way through a narrow passageway, which had been cut into the wall behind the backside of the dining room, to the small, separate toilet which was just beside a tiny but cute bathroom. Both of which were obviously new and had been built on at the same time as the new kitchen during the past months since Keith and Margaret had purchased the property. Adrian could not help but notice to the right of the toilet another space which contained a work bench and one or two shelves, which Margaret explained was the workshop in which Keith spent a fair amount of time, as he was very practical and had a gift for making furniture and other wooden objects with his hands, using the various tools which he had brought down with him when they moved from their former home in Pinner.

From the other side of the dining room a narrow staircase led upstairs, where Keith and Margaret had their reasonably sized bedroom right above the sitting room, whilst there was only one other, very small bedroom, which was above the dining room, containing a small single bed and one wardrobe, which, Margaret told Adrian, would be his bedroom. When he realised that this was in effect a very small "two down, two up" cottage, which made him think that it resembled a dolls' house, Adrian understood better why Mrs Packman had said during the journey down that there was no room for her to stay at the cottage and she would take a room at the hotel in Cullompton.

When they were all seated on the settee and the two armchairs in the sitting room, Margaret told her mother and Adrian that this cottage, with its thick cob walls and thatched roof, had been built in the Tudor era about four centuries earlier at the same time as several other cottages on the Bradfield estate as homes for the labourers who worked on the farms which formed part of the estate in those long by-gone days. It was only in the first part of the twentieth century that two of the farms and all the labourers' cottages on their land had been sold off by the Walrond family. This cottage had been owned by a couple

for many years and it was after her husband's death that his widow decided to sell the property and move to another part of the county to be nearer her son and his family, which gave Keith and Margaret the opportunity to purchase it.

***

The ensuing months were very difficult and trying for young Adrian and during the first year after his arrival at Stenhill Cottage, he found it almost impossible to adjust well to this new life with Keith and Margaret and these new surroundings. He felt more cut off than ever from any contact with his brothers and his anguished worry that he would never be able to see them again overwhelmed him, became all-consuming and rendered him more unhappy and miserable than he had ever been before. Keith and Margaret were good to him, bought him new clothes and toys, provided him with pleasant food skilfully cooked by Margaret on her beloved Rayburn stove in the new kitchen at the cottage, and bestowed some acts of generous kindness upon him such as offering him for his twelfth birthday a tiny, new-born Jack Russell terrier puppy from among the litter of seven such dogs born down at the local farm.

However, they behaved towards him in a practical, straightforward and functional manner as if ensuring a mere guardianship and protection for his wellbeing, but neither of them ever took him in their arms, gave him any hugs or kisses or said to him that they loved him.

As he had been deprived of signs of love and affection and acts demonstrating that he had some worth in the eyes of others for so many years, his mental, emotional and physical need for love, affection and consideration had become terribly acute and he was submerged by a black cloud of depression, negative thoughts and the conviction that he was worth nothing in the eyes of everybody, including Keith and Margaret.

Mrs Packman had taken up residence in her spacious rented flat on the top floor of a large individual house in a very pleasant street in a residential part of the coastal town of Sidmouth. Twice each month early on Sunday morning Keith, Margaret and Adrian drove in the little green snail on wheels on the country roads from Stenhill through the village of Kentisbeare, then along the high street of the town of Honiton, up the hill onto the common then down the steep hill the other side of the common through the small villages of Sidbury and Sidford into Sidmouth, where they attended Sunday mass with Mrs Packman at the Sidmouth Catholic Church then ate a pleasant lunch with her in one of the restaurants in the town. It became their regular habit to digest and walk off their lunch with a leisurely stroll along the esplanade, watching the waves of the English Channel lapping up or pounding against the pebble beach, depending on the direction of the current and the strength of the wind.

Then the adults took a nap, sitting on deckchairs lined up on the esplanade, if the weather permitted, while Adrian careered down onto the beach and threw stones into the water or took off his clothes and put on his swimming trunks, in the summer months. And showed his prowess as a swimmer by ploughing

through the waves at top speed and practising energetically his backstroke, which became his favourite stroke, although he also became a very strong adept at the crawl.

Whilst in the water he often thought of Neil and Justin and hoped that with age he would become as strong and proficient a swimmer as they both were. Each time he was in the sea, he called out loud the names of his brothers and told them how badly he missed them and he imagined that the wind carried back to him their voices sending him a message saying that they missed him too and thought about him just as much as he thought about them. Near the end of the afternoon, Mrs Packman invited them all for a delicious Devon cream tea in the old-world, cosy tearoom nestled against the wall boundering the Sidmouth cricket ground and looking towards the esplanade on the other side of the road. Finally, they drove her back to her flat and, after a very pleasant day spent in Sidmouth, made their way back on the country roads to Stenhill Cottage.

After the Easter holidays of 1960, Adrian was obliged to spend just one term at the local primary school in the very small town of Uffculme until the summer holidays, before graduating to the large grammar school in the town of Tiverton. That three-month long term seemed never ending and was excruciatingly painful for him. He was constantly mocked and bullied by many of the other children in his class, who ganged up on him. Firstly because of the strange Norfolk accent and use of language that he had taken on during his four years of imprisonment at the two orphanages in Norfolk, which appeared like gobbledygook and a language from some other planet to these children, who did not think for a moment how weird and difficult to comprehend their Devonian accent and vernacular way of speaking it was for poor Adrian!

Secondly, and much more importantly, these new acquaintances, who all happened to be children from normal, stable family households living with both a father and a mother and their respective brothers and sisters and having contact in most cases with grandparents, uncles, aunts and cousins, treated Adrian abominably with contempt, disdain and physical and mental taunts and abuse, in that very cruel way that children are fully capable of, there being nothing innocent about children except for the sweet smiles on their faces.

This was because Adrian was so very different from them. These children were enjoying normal, loving upbringings and were well-adjusted, well-balanced and as stable and happy as it was humanly possible to be, taking into account the specific circumstances of each one of them.

On the contrary, Adrian had lived dramatically traumatic and damaging experiences since a very young age, had suffered rejection, abandonment and betrayal by his father and mother, a very unhappy and unloving existence in two orphanages and the misery of separation from his two much loved and adored brothers. He was terribly damaged and warped mentally, psychologically, emotionally and even physically, for, with his immense sense of guilt and hatred of himself, he was convinced that he was very ugly in appearance and had no worth or value. He had no belief or confidence

whatsoever in himself, absolutely no self-esteem, had great difficulty to concentrate, had no sense of humour or fun and was incapable of cracking any jokes. He carried himself with a bowed head and slouched shoulders, with a sad, hang-dog look on his face and in his eyes, with no glimmer of hope or light of enthusiasm in those blue eyes, for he suffered continuously under a black cloud of depression and despair.

Adrian never uttered a word to Keith, Margaret or Mrs Packman about the suffering that he had to endure at the cruel hands of these primary school children. On one or two occasions, after he had received a beating from some bully boys and never fought back due to his feeling of nothingness and lack of value and a mental acceptance that he deserved to be beaten and punished, Keith and Margaret asked him how he had received his bruises and a black eye. Adrian merely shrugged and sheepishly replied that he had been hurt during some games with other boys involving some rough, tumble and horseplay, which seemed to appear plausible and convincing to them, as they readily believed the adage "boys will be boys".

When Adrian started to attend the Tiverton Grammar School in the first days of September, just before his twelfth birthday, going there by bus each day as the bus collecting the grammar school children actually stopped at the Stenhill crossroad, he continued to suffer the same type of mistreatment, bullying and taunts at the hands of other boys at his new school, including boys who were a little older than him and in higher classes. Due to his deep sense of guilt caused by his warped and automatic conviction that he was to blame for the breakdown of his family unit and the separation from his brothers, Adrian continued for a long time to feel that he had to endure all this suffering as it was an inevitable part of his punishment for his sins.

After Christmas that winter, Keith and Margaret told Adrian joyfully that in a few days' time in early January, before the new school term started, they were all going to drive in the little green snail on wheels to Exeter St David's Railway Station in the city of Exeter, would leave the car in the station carpark, board a train going up to the railway station at Paddington in London, the country's capital city. And spend a week staying in a small hotel in the Paddington area and seeing some of the most important sights that London had to offer. They looked at one another in bewilderment when Adrian merely looked blankly at them, shrugged his shoulders, then nodded meekly and turned on his heels and walked away, with no sign at all of enthusiasm, excitement or anticipation as to the upcoming week's holiday in the big capital.

When the week's stay in London was over, there was a very heavy, tense and silent atmosphere in their carriage as the train took them back down from Paddington to Exeter and no word was exchanged while Keith drove the little green snail on wheels home to Stenhill Cottage. However, after they had taken their suitcases up to their two bedrooms and were sitting on the settee and in the armchairs in the sitting room, Margaret gave a black look in the direction of Keith then stared ominously at young Adrian and exploded into a fit of anger and desperation as she shouted at him in a harsh tone of voice,

'What on earth is the matter with you, Adrian? We have just given you a superb week, touring some of the most famous and favourite sites of London and we paid a lot of money for this holiday! We are very disappointed by your complete lack of enthusiasm, your apathy and your lack of enjoyment during our various outings in the capital. You pulled a glum face all the time, walked around everywhere with a bowed head and slumped shoulders and you did not even smile or laugh on one single occasion. You have shown no appreciation at all for our generosity. I am at a loss to understand what is the matter with you!'

Adrian could barely look Margaret in the eyes, as her glare was so angry, reproaching and full of bitterness and blame. He was struck forcefully by her use of the word "I" in her tirade against him. He glanced over at Keith and seemed to detect a slight warmth, kind sensitivity and compassion in his eyes, but he sensed once again, as he had on several occasions before, that Keith was dominated by and under the thumb of his wife and was going to remain silent. He looked again at Margaret and what he saw in those hard eyes was so unpleasant that he could not face it anymore. He stood up with wobbly legs, which almost buckled under him as he trembled, and he fled out of the room, rushed up the stairs two at a time, shut himself in his bedroom and spent what seemed like hours lying on his bed and crying his heart out. Whilst sending out tortured thoughts to his two brothers and muttering prayers to them, beseeching them to help him somehow to cope with his wretchedly unhappy situation and to send him the strength to endure and bear this depressing existence.

Margaret had acquiesced to her mother's entreaty to accept to take on and adopt this poor orphan. But Margaret somehow made the essential and fundamentally grave mistake of thinking, with her specific frame of mind set in its inflexible ways at forty-one years of age, that just because she and Keith had taken him to live with them and were going to adopt him legally, there was no further problem. She simply and adamantly expected Adrian to think, behave and react just like any normal twelve year old boy. She was not able to realise and understand that this boy was not normal, but was in actual fact totally abnormal. And that the damage that he had suffered through such a dreadfully unhappy and hurtful early childhood was extremely deep and had caused him to be so mentally and emotionally maladjusted, warped, unstable and depressed about his existence in this miserable life that it was going to require several decades before he would be able to think, behave and react like a normally adjusted, stable and happy person.

***

Life for Adrian at Tiverton Grammar School continued to be very difficult and in class he found it an enormous and mentally and emotionally exhausting effort to be able to concentrate on the various scholastic subjects. He found it impossible to relate well to the other schoolchildren and could not make friends, due to his troubled psyche, lack of confidence and self-esteem and fear of being hurt again by people, so he tended to keep to himself during the breaks

and to become a sad loner. The feeling of his unworthiness, the inferiority complex and his lack of self-esteem were so deeply engrained in his being that it prevented him from making any friends.

He woke up each morning with a crushing weight on his chest, a painful lump in his throat and pressure in his head and behind his eyes, as well as a psychotic fear as to how he was going to live through and survive the day. He had to endure many unwanted and very invasive negative and depressing thoughts, which increased his overwhelming sense of nihilism. He discovered over the weeks and months that the best way for him to manage to cope with his dreadfully crushing anxieties and to release somewhat the continuous emotional and physical tensions and pains that he suffered in his head and his entire body was to take regular exercise and practise sport.

As Keith and Margaret had bought him a brand new bicycle, he developed the habit of riding his bicycle as fast as he could up and down the country lanes near their home after school in the light of the summer and autumn evenings and at weekends whenever he had the opportunity.

In early March 1961, it was announced at the grammar school that staggered long-distance running races were going to take place over three days in early June around the streets of the town of Tiverton, with the distance of each race varying according to the age category of boys and girls respectively. Adrian read on the notice board that the distance would be ten miles for the boys of his age who wanted to take part in the race and it sufficed to write one's name in the appropriate spaces on the suspended notice. Upon returning home after school, he took out his bicycle, rode for two miles until he reached a favourite tree by the roadside, shinned up the tree and sat in the crook of two branches, then sent telepathic messages to Neil and Justin, asking for their advice as to whether or not he should undertake this race, for his lack of confidence in himself and his capabilities drew him back and caused him to hesitate.

Suddenly, he felt that they were both replying to him as his mind went back dreamily to those days so many years earlier in Kenya when all three of them used to run across the African fields, countryside and plains for miles and would admire local Kenyan boys as they ran with such ease and elegance and supreme fitness. Adrian and his brothers were all very fit themselves back in Kenya and they were all strong swimmers as well. Adrian felt physically fit through riding his bicycle so often, and as he felt that his brothers were urging him on and encouraging him and wanted him to do it, the following morning he headed for the notice board as soon as he arrived at school and wrote down his name for the ten mile race in his age category.

Three of the other boys in his class, who had already written down their names, came up behind him, started pushing and jostling him and one of them blurted out mockingly, 'You puny little maggot, you will not survive even two miles, let alone finish the entire ten miles! We will all be far ahead of you and out of your sight before you have run even half a mile, you'll see, you pathetic runt!'

Adrian's enormous inferiority complex and lack of self-esteem almost caused him to be convinced by their taunts and to be overwhelmed so much by negativity that he almost scratched out his name there and then.

However, some small inner voices, which seemed to him to come magically but perceptibly from his beloved brothers, told him not to listen to the bullies but to maintain his name on the list and to prepare himself to run the race.

So, over the following three months, he developed his road-running training, in the early evenings after school and in the morning each Saturday, and built up the distances he covered until he was sure that he could easily finish ten miles. He earned the admiration of Keith and Margaret, as well as Mrs Packman when she heard about his efforts, and the close neighbours who cheered him on as he ran past their houses.

Keith said to Margaret one day soon before the date of the race, 'You know, despite the first appearance, this young fellow has a lot of character and determination!'

Adrian felt fit and ready, but he was truly astounded when he finished the race in tenth position among about one hundred boys in his category, and he felt very relieved to hear that he had finished far ahead of the three bully boys who had taunted and mocked him! He hoped and prayed that they would have a little more respect for him and would leave him alone and stop their nasty behaviour towards him.

From then on, Adrian started to participate in the athletics programme at the grammar school and, during that summer term, discovered that he was quite a reasonable middle distance runner.

At the start of the autumn term, when he had just turned thirteen years of age, he began to show an interest in the somewhat strange game of rugby. After having participated in a number of very physically gruelling training sessions, he was selected as a member of the school's junior team playing as the number seven wing-forward. He found that playing the rough and very physical game of rugby was an unexpected and welcome release for some of his mental and emotional anxieties, tension and torture and the physical discomfort and pains in his body caused by them. He rapidly became a very keen player and earned a small reputation as one of the most ferocious and fearless tacklers in his team. As he had developed the technique of rushing at an adversary who was carrying the oval ball from just behind him at an angle and wrapping both arms around his thighs and resting his head comfortably on the boy's buttocks as he brought him crashing to the ground.

However, off the rugby pitch it was impossible for Adrian to prevent his lack of confidence in himself from returning and his sense of unworthiness and lack of any value from overwhelming him again. Whilst he so desperately wanted to win the affection and friendship of some of the other schoolboys, his over-anxious and unnatural attitudes and behaviour due to his great instability, tortured soul and hypersensitivity caused the opposite effect, as he could not be natural but over-reacted. And he continued to be subjected to the mockery,

contempt and bullying practices of many of the other boys who showed in many clear and forceful ways that they disliked him and did not accept him as he was so very odd and different.

In particular, he was set upon on several occasions by a gang of four boys one year older than him whose leader was a pugnacious, very rude and highly obnoxious character. During one morning break from class, when Adrian was walking around solitarily on the school playing field with his head bowed low, his shoulders slouched and a sad expression on his face, he sensed suddenly that he was being surrounded by the four gang members, who were preparing to attack him and give him yet another beating. In a flash, he seemed to hear faint inner voices deep down inside his frame, coming from his two brothers, urging him to show some character, to stop being a coward and to defend himself bravely against his tormentors.

As if independently from his own will, which would have wanted to rush through the small gap between two of the bullies in a feeble attempt to escape, he felt a strong anger swelling up in his chest. He clenched both his fists in the way he had seen in some boys' magazines several images of professional boxers clenching their fists in the ring as they prepared to fight. He pivoted on his heels in a circular manner, looking in turn at each one of the four bullies in the eyes, and although he felt terrified, he seemed to overcome his fear with the silent voices of Neil and Justin encouraging him to show bravery and defiance. Then, as he tried to straighten his usually slouched and rounded shoulders and appear taller than he really was, he said to the gang members in as deep and manly a voice as he could muster,

'I am getting totally fed up with being harassed and bullied regularly by you cowards. It is very easy for you to beat up someone when you are four against one. There is no way I can fight off all four of you together, but it would only be fair if you will agree that I will fight your leader here, one on one, and if I beat him you will leave me alone and never bully me again. Do you agree?'

The three boys hunched their shoulders, tilted their heads to one side and opened the palms of their hands in an enquiring manner as they looked simultaneously at the undisputed leader of the gang.

After a moment's silence, he smiled cockily to them then looked over at Adrian with black and hate-filled eyes and a sneer on his face, clenched his teeth then growled like an aggressive wolf in an arrogant and self-confident manner, 'Yeah, OK, this will be good fun, for I will smash your ugly face into pulp, you pathetic little shit!'

As the other three gang members stood around Adrian and their leader, the latter raised his right fist and hurled himself with full force at Adrian whilst emitting a blood-curdling cry. Adrian's rugby training came to his assistance, as he sidestepped the rush instinctively then tripped the assailant with his left foot and pushed him hard in the back. As the other boy crashed headlong to the ground but managed to turn himself onto his back to face his enemy as he lay on the ground, Adrian pressed home his advantage and sat forcefully on his

chest, pinned down his arms with his knees and legs and started pummelling his face and the top of his chest with both fists as hard as he could.

With his teeth clenched and whilst grunting and groaning and shedding tears which filled his eyes and streamed down his cheeks as he kept throwing his punches in a blind rage. It was as if he was attempting to exorcise all the unhappiness, frustration and dreadful suffering which had ruined his life and that of his brothers over all these past years.

As several other schoolchildren saw the fight and came over to swell the numbers in the circle around the two belligerents, and as Adrian continued to throw punches at the blood-stained face below him as if he had lost all self-control, one of the gang members screamed out in desperation, 'He is going to kill poor Sandy! Someone must stop him and pull him off, please, or he will kill him!'

An older boy, who was in fact one of the prefects at the school, was walking across the playing field and when he saw the crowd of youngsters and heard their raised voices and the loud appeal of one boy, he rushed over, pushed his way through the spectators, grabbed Adrian by the shoulders and dragged him off the other boy, who was lying flat on his back, with blood-shot eyes and several bruises already welling up and some cuts seeping blood on his battered face. However, he was not unconscious and after a couple of minutes was able to sit up then stand up shakily with the aid of the other three gang members.

As the prefect took Adrian's arms and started leading him away from the scene, Adrian turned to the four gang members who were also starting to walk away in the opposite direction and he shouted, 'Remember, you all agreed that if I beat your leader you will stop bullying me. So keep your word and leave me in peace. As for you, the one they call Sandy, if you trouble me again I will thrash you so hard you will need an ambulance to take you to hospital!'

From that day onwards, the reports of the fight spread quickly around the grammar school and no boys bullied or ganged up on Adrian again. However, his victory against that gang leader did not help him to win any friends, for he already had a reputation as being a weird and very unstable and unsettled boy with whom no one wanted to make friends. He continued to feel very lonely and unloved and became a sadder figure than ever as the months passed by.

***

In his misery, due to his incapacity to behave normally like other children who enjoyed a stable and loving family life with their parents and siblings and his overwhelming feeling of utter worthlessness, great inferiority and fear of being hurt again by people which warped and distorted his awkward and somewhat bizarre behaviour in the company of others, Adrian gradually felt a slight compensation as he developed a pleasant, warm and easy relationship with Keith.

This man was gentle, kind and well-meaning in his treatment of Adrian and he took him under his wing, never raising his voice in any anger and always exercising a good measure of patience towards Adrian's sad, gauche, unstable, unbalanced and very troubled psyche and personality.

Keith had a strong artistic bent, which he showed to Adrian as he included him in designing the lawn in the garden and then creating it in the unexpected form of an amoeba, together with two holes in the grass such as those which he explained to Adrian formed part of the amoeba's curious shape. Keith was also very talented with his hands, had taught himself to be ambidextrous and in his workshop, which was a lean-to attached to the back wall of the cottage, he first of all arranged all his workman's tools, which he had brought down from his previous home with Margaret in Pinner in the County of Middlesex. Then in the presence of Adrian one Saturday, he constructed with his own hands a long and wide workbench with wood that he had bought in the local town called Cullompton.

Over the next several weeks, he designed and built on the work-bench a lovely oak-wood table with its legs, which he and Adrian carried into the small dining-room. Then a round stool on three legs from chestnut wood which he entrusted to Adrian who took the stool into the lounge and set it down in one corner near the bay window and sat on it with a proud smile on his face. And a few other wooden items of furniture for various spots in the cottage.

Adrian's admiration for Keith's skills knew no bounds when he was allowed to participate in Keith's construction of two wooden benches for the garden and helped him carry each one to a chosen strategic spot enabling one to sit and admire the two large flower beds and the two sizeable vegetable patches which both Keith and Margaret had worked so hard and efficiently to create.

As the months went by, Adrian could feel in his warped and miserable frame an increasing affection for Keith, but his instinct told him to be very cautious, as he was terrified of being disappointed yet again by a human being. His love for his father and mother had been very deep, overwhelming and all-engulfing, but they had shattered his life and that of his brothers through their selfishness, violence, treachery, rejection and abandonment. He still loved his parents in his innocent childlike way, he thought about them constantly, wondering where they were and what they were doing in life, but his pain, anguish, acute suffering and awful sense of guilt were such that he still had the most dreadful nightmares, in which the dark swirling vortex hurtled him down into the black hole in the bowels of the earth. He thrashed his body from side to side and wept bitterly in his bed each night and slept so badly and fitfully that he felt haggard, exhausted and almost incapable of facing the day each morning. However, his need for love, recognition, affection and consideration was so great that he found himself allowing his tender affection for Keith to grow stronger, despite his constant anxiety and worry about the risk of being rejected and abandoned once more.

Although he could not banish from his mind the memory of his birth father, he allowed himself very timidly, but with a guilty feeling, to start calling Keith

"Dad" and when Keith showed his pleasure at this each time by tousling Adrian's jet black hair in a gentle, affectionate and playful way, Adrian would look up into his face with his bright blue eyes and smile proudly and emit a low sighing sound rather like the purr of a satisfied cat.

On every other weekend, Keith, Margaret and Adrian continued to make the drive in the little green snail on wheels over to Sidmouth to visit Mrs Packman. If they went over on Sunday, they attended Mass with her in the Sidmouth Catholic Church and Adrian, who was always seated between Mrs Packman and Margaret, marvelled each time at the glorious soprano voice of Mrs Packman on his left side, as her beautiful singing made the notes soar up above the congregation, bounce off the wooden beams in the ceiling, swirl around and into all the recesses of the church then float up again into the sky to enchant all the saints and angels in the celestial Heaven.

On his right side, poor Margaret tried her best to sing but, as she admitted herself, she did not inherit the wonderful singing talent of her mother for she was tone-deaf and in her pitiful attempts she only emitted false notes and off-key groans causing quite some discomfort in Adrian's right ear. He could not remember having heard his father or his mother sing but he did enjoy singing and discovered that he must have inherited his rather pleasant, tenor voice from one or other of his Welsh relatives. He had been told by Mrs Packman that the Welsh people in general had superb singing voices and cultivated the love and art of singing in their organisation of an annual singing festival called Eisteddfod in their local Celtic language.

Adrian became aware that his affection for Mrs Packman was also increasing. Firstly, he felt a genuine gratitude to her for having extricated him from the hellhole of the orphanage. Secondly, and much more importantly, he could see how pleased she was each time they met and he felt warmed by her sincere concern for his well-being and happiness living with Keith and Margaret. Which she understood would not be easy for him, as he was so maladjusted, disturbed and unstable after all that he had endured and suffered in previous years. Nor easy for them as they had not yet had any experience of bringing up a child, not having their own child, let alone the difficult experience of handling a very damaged eleven-year-old orphan.

Mrs Packman showed true affection and kindness towards Adrian and he could sense that she was a loving and caring person who had acted generously and unselfishly on many occasions to help others less fortunate than herself in life. She encouraged him to call her "Granny" and he started feeling very pleased to do so, as he had never met his grandparents on his mother's side, who he had been given to understand were still living in Cape Town, South Africa. And he did not harbour a pleasant memory at all of his meeting with his father's battle axe of a mother and he had been told that his paternal grandfather had died many years earlier.

Adrian's reactions and attitudes towards Margaret were ambivalent. On the one hand, she had accepted to give him a new home and a new life and she was a very capable, practical and efficient person who worked hard to make the

cottage as comfortable and pleasant as could be and the garden a delightful place with all its flowers and a source of well-being and good health with all the varied and fresh vegetables grown in the two vegetable patches. On the other hand, she appeared to be a very no nonsense, down to earth and hands-on person with a very strong, domineering and bossy character who always needed to be in charge and control of everything, but who showed very little warmth, gentleness, tenderness or emotion.

On several occasions, Adrian was appalled, scared and saddened to witness the unpleasant and harsh way in which Margaret treated her mother, often criticising her mother's way of approaching matters and trying to order her about with a domineering manner and even shouting at her in a bullying and overbearing way when her mother did not agree with her on certain subjects.

Adrian felt afraid that this woman was not going to be able to love him and give him true affection and help him to heal his deep wounds, nor to comprehend the root cause of his mental, emotional and psychological suffering and scars, but would merely oversee and take care of his material needs and education.

With some reticence and hesitation, he forced himself to address her as "Mummy" after she insisted on it several occasions in her forceful manner, but for quite some time he had to admit to himself deep down that his heart was not really in it. He found it impossible to allow Mummy to displace his birth mother in his affections, for he thought continuously of his real mother and wondered how she was faring and what she was doing with her life.

***

A few days before Easter 1962, Margaret asked Adrian to join her and Keith in the sitting room, as they had some important news to give him. He came into the room with alacrity and a pleasant sense of anticipation, for he felt sure that they were going to provide him with some information about the events in the lives of Neil and Justin and how they were both faring.

However, as he sat on one of the armchairs opposite Keith and Margaret, who were seated side by side on the settee, he became nervous when he saw the look of apprehension on Keith's face and in his eyes. Keith did not say a word and merely turned his head towards Margaret.

In her usual brusque, business-like and straightforward manner, Margaret, the dominant one in the couple, who was holding a sheaf of paper in her right hand, said simply and directly to Adrian, with no trace of any emotion, 'Since early September 1960, you have been attending the Tiverton Grammar School. However, there is soon to be a change concerning your education. Keith, your adoptive father, who you now call Dad, has not always been a Roman Catholic. He was born in a Protestant family and was brought up as a member of the Church of England. After we met and when we decided to become married, at my request he followed instruction in the catholic faith with a catholic priest and became a convert and has since then practised as a Roman Catholic. I have

118

always been a catholic, as I was born into a family where both my father and my mother were Roman Catholics. My father in particular was a very staunch and devoted Irish catholic with a deep faith and, under his impulsion and using their savings from my father's hard work and good salary in an insurance company, my parents had me educated at a first-class catholic convent where I was a boarder for a few years. My brother Patrick, who is six years younger than me, was educated at Ampleforth College, the best catholic school in England according to my father, where he was a boarder for several years. I have decided that the time is now right for you to start attending a catholic school as a boarder, since it is a tradition in my family going back a long way, for my father, my grandfather and my great-grandfather were all educated as boarders at catholic schools. I have naturally discussed this with Keith and he agrees with this decision, don't you, darling?'

'Well, yes, of course,' Keith replied hesitatingly with a very timid and sheepish look in his eyes and a begrudgingly acquiescing expression on his face.

Adrian glanced from Margaret to Keith and surmised, with the perspicacity of a young teenager, that the latter had not had any choice in the matter. He noted, yet again, that Margaret constantly said "I" as she talked out the decisions.

'As Dad and I do not have much money and most of our savings were used to purchase this cottage just before Dad retired, we cannot afford to send you to Ampleforth College, where I would absolutely have loved to be able to send you. I have made some enquiries in the catholic diocese down here covering Dorset, Somerset, Devon and Cornwall and have discovered that there is a good quality catholic school in Plymouth in south Devon called St Boniface's College, which is mainly a day school but has also one house catering for boarders in its very large grounds. It is managed by the reputable catholic order of Irish Christian Brothers. And, as it is a direct grant school, I have received an agreement from the college's Board of Governors in this letter that I am holding that they will grant us financial assistance. You can attend the school as a boarder as from this coming early September during the next four years enabling you hopefully to obtain firstly your O Level examinations and then your A Level examinations. I have spoken with the headmaster by telephone and agreed with him that we will drive down during your Easter holidays one day in the week following Holy Week to meet him and another staff member, who will show us around the premises.'

After their return from the visit to see St Boniface's College, it truly sank into Adrian's petrified mind that it was a reality that he was going to be sent away to this school, without any personal say in the matter, and would live there during the whole of each term for the forthcoming four years, away from his new family environment. Adrian slumped inexorably into a state of confusion, depression and wretched unhappiness.

He never said a word to his adoptive parents, as he sensed that he could not argue with Margaret's overbearing, controlling and determined character nor

attempt to persuade her to reverse her decision and allow him to continue attending Tiverton Grammar School and living at home.

As for Keith, the affection that Adrian had for his adoptive father had developed into a real love for this gentle, sensitive and considerate man. But Adrian concluded that it was pointless confiding to him his disarray and anguish caused by Margaret's harsh decision, as he had seen on countless occasions that it was Margaret who wore the trousers, so to speak, and Keith bowed to her every decision, did all he could to avoid any frictions or arguments and simply kept the peace and let her have her way. Adrian started to feel as sorry for poor Keith as he did for himself and to conclude that they were two partners in misery!

Adrian slid into a state of bewilderment, blind panic and desperation. He had already been betrayed, rejected and abandoned by his birth parents. He now felt with dreadful mental and emotional pains, which caused actual physical pains in his head, heart and limbs, that by banishing him far away to a boarding school for the next four years his adoptive parents were also betraying the trust he had placed in them and were rejecting him and abandoning him to an awfully miserable and bad fate like a sacrificial lamb on the altar of Roman Catholic traditions.

What he needed more than anything, after his ghastly and unhappy childhood, was to remain all the time in a stable, reassuring, comforting and loving family home with his adoptive parents. Margaret's decision to send him away to this boarding school many miles away created in him an even greater mental and emotional imbalance, instability, distrust of other people and acute hurt stemming from his deep conviction that this woman did not love him at all and had taken the first available opportunity to get rid of him for as many months of each year as possible.

Furthermore, his all prevailing sense of guilt made him think as well that the decision to banish him to a boarding school many miles away from home was a continuation of the punishment being meted out to him by some higher force for having caused the breakdown of his family unit several years earlier. He did not dare to say a word to Granny about the unhappy situation, as he felt a commiseration and sympathy with her due to the domineering way Margaret treated her and he felt convinced that Margaret had taken her decision on her own without consulting her mother and that Granny would be powerless to obtain any reversal.

Adrian was taken down to St Boniface's College with his trunk containing his clothes and some other personal effects in early September 1962 and a few days later had his fourteenth birthday at this boarding school, which he could not call a celebration by any means. It reminded him acutely of the day of his arrival at the orphanage called The Grange on his seventh birthday. The pain in his chest was so searing that he doubled his body up into the foetal position in bed that night and wept bitterly. But he had to choke his tears and sob softly without making any noise for his bed was one of thirty-five others in a massive, dark and depressing dormitory up on the top floor of the boarding house. He

hated the place from the first day, felt more unhappy, insecure and fragile than ever and due to his increased distrust of and fear of being hurt by other people and his utter lack of confidence in himself he found it impossible to smile to the other boys and to make any friends among them. He lived there in a sad, solitary and wretchedly miserable state like a lone wolf cast out of and distanced from the pack. His only solace came from the fact that he attended rugby-training sessions and, due to his dexterity and speed as a wing-forward and his ferociousness and crazy courage on the pitch, was quickly selected to play in the school's second team during that first season.

On a Wednesday afternoon, about a month later in early October, Adrian was running with the other team mates around the rugby pitch during training when one of the schoolteachers came rushing out of the nearby building, hurtled onto the pitch and shouted out loudly, 'Walton-Mornick, follow me! There is a very urgent telephone call for you.'

Adrian ran off the pitch, took off his rugby boots as quickly as possible beside the open door and followed the teacher inside. When he took the telephone handed to him, a feeble and tired voice spoke in such a soft tone that he could barely hear but he recognised it as that of Mrs Packman.

'Adrian, my dear, this is Granny. I am afraid that I have some very sad news. Dad has fallen gravely ill, has been taken by ambulance to the hospital in Exeter and, after a series of tests, a team of doctors have diagnosed that he is suffering from a brain tumour. They do not yet know if the tumour is benign and can be dealt with through a surgical operation or some other treatment or is malignant with possibly dire consequences. They are carrying out further tests, so as soon as we have been told the results I will call again. In the meantime, we must just hope and pray that the tumour is benign and that Dad will recover. Mummy is visiting him in hospital each day. As she is a trained nurse, she is fully aware of the potential effects of this dreadful illness. God bless you, my love, be strong and please do pray for a good turn of events.'

After replacing the receiver on its hook, Adrian looked around him but the teacher had disappeared and there was no one else in the corridor. He left the building in a daze, felt a painful and constricting lump in his throat making it difficult for him to breathe and warm tears streaming down his cheeks, but decided in a flash that the best thing for him to do immediately was to return to the rugby pitch and get stuck into the training again and run around as much as possible to help ease the internal pain that was like a vice squeezing his throat and chest and throbbing in his head. He put his boots on again, careered onto the pitch, continued with the training session in a blind rage and did not say a word to anyone about the sad news and his fears for his adoptive father.

During the next three weeks, Adrian visited the chapel in the building as often as he could. He was not sure whether he had a real faith in the existence of God, Jesus Christ and Mary the mother of Jesus which catechism classes that he had attended over the years had taught him. Nonetheless, on each occasion he lit some candles, knelt down in a pew and prayed as hard and reverently as he could asking Divine Providence to save his beloved adoptive father. In

addition, each evening when he had put on his pyjamas and brushed his teeth he knelt down beside his bed, clasped both hands together tightly and prayed again to the Almighty Father and to Our Lady in Heaven beseeching them to allow Keith to be treated and to recover all his faculties. He did not care that all the other boys in the dormitory scorned and mocked him and contemptuously shouted to one another with blasphemous words, jeering jokes and mock prayers. He did not blame them for he had not said a word to any of them about his plight.

However, as all the staff had been told about the situation, the staff member in charge of supervising the large dormitory in the late evening and during the night felt very sorry for Adrian when he witnessed the cruelty of the other boys towards him. But Adrian begged him not to divulge anything to the boys, for the last thing that he wanted was anyone's pity. The staff member decided that the least he could do for Adrian was to request the manager of the boarding house to allow Adrian to move from the hateful dormitory to a single room and he felt very relieved when the request was accepted and Adrian was able to occupy this room.

In early November, Mrs Packman telephoned again and told Adrian in between her sobbing noises as she tried to stem back her tears, 'I am so sorry to have to tell you this. There is sadly no hope for Dad. The further tests and analyses have shown that his brain tumour is malignant and is inoperable due to its position in the brain. The doctors have told Mummy that he has about three to four months left to live and the only possible treatment is to give him certain drugs and pills to help ease the terrible pain and frightful pressure in the brain, which are unfortunately but unavoidably increasing more and more as the weeks go by.'

'Due to her training and her practical experience over the years as a nurse, Mummy has decided she wants to treat him herself at home from now right up until the end. The doctors have agreed with this, he is going to be transported home tomorrow by ambulance and one of the doctors will make a visit to see him and Mummy once a week. A special bed for him will be placed in the lounge of the cottage, for the stairs are so narrow that it is impossible to carry a coffin down and negotiate the bend near the bottom of the stairs. You have no doubt seen in the first left-hand corner of the lounge of this sixteenth century cottage, when you walk through from the small dining room, that there is a trapdoor in the ceiling and a wide sloping indentation carved vertically into the lounge wall below it. This was done when this small workman's cottage was built in order to allow a coffin to be lowered through the trapdoor from the bedroom above containing the body of a person who had died upstairs and to prop up the coffin vertically against the wall until the undertakers could come to take the coffin away for the funeral. Mummy does not want this and has told the medical team that it is better to have Dad's special bed installed in the lounge as it is nearer the kitchen from which she can carry him his meals and water in a basin to wash his body each day during the illness. You should stay at the college for the rest of the term and try to concentrate as hard as you can

on your studies and other activities, then come home for your Christmas break to be with Dad, Mummy and me.'

When Adrian returned home in mid-December, he had tried to prepare himself mentally and emotionally for what he would find. However, when he saw Dad lying under the covers in the bed in the lounge without any hair left and his face dreadfully emaciated, the skin very yellowish and his eyes bloodshot and almost closed when he looked absently at his adoptive son, Adrian experienced the worst emotional shock and reaction that he had had since his birth father had turned away and abandoned him. He shook off his misery the best he could and tried to concentrate on being there for Mummy and assisting her in every way possible. He admired her tremendously for her strength of character, her stoicism with a stiff upper lip courage and dignity and her devotion to giving her husband the best care possible.

He was able to witness in many of her gestures and practical tasks how experienced and good a nurse she was. And he felt very proud of her for having decided to care for Dad herself here in his home that he loved so much rather than leaving him in the hands of unknown and impersonal nurses in a cold and clinical hospital. Granny had driven over from Sidmouth in her little blue snail on wheels some days before Adrian arrived, slept in Keith's place in the double bed upstairs beside her daughter and she gave her as much moral support and practical assistance as she could. She told Adrian that she would continue living at the cottage to help Mummy until the inevitable end of the ordeal.

When Adrian told her he wanted to stay as well, she told him to be reasonable and said that the correct and best thing for him to do, which she knew Mummy would also want, was to return to St Boniface's College for the new term and to throw his energy into his studies, his rugby and his life at the college to the best of his ability.

The telephone call came in the late afternoon on February 5th 1963 while Adrian was doing his homework in the boarding house library along with several other boarders. His adoptive father Keith had died one hour earlier from a large malignant brain tumour, which had made him suffer like a martyr and had literally driven him crazy in the head. Adrian returned home the following day, after a fretful and sleepless night weeping and gnashing his teeth and thrashing his body from side to side in terrible anguish, then praying for the repose of Keith's soul.

He could not understand for what reason fate had dealt him yet another very bad card on the table of destiny unless it was meant to be further punishment. His adoptive father had given him a new hope in life and in people but that hope had now been cruelly dashed. He had grown to love this man like a son, had felt deep inside him that that love was reciprocated, but it had just been shattered with the gruesome and terrible shattering of this lovely man's brain.

Adrian plummeted rapidly into the deepest state of depression that he had ever suffered and he told himself that he could not carry on in this miserable and unjust life and had no choice but to commit suicide and put an end to all

the unbearable pain. However, as he lay on his bed one night bunched up in the foetal position, rocking his body from side to side and thinking about the best and cleanest way to end it all, he heard deep inside his being very faint little voices haranguing him with a telepathic message and sensed the presence of the spirits of his two beloved brothers appealing to him in his heart. The little voices told him that suicide was cowardly and for weak people, but not for him, as he was a survivor and had to be strong and courageous and bear whatever suffering life threw at him.

However, with his mind more tortured and disturbed than ever, almost tipping him over into madness, Adrian interpreted this new suffering as an integral part of the overall punishment he was having to endure for having caused the breakdown of his family unit. His sense of guilt felt greater than ever and he told himself that he was meant to continue to suffer and would never be able to regain the happiness of a full and satisfying family life.

After the funeral Mass in the small Catholic church in Cullompton and the burial service in the Cullompton cemetery, Margaret put on a very brave face and she, her mother and Adrian did their very best to resume some semblance of a normal life, but it was extremely difficult and there was a heavy sadness and absence in the little cottage.

On the eve of the day when Adrian had to return to St Boniface's College and he and Margaret were sitting alone together in the lounge, as Mrs Packman had returned to her flat in Sidmouth, Margaret said to him, 'I think it is important that I relate to you two things that Keith said to me on two separate occasions near the end of his ordeal. On the first occasion, as I was about to give him his daily wash, he placed a hand on my wrist, he looked straight into my eyes, his face seemed to glow, his eyes seemed to glisten as if illuminated by a bright light and he whispered that he had had a glimpse of Heaven. I was amazed and felt very excited and I asked him to tell me what Heaven looked like. Immediately, his face became ashen again, his eyes dimmed and their expression hardened, he turned his head away from me and he refused to say any more. I realised that I had made a mistake and should not have asked that question. On a later occasion, just a week before he died, he confided to me that he felt that the tumour was addling his brain and he was going mad, but he accepted it serenely for he knew where he was going in his afterlife. These two declarations have given me great comfort in my loss, for I feel certain with my faith that his soul is now enjoying full peace and happiness together with Our Lord, Our Lady and all the angles and saints in Heaven. I am hoping very much that you will also derive some comfort from this.'

Adrian never forgot those words and sometimes pondered on their depth of meaning, especially during many ensuing occasions when he found himself struggling over questions concerning religion in general and his own faith in particular as he struggled to cope with the overwhelming difficulties which were thrown at him in his earthly life.

***

At St Boniface's College, it had become a tradition over the past few years to project a film for all the boarders one Friday evening during each term in one of the largest classrooms, which contained many rows of long benches for pupils to assist at lectures given by various schoolmasters. The headmaster of the college always selected the film which the boys would have the privilege and pleasure to watch. The title of the film was always kept secret in order to maintain the suspense and excited anticipation so the boys only discovered the title when it was projected onto the screen at the front of the classroom which had been erected for the occasion.

On the second Friday evening after Adrian had returned to the college in late February 1963, still struggling hard to come to terms with the appalling illness and sad death and burial of Dad, he, a depressed and solitary figure, reluctantly followed a boisterous and joyful group of other boarders into the designated classroom and told himself that he should force himself to watch the film as it might well help to cheer him up a little.

He had not managed to make any friends among all the boarders, so was not part of any group. But as all the boys tumbled into the classroom, a queue quickly formed, Adrian was swept along in the tide of impatient and jostling cinema goers and was pushed by the force of the swelling tide into one of the farthest benches from the screen near the back of the classroom and found himself wedged in the middle of the bench with several boys contentedly smiling and chattering among themselves on either side of him. As no one smiled or spoke to him, he sat sullenly with his arms crossed over his chest waiting for all the boys to be seated in the classroom and for the lights to be dimmed for the projection of the as yet unknown and mysterious film.

As the title and the first violent, gory and bloody scenes of the film appeared on the screen, rolling waves of surprised and excited murmurs, punctuated by "oohs", "aahs" and "wows", rose among the boys from the front bench right up to the back bench, like rippling waves soaring and gathering in strength on the surface of the sea. Then the murmurs died down and were followed by a hushed silence, like the waves arriving on the shore and transforming into silent foam, as the boys settled down to see the dreadful story unfold.

A horrified Adrian recognised that this was "Simba", the film that he had already been forced several years earlier to watch in part by his cruel and unfeeling birth father until he had revolted. As the violent images continued to fill the screen, his mind was instantly thrown back to those ghastly *Mau Mau* attacks and the bloody deaths at his farm in Kenya when he was just a very young and innocent boy.

He nearly vomited and was thrown into a blind panic, visceral emotional reaction and raging revolt and, as he stood up abruptly, he screamed at the top of his voice, 'Let me out of here! Let me get out! I cannot watch this, the memories are too horrible!'

The boys in his bench were shocked by this dreadful outburst but none of them moved and their attention remained glued to the screen as the extreme

violence and appalling murders continued to unfold. Adrian, his eyes full of tears and his emotions now uncontrollable, scrambled headlong in the dark like a scared rabbit along the knees of the boys sitting to his right, tumbled down roughly at the end of the bench hitting his head on the wooden floor, picked himself up in a daze and rushed down to the front of the classroom, pushed the door open and once out slammed the door shut with a loud bang.

His vision very clouded by the tears filling his eyes, he ran as fast as he could to his bedroom, threw himself on his bed, automatically assumed the foetal position, rocked his body violently from side to side and called out to his beloved brothers Neil and Justin, pleading with them to help him to cope with this renewed and terrifying anguish and nightmarish reminder of excruciatingly painful experiences.

No other boy left the makeshift cinema and if the many remarks after the film were anything to go by the great majority of the young viewers revelled, as they stared goggle-eyed, in all the gore, violence, butchery and slaughter perpetrated by *Mau Mau* warriors with *pangas* against white colonialist families and those black servants who worked for such victims. Such revelry and sense of entertainment was easy and safe for these boys from the comfort of benches in a school classroom thousands of miles away from Kenya with a prevailing sentiment that this was pure fictitious Hollywood cinema to be consumed, enjoyed and even laughed at.

The following morning, Mr Simpson, one of the lay teachers in charge of the boarders, had Adrian escorted by a prefect to his office and when the prefect had gone he shut the door and asked Adrian to give an explanation for his strange, rude, excessive and unacceptable conduct during the film the previous evening and for rushing out of the classroom without asking the permission of the supervising teacher present in the room.

When Adrian broke down completely, wept and told the teacher in between sobs and gasps of breath and pains in his heaving chest that his family had lived on a farm in Kenya and had directly suffered violence, butchery and murder perpetrated by *Mau Mau* warriors, Mr Simpson put an arm around his shoulder, spoke calmly to him saying he now understood Adrian's reaction the previous evening, and comforted him by stroking his cheek, caressing his chest soothingly and patting him on the head. He told Adrian that he would tell all the lay teachers and the Irish Christian Brothers in the college's boarding house about Adrian's horrifying experiences and ask them to put out the word among all the other boys who had seen the film so that they would show understanding, commiseration and sympathy over Adrian's extreme reactions to the film. As Adrian started to move towards the door to leave the office, Mr Simpson put both his arms around him, drew him towards his body, kissed him lingeringly on the left cheek, then placed his left hand firmly on Adrian's left buttock as Adrian turned to free himself from this clutch, feeling very surprised and confused by this effusion of affection meted out by a teacher to a fourteen year old pupil.

Over the next two weeks, whilst Adrian had hoped that Mr Simpson had kept his promise by having the reality about Adrian's awful African experiences explained to other staff members and the other boys in the boarding house, Adrian became more confused and destabilised because many of the boys, instead of showing him some understanding and sympathy, avoided talking to him when they saw him, or threw him nasty glances, insinuating that he was completely mad. Or sniggered among themselves behind his back and treated him with harsh and cruel contempt and some said in a loud way so that he would hear that his behaviour over the "Simba" film had showed that he was even more bizarre, crazy and downright weird than they had thought! He was also bullied by some of the boys who made his life even more miserable. Adrian began to sense that the trust and confidence that he had placed in Mr Simpson had been betrayed, he felt even more isolated, lonely, fragile and marginalised in the school, had even greater difficulty than before in finding sleep at night and started to suffer worse nightmares than ever before.

In the early evening one week later, Adrian was attempting to concentrate on finishing his homework in the boarding house library before supper. He was alone in the library, as the other boarders had already accomplished their tasks, for Adrian was much slower in his studies due to his emotional problems, lack of confidence in his abilities and difficulty to concentrate. He suddenly felt the shadow of a tall human presence standing in front of the table. He looked up and saw Mr Simpson standing there with a beatific smile on his face and an inviting expression in his brown eyes. There was a moment's silence, during which Mr Simpson fixed Adrian with an ambiguous gaze as he looked down intently into Adrian's lovely blue eyes.

Adrian felt ill at ease and became red in the face as Mr Simpson said to him, 'Adrian, my dear boy, please come with me to my office. There is something about which I must speak with you. Bring your books and notepad with you and you can finish that homework tomorrow after school.'

After Adrian had assembled his books, notepad and pencils and placed them in his satchel and swung the satchel onto his back, he followed Mr Simpson, with curiosity and anxiety dominating his mind, out of the library, down the long corridor, around a corner, along another corridor and into Mr Simpson's office. As the teacher held the door open for him, stepped after him into the office and shut the door, Adrian could not help but hear as Mr Simpson slowly and quietly turned the key and locked the door, causing Adrian's heart to thump in his chest and his level of anxiety to rise rapidly like the mercury in a thermometer shooting up when placed in a warm room. Adrian stood rigidly still as Mr Simpson walked past him, took off his jacket, placed it neatly on a chair and turned slowly to face Adrian.

Then, with a lascivious, twisted smile on his face, he said in a seductive and cajoling tone of voice, 'My dear Adrian, I will not beat about the bush, for we do not have very much time, as the gong will ring shortly calling all the boarders to supper. You may not be aware of it, but you are a very attractive

Adrian remained prostrate and trembling over the desk for a long minute trying to overcome the state of shock, bewilderment, physical pain and discomfort, whilst a flash photo appeared in his mind of the scene he had witnessed of the sodomy that his eldest brother Neil had had to endure a few years earlier.

As he tried to stand up, his knees buckled, the intensity of the soreness and discomfort still throbbing inside his body overwhelmed him and he fell headlong to the floor. His whole body shook in utter shock and with rage and disgust at the brutal aggression and indignity he had suffered as he felt the powerful arms of Mr Simpson gripping him under the armpits and raising him up again. He nearly toppled over again as he stood very unsteadily with his legs trembling and he felt with a sense of great humiliation some seminal fluid dribbling out of his backside and down one of his thighs. He saw Mr Simpson pulling his own underpants and trousers up again and buckling his belt and he decided, whilst shaking his head vigorously in an attempt to clear his mind and evacuate his feelings of outrage, shame and humiliation, that he had no choice but to do the same.

'That was rather good, wasn't it? I hope that you enjoyed it for your first time?' Mr Simpson said laconically as he grinned cruelly like a satisfied wolf after a hearty meal of fresh meat.

'You utter bastard! You are nothing but a cynical, bullying monster! I had placed my trust and confidence in you but you have betrayed that trust and used me for your own pleasure with that brutal aggression. I shall report you to the headmaster for buggering me!'

'You will do no such thing, you measly little maggot! You have such a bad reputation in the school for being a pathetic, bizarre, crazy and unstable kid of unsound mind that no one would believe you and everyone would say that you had invented the story and told a fantastic lie in an attempt to draw attention and sympathy towards yourself. If you say one word to anyone, I can assure you that I will arrange for you to be expelled in ignominy and shame from this college and interned in a mental institution for deranged people, where you will stay for many years and your whole life will be ruined!'

Adrian was totally crestfallen and crushed, despite his furious rage against his tormentor, and knew instinctively that he was defeated. This unscrupulous, perverted and heartless teacher had taken advantage of his emotional and mental vulnerability and instability and very fragile state, was blackmailing and bullying him in the cruellest manner. But there was nothing he could do to fight against it, for he felt with his crushing inferiority complex that the teacher was right and he was indeed a weak, pathetic and utterly worthless little worm whose version of events nobody would ever believe. When he returned to his bedroom, after making an excuse of feeling unwell to avoid having to go to the dining room for supper with the other boarders, he lay on his bed, curled up in the foetal position and wept until his wracked, soiled and exhausted body seemed to be empty and dried out and he had no more tears to expel.

He thought back to the words that Neil had uttered after he had been brutally sodomised. And he knew that he could not tell anyone about the aggression that he had just suffered and had to keep his misery sorrowfully pent up inside him and try to cope with the emotional and mental agony and the shame and humiliation of his situation. Indeed, he was overcome by dreadful shame and guilt and became convinced that he was at fault and must have done something to attract Mr Simpson's attention and cause Mr Simpson to treat him with such contempt and cruelty. He sensed that his state of shame and guilt would be impossible to shake off.

Adrian was taken like a pathetically weak and defenceless lamb to the slaughter by Mr Simpson to his office and callously and brutally sodomised on one further occasion, but for slightly longer and even more violently than the first time, before the relief of the Easter holiday arrived in early April and he was able to distance himself from this monstrous and immoral pervert for a couple of weeks.

When he arrived home, he missed Dad achingly but was very pleased and grateful to see Granny and Mummy again and he tried his best to behave as normally as possible. But he felt wretchedly miserable and depressed that he could not unburden himself and had to keep his dark and dreadful secret buried deep inside his damaged body and tortured psyche.

On several occasions during the Easter holiday, he was almost drowned by his sense of shame and guilt and overcome by a gruesome desire to put an end to his depressed state and terribly unhappy life by committing suicide. But each time he seemed to hear little voices deep down inside his being admonishing him for such cowardice and commanding him to be brave and strong and to carry on enduring all the suffering and mental and emotional pain in a vague hope that the path of his life might improve in some way one day.

In mid-morning on the Wednesday after Easter Sunday, Margaret asked Adrian to come and sit down with her and Granny in the living room as she had some important news to give him. When they were seated, Granny smiled meekly at Adrian but remained silent with her hands clutched together resting on her lap.

In her usual role as head of the small household, Margaret passed a sheet of paper to Adrian, who saw that it was an extract from The London Gazette dated April 11th 1963, just a few days before Easter Sunday, which read:

Notice is hereby given that by a Deed Poll dated the 26th day of February 1963, and enrolled in the Supreme Court of Judicature on the 10th day of April 1963 the Norfolk County Council, the legal guardians of ADRIAN TUNNINGTON an infant and a citizen of the United Kingdom and Colonies by birth renounced on behalf of the said ADRIAN TUNNINGTON his former surname of WALTON-MORNICK.

As Adrian stared at the paper for several seconds then looked first at Granny then at Mummy in bewilderment and astonishment, Margaret said to him in her blunt, matter-of-fact manner, 'As we had legally adopted you and had received the documents from the court authorising the adoption, under the

auspices of the Norfolk County Council who remained your legal guardians with the duty to supervise whether the adoption was a good experience, and as some time has now passed since you started living here with us, Dad and I decided some months ago, before his brain tumour became known, that it was now time to change your surname from Walton-Mornick to ours, which you know is Tunnington. To do that it was necessary to ask the Norfolk County Council to proceed through a specific legal procedure by Deed Poll and to have your change of surname published in the London Gazette, the official newspaper in which various legal acts must appear for them to be legally valid. The document in your hand is our copy of the official publication of your name change in the London Gazette, which we have just received in this morning's post, so from now on for all purposes, including at your school, at our local church in Cullompton, and anywhere else, your name is to be Adrian Tunnington and no longer Adrian Walton-Mornick.'

This new and unexpected turn of events had a devastating effect on Adrian. He was appalled that the decision to change his surname had been made behind his back, without consulting him, asking whether he was in agreement or even keeping him informed as the steps in the procedure progressed. He felt convinced that it was in fact Margaret, with her strong, forceful and domineering character and personality, who had made the decision and that meek and gentle and unassuming Keith had no choice but to go along with it. Adrian felt a bitter anger and resentment against his adoptive mother for what he felt subjectively was a heartless attitude and manner lacking in sensitivity towards him. Worse than that, he suffered an enormous amount of grief, shock, mental and emotional anguish and physical pain in his head, throat and chest and even panic attacks from the feeling that he had been totally dislocated from his true and original family and especially from his two beloved brothers, as his surname was now different from theirs, an extremely important and painful change in his miserable life. It felt as if his brothers were being obliterated from his life like an image being effaced from a page by a rubber.

Adrian encountered severe psychological traumas and a big identity crisis, with feelings that he did not know what his true identity was and who he really was.

On several occasions, he thought back over the past nine months and sadly reflected that during such time he had been betrayed, rejected, displaced and banished by his adoptive parents, or rather by his adoptive mother, to a far off and rotten boarding school. He had lost his beloved adoptive father, he had been betrayed and horribly abused by a cruel and perverted teacher and he had lost his real surname for another one with which he could not properly identify. He felt entirely lost, like the empty bottle that he had once seen bobbing up and down with the waves on the surface of the sea and being swept first in one direction then in another, not knowing where he was going, without any sense of direction and being utterly confused as to who he was and what was his true identity.

He was completely insecure and his conviction that he was utterly worthless and had no purpose and felt grievously guilty about being alive at all became deeper than ever. He had to use all the inner strength he had to combat and overcome his frequent thoughts about suicide and he felt totally drained and emotionally exhausted at the end of each day. But had great difficulty to sleep and the most dreadful and hideous nightmares, so that he was caught up in a vicious circle and sometimes felt he must appear to resemble a zombie.

From that time onwards, Adrian, who was badly scarred by all the traumas, lack of love and unhappiness he had suffered from his very early childhood and by the abhorrent sexual abuse he was enduring, became more sullen and withdrawn than ever, could hardly ever smile, was incapable of any humour or any production of jokes and funny stories, was submerged often by black thoughts, incapable of being relaxed and could not make any friends. His back became more bent over and his shoulders became more slouched and rounded than before as he carried the heavy burden of his psychological and emotional sufferings, insecurity and unshakeable sense of shame and guilt. He was always on the defensive, subconsciously and in a way beyond his control, due to his feeling of utter worthlessness, immense inferiority complex and overwhelming fear of being betrayed, rejected, abandoned and mistreated by all the persons he came into contact with.

In public, he had to learn to play-act and to develop a pathetically sad and difficult comedy of dissimulating his distress and pretending that he was normal, content and at ease with life whereas the total opposite was true. On many occasions he sounded false and acted strangely and over-reacted so that some people found him somewhat bizarre, abnormal and unbearable and were impatient, mocking, harsh and even cruel in their attitudes and behaviour towards him.

After his return to the boarding school at the end of the Easter holidays, Adrian was taken by Mr Simpson to his office on two further occasions. As he was consumed by shame, humiliation and guilt, he just resigned himself to his fate and felt convinced that the barbaric acts of sodomy perpetrated on him by the teacher were entirely his own fault.

However, his unhappiness and depression reached such a level that he went one Saturday evening to the telephone booth in the boarding school reserved for use by the boarders, dialled his adoptive mother's home number and, when she came on the line, said to her in a pathetically sad voice, 'Mummy, please forgive me for disturbing you, but I have a request to make. I miss both my brothers dreadfully; I think about them constantly and wish that I could see them again. I have no idea where Neil is, all I know is that he is in the Royal Navy somewhere. However, both you and I know that Justin is being brought up by my Uncle Henry and Aunt Clotilda in Dickleborough in Norfolk. I want dearly to be reunited with Justin and spend a few days with him. Do you think you could contact Aunt Clotilda and ask her if I could come up to their house and stay with them and be with Justin for as many days as possible during the coming summer holidays?'

At first there was silence at the other end, and with a sinking heart Adrian feared that his adoptive mother was angry about his request, wanted to keep him close to her at home during his summer holidays and would refuse to attempt to arrange a visit for him to see Justin.

However, after several long seconds she said with a hesitating and unenthusiastic tone in her voice, 'Well, I do not know the telephone number of your aunt but I think that Granny must have it. I will check with her and ask her if she is prepared to call your aunt and relay your request. We will get back to you on the subject in the coming days.'

Adrian's relief and delight knew no bounds when Granny telephoned him and told him with her cheery and musical voice that she had spoken with Aunt Clotilda over the telephone and she had willingly agreed, after speaking with Justin, that Adrian could stay with them for ten days in the second part of July. Adrian started dreaming about his forthcoming reunion with his brother, whom he loved so much and had not seen for so many years, both with joy and a slight feeling of apprehension. For he wondered how Justin had evolved and might have changed over these past years and whether his elder brother would be pleased or not to spend some time in his company, since Adrian felt so hopelessly inadequate and worthless.

Adrian felt that life was definitely taking a slightly better turn, after the wonderful expectation of seeing Justin again during the summer holidays, when he heard the news among the chattering gossips in the boarding house that Mr Simpson was going to leave St Boniface's College at the end of that term as he had accepted the offer of the prestigious post of headmaster of another school located somewhere in the County of Dorset, which he learned with immense relief was a very long way from Plymouth.

To his even greater relief, he was not taken again by Mr Simpson to his office and he started wondering whether the sadistic and perverted teacher may have transferred his attentions to some other boy who might have taken his fancy until his departure from the college.

However, he said to himself that that was none of his business and he was just pleased to be left alone by this monster and would simply say good riddance when he left the school at the end of the term. Two days before the term ended, he became terrified when Mr Simpson told him to follow him to his office, but once inside the teacher did not attempt to abuse him but repeated his earlier threats with a growling and menacing voice and told Adrian forcefully that if he said a word to anyone about their secret he would vehemently deny his accusations, which nobody would ever believe. And that he had the power from his important position as the headmaster in the other school to have him expelled ignominiously from St Boniface's College and interned indefinitely in a mental institution for mad people. Adrian knew inside himself that, just like his brother Neil, he would never tell anyone and would always keep the dark secret buried deep in his heart and mind.

As Mummy had been obliged for financial reasons after Dad's death to start work on a full time basis as a nurse at the Tiverton Hospital, Adrian was

very excited as Granny drove him in her little blue snail on wheels early on the appointed Wednesday morning to the Exeter St David's railway station. Then she gave him a big hug and kiss on the platform, wishing him a very joyful reunion with Justin, and waved goodbye as the steam locomotive pulled the carriages out of the railway station. After a very long and slow journey, which required changing trains at the large and bustling Paddington station in London and taking a second train with fewer carriages up to the large town of Norwich then a smaller local train, Adrian felt somewhat weary as he descended in the late afternoon from the carriage onto the platform of the railway station at Diss, the small Norfolk market town which was only a few miles from the village of Dickleborough.

Adrian recognised immediately the slight frame, piercing blue eyes and slightly greying hair of Aunt Clotilda, who was puffing on a cigarette, but he drew in a gasp of air as he looked at the very tall and broad-shouldered young fellow standing beside her. He hardly recognised Justin after all these years. He had shot up like a beanstalk and Adrian strained his neck as he gazed up at this young man, who had just had his seventeenth birthday and was already six feet tall and appeared like a giant to the much smaller Adrian.

His frame had also filled out and he was impressively broad-shouldered and looked to Adrian to be as strong as an ox or, if not an ox, a very fit and well-trained wrestler with whom you did not want to argue or get on the wrong side of. Adrian looked up to the slightly rounded face, which had become pleasantly handsome, and into those marvellous blue eyes, which seemed to have a warmer and wiser expression than in past years. Without saying a word, ever the strong silent type who did not waste words, Justin gave him an expansive smile and opened his long arms. Adrian rushed forward, blotted his face against Justin's large chest, wrapped his arms as best he could around his broad back and sobbed gushing tears for several seconds as he felt those strong arms wrapping themselves easily around him in a warm and protective embrace.

As Adrian stepped back and looked up, he felt very moved to see Justin's eyes reddened and filled with tears as well. No word passed between them just then, the exchange of affectionate looks in their wet blue eyes sufficed. Justin wiped his tears away then took Adrian's suitcase in one hand as they walked behind Aunt Clotilda to her black car and he placed his other arm over Adrian's shoulders and drew him towards him so their bodies pressed against each other as they walked happily in step to the small station car park. They sat together on the back seat as Aunt Clotilda drove home to Dickleborough, holding hands in brotherly union, and they agreed as they started chatting that they would have great fun getting to know one another again and catching up on each other's news over the next ten days of the holiday together. Their love for one another was as strong as ever, despite all those years of unjust and sad separation, and they felt immensely happy to be reunited, if only for a short while.

Whilst Adrian was not very pleased to see Uncle Henry again that evening over supper, he was delighted to be with Cousin James once more and he

played all sorts of games after supper with Justin and James. The latter had naturally grown up as well, but he was nowhere near as tall as Justin and his height was somewhere in between that of Justin and Adrian, who said proudly to himself that no other seventeen year old fellow anywhere on earth could be as tall, broad-shouldered, handsome or wise as his beloved brother Justin! He was quite surprised by James' physical strength as they played some rough-and-tumble games and wrestled together. James expressed his glee with loud grunts and groans and grinned cheerfully like a self-satisfied chimpanzee.

As they were finishing breakfast the following morning and about to clear away the table and do the washing up, Justin came round the table, put one long arm around Adrian's shoulder, patted him on the cheek and said to him as he gave him a very affectionate smile, 'Little brother, I have a big surprise in store for you on Saturday morning. Something very special is going to happen then. In the meantime, James and I will entertain you today by taking you for some walks to great places in the vicinity and Aunt Clotilda has accepted to drive us all to Norwich tomorrow, where you can discover some of the sights of the town and we can visit the very old castle and its scary dungeons.'

'What is the surprise? Please do tell me, Justin! I cannot wait until Saturday to know. You must tell me now or my curiosity and impatience will make me burst into little pieces!'

'Aha! I remember very well, even when we were little boys in Kenya, that you were an impatient rascal. As you will be fifteen years old in early September, it is high time that you learnt some patience, so I am not saying any more and you must wait until Saturday!'

'I remember as well, even back in our days in Kenya, that you were always the most reasonable, smart and wise one among the three of us! Okay, you are the boss, I will try to be patient and will force my head and body to wait until Saturday – but this surprise had better be worth the wait!'

When they were having their breakfast on Saturday morning, Adrian's excitement and anticipation were getting the better of him and he could barely sit still. After they had finished the washing up and were lounging on the settees in the living room pawing through some comic books, the front door bell suddenly rang.

Neither Uncle Henry nor Aunt Clotilda appeared and Adrian was astonished when Justin looked over at him and said laconically with an impish grin on his face, 'Little brother, will you go and open the front door please? At this hour I imagine it is the milkman delivering two bottles of milk.'

Adrian glanced from Justin to James, feeling somewhat irritated, as he thought to himself that this was their home and that one of them should surely go to open the door for the milkman. However, he just shrugged his shoulders, not wanting to argue with his elder brother, pushed himself up from the settee and ambled slowly and unenthusiastically across the room into the small hall and opened the front door, preparing himself to take the two bottles of milk.

As the door opened fully, he had a double take, could not believe the vision before him and had to rub his eyes twice with his hands for he wondered if his mind was playing tricks with him and he had just seen a ghost.

'Oh my God! Oh my God!' Adrian shrieked, as he heard Justin bursting out in laughter and gleefully clapping his hands somewhere behind him. 'Is it really you, Neil? Is it really you?'

'Hi there, little brother! It is wonderful to see you again after this separation of five years! Into my arms! Let me give you a big hug!'

The eldest brother and the youngest brother clung on to each other for several minutes in a long, warm embrace, pecking each other on the cheeks. Neil passed a hand with tender affection through Adrian's hair and his beautiful blue eyes looked down into Adrian's blue eyes and his deeply loving expression warmed Adrian's heart so much that he could not prevent himself from bursting into tears as he gazed up at his big brother whom he loved immensely and had always hero-worshipped since his birth and those young days when they had had so many adventures together with Justin back in Kenya.

As Neil and Adrian walked arm in arm into the living room, Justin rushed over to them with tears rolling down his cheeks and the three brothers stayed locked in a warm, loving embrace for what seemed to James like a very long time as he looked on enviously at this scene of affectionate brotherly reunion and he wished that he too had a brother to love him.

When they finally separated and stood huddled together smiling and laughing and saying how happy they were to be together again, Adrian looked at Neil and Justin and saw that Neil was taller than himself but several inches shorter than Justin. Whilst Adrian and Justin had inherited the roundness of their mother's face, Neil resembled their father and Adrian looked adoringly at Neil's strikingly handsome, rectangular face with almost exactly the same aristocratic elongated nose and regular features as their father. Neil was wearing his naval uniform, which greatly impressed Adrian and increased immediately the level of the hero worship.

He saw that the band around the naval cap perched on Neil's head contained in gold capital lettering at the front the mention "HMS ARETHUSA".

They walked towards the settees and Neil greeted Cousin James with a friendly hug.

When they were comfortably installed on the settees, Neil turned his attention to Adrian and said, 'I let Justin know some time ago that I had been transferred from HMS GANGES to HMS ARETHUSA. He telephoned me a few weeks ago, told me that you were coming here for a ten-day holiday and asked if I could get away so that we could all be together again. I have managed to obtain permission from my superiors to come up here for the weekend. I arrived by train late yesterday evening at Diss railway station, spent the night in a small hotel and a taxi has just driven me here. I can stay here tonight but I will have to return back down there by train during the afternoon

tomorrow, as we have important sea exercises starting on Monday morning. I will ask Uncle Henry if he can drive me back to Diss station in time for my train tomorrow afternoon. I imagine he and Aunt Clotilda are still up in their bedroom, so I will greet them when they come down later.'

Neil, who had turned nineteen some weeks earlier in June, told Adrian, as Justin already knew this, that HMS ARETHUSA was a Royal Navy training centre situated at Lower Upnor in the County of Kent.

He said that in 1849 there had already been a training ship named HMS ARETHUSA moored there on the River Medway and since then each new training ship replacing an old one was named HMS ARETHUSA. As the ship was moored near the entrance to the wide estuary of the River Medway, there was easy access for it to the North Sea. He added proudly that he was enjoying his life in the Royal Navy. Although he sadly had not managed to make more than two real friends, as he found it very difficult to relate to the other boys as he felt he was a tortured soul, over-sensitive and lacking in self-confidence due to all the traumas, lack of love, rejection and unhappiness that he had endured in his early years.

Both Justin and Adrian assured him that they understood extremely well what he meant and were having similar difficulties themselves. Neil told them that one of his superior officers was encouraging him to study hard and to undergo a training to become an electrical engineer, which he had accepted to do, although he was aware that his weakness was his difficulty to concentrate due to his inner anxieties and lack of faith in his own abilities. That also rang a bell in both Justin's and Adrian's minds and they told Neil about their own respective difficulties to concentrate.

The three brothers compared notes orally and gave one another examples of some concrete instances of lack of concentration that they had suffered.

Justin then jumped up and said with an excited voice, 'As I have just turned seventeen, and I did manage to obtain seven O Level exams, I have one more year to go at Buckden Towers in the normal school and hope that I will manage to pass the three A Level exams. The priests at the school are trying to push me to undergo the long novitiate training in the seminary to become a priest, but they push religious studies down our throats, which is really beginning to turn me against religion, and there is another fundamental reason why I have decided not to become a priest.'

'During my various holidays, I have met a couple of rather pretty girls here in the village on different occasions and each one has introduced me to the delightful pleasures of sexual conduct between boys and girls. As Roman Catholic priests are not allowed to marry or to have any sex at all with women and must take the vow of celibacy for the rest of their lives, there is no way that I will become a priest as there is no way that I am going to become celibate! As to my future, I have already told Neil over the telephone that I have decided that after I leave Buckden Towers I will join the Royal Navy, following in big brother's footsteps, and I like the idea of training to become an electrical

engineer as well.' Adrian smiled at this and thought to himself that he was not the only brother who had succumbed to practising hero worship!

The whole weekend was wonderful for all the three brothers, who enjoyed themselves immensely being together, doing various activities together and chatting away together like excited magpies about all sorts of subjects, whilst including James in all these happy moments, as Cousin James was an important member of the family in their eyes. The moment when Neil had to say goodbye to them and be driven away in Uncle Henry's car was exceedingly wrenching and very sad for all of them and the three brothers prayed together that they would be able to be re-united again before too long.

One day during the next week, before Adrian had to leave to return to Devon, Justin told him that he had learned, although merely superficially, some fascinating things about their Walton-Mornick family both from Aunt Clotilda and from Aunt Patricia. He said that the three brothers had been born into an aristocratic, upper-class family and both the Walton and the Mornick branches dated back to the Doomsday Book, a manuscript record of the great survey of much of England and parts of Wales completed in the year 1086 by order of King William the Conqueror to record how much each landholder had in land and livestock and how much it was worth, in order to determine what taxes had been owed by wealthy landowners during the reign of King Edward the Confessor.

Justin told Adrian that the two families had merged to become one through marriage many centuries ago and counted many illustrious and successful people among their members down the ages. However, he said that it appeared that the Walton-Mornick family in the modern era had some bizarre and eccentric, self-centred and unpleasant members. Whilst they knew to their cost and sad fate that their own father was one of them, Justin said that their Aunt Celestina seemed to him to be somewhat strange and eccentric as well. She had one daughter called Roberta, who was about three years older than Justin, but poor Roberta did not know who her father was and had never met him and, despite her entreaties, her mother always refused cruelly to tell her the identity of her father. It turned out that Aunt Celestina would take herself off sometimes and would come to Dickleborough with Roberta first, literally dump Roberta on Uncle Henry and Aunt Clotilda and be away somewhere for weeks and even months on end, without them knowing where, and would re-appear suddenly one day and take Roberta home with her. Justin said that he had naturally seen Roberta many times, since he had been taken in by Uncle Henry and Aunt Clotilda several years earlier, and she had been deposited with them by her mother on several occasions. He added that he found Cousin Roberta to be a lovely but very sad, insecure and unhappy girl suffering terribly from the total lack of a father and the unloving and detached treatment of her mother every now and then.

Adrian listened to all of this with an increasingly heavier heart and he felt a certain confusion and a little resentment against some of the members of his weird, grotesque and highly dysfunctional family.

It so happened that a few days before Adrian's departure Aunt Clotilda informed him, Justin and James that Aunt Celestina would be arriving with Roberta about teatime that afternoon to see them all, as she had telephoned her sister and told her that Adrian was staying there and had invited her and Roberta to come over to meet him.

During the day, Adrian felt an anxiety and apprehension about meeting Aunt Celestina and Roberta welling up inside him but, when they arrived, he took to cousin Roberta immediately and found her not only very pleasant to look at but very entertaining and amusing in her conversation. However, he felt somewhat reserved about Aunt Celestina and, whereas he had a deep affection for both Aunt Clotilda and Aunt Patricia, he found he could not make up his mind whether he liked Aunt Celestina or not, as she did appear to him to be rather odd, eccentric, coldly aloof and detached.

Chapter 7
Discovery of Soulmate

Adrian celebrated his fifteenth birthday on September 7th 1963, a few days after returning to St Boniface's College for the start of the new scholastic year. But "celebrated" was not, in fact, the right word for there was no birthday party, none of the boys in the boarding house celebrated with him and he felt completely isolated, ostracised and miserably lonely.

He found some consolation and relief from his anxieties by throwing himself more than ever into the gymnastics sessions and rugby training after school twice each week and matches each Saturday afternoon.

He was delighted and somewhat proud to be promoted as number seven wing forward from the school's second team to the first team. He was so keen on playing rugby, a sport that he loved and which was an antidote to his psychological and emotion problems and a means with which to fight against his insecurities and sense of worthlessness, that he was able to manage to maintain his place, against strong competition from other players, in the school's first team as its number seven wing forward over the next three years until he left the college at the age of eighteen.

Scholastically, the situation was far less brilliant. Despite enormous mentally exhausting efforts, Adrian could not rid himself of the overriding inferiority complex, lack of self-assurance and the deep-seated conviction that if he had been rejected and abandoned by his parents it was because he was worthless, useless and unlovable. He suffered constantly from problems of lack of concentration, which were exacerbated by the cruel taunting, mocking and bullying meted out on frequent occasions by normal, stable and self-confident boys of his own age and some who were older than him, who saw and felt that there was something fundamentally wrong with him and lacking in him and that he was abnormal, strange and different from them.

After the O-Level exams in late June 1964 Adrian was appalled to learn that he had failed Geography and Chemistry and had obtained passes with very low and humiliating marks in seven subjects and had only just scraped by in Maths. When he learned that most of the boys in his year had obtained nine O Levels with very high marks, his meagre results only deepened further the terrible inferiority complex, lack of self-confidence, inner conviction that he really was worthless and the concentration difficulties. He became the butt of even harsher and crueller jokes, mockery, bullying and clear messages from

many of the other boys that he was set apart, stigmatised as a "wierdo" and an inferior being and could never become one of them.

Two years later, the dreadful nightmarish situation repeated itself when Adrian only just scraped through his three A Level exams in English language and literature, French language and literature and Latin with the lowest marks possible to obtain a pass. He felt crushed, humiliated, ashamed and very confused. For during the past two years, he had been the top of his class in Latin, as he seemed to have an ease and facility with that subject. But he realised that his difficulties to concentrate made him have to work extremely hard to prepare for the regular tests and learn the Latin words, phrases and citations by heart and had exhausted him mentally, emotionally and physically. And his inferiority complex and extreme nervousness during the exams caused a memory failure and difficulty to recall much of what he had learned so that his marks were unexpectedly low.

Adrian left St Boniface's College at the end of that summer term with his tail between his legs and a sentiment of failure and intense personal unhappiness, especially as he had not managed to make even one true friend at the school with whom he could look forward to maintaining some contact. When he returned home, his emotional stress and depression was compounded as he had to face the disappointment and severe criticism of his low academic achievements from Granny and Mummy. They were just unable to understand the deep problems inside Adrian, who just clammed up and could not find the words to attempt to explain the deep pain and suffering which were his lot on a daily basis in his distorted and unhappy life. It seemed that Granny and Mummy both thought that since he had been adopted he should automatically be a perfectly normal and stable boy without any psychological, mental or emotional problems and that any consequences of the lack of love, betrayal, rejection and abandonment by his parents and the experiences in two orphanages should have simply disappeared into thin air. How wrong they both were, but Adrian could not summon up the mental strength to put them right on that score.

Whilst Granny and Mummy had dreamed that Adrian would be able automatically to go to a university after leaving St Boniface's College, it became evident after several enquiries were made that there was no way any university in the country would accept to give Adrian a place due to the low marks that he had obtained in his A Level exams.

In discussions with Granny, Mummy, Uncle Patrick, Mummy's brother who was an Army officer, and some other persons of good counsel, it was agreed that Adrian should find an educational institution which would allow him to study the same three A Level subjects again during the coming academic year as from the end of August and attempt to obtain higher marks in the exams at the end of the following summer term.

It transpired that Exeter Technical College was prepared to give him a place and a second chance and the head of the college suggested that, as he had already studied those three subjects during the past two years, it would be

beneficial and might increase his chances of obtaining a place at a university if he also studied the additional subject of British Constitution.

Adrian accepted this challenge and started the one-year courses in the four subjects in late August 1966. He lived at home and drove to and from the college each day during the week in his little, very old Austin A40 car, which he had managed to buy out of his meagre savings from the jobs that he had always done during his holidays over the past two years, especially one loading piles of roofing tiles onto lorries at a local tile factory a few miles from home, which kept him fit and developed his arm and chest muscles.

Adrian felt that he owed it to his adoptive family as well as to himself to study as hard as possible and ensure success at the exams. He fought the best he could against his concentration difficulties and was sure that because they were still very strong he had to put in many more hours of study and revision than most of the other students. Also, as his psychological and emotional problems were still overwhelming him and causing much inner suffering, he worked hard to combat them and gain some degree of mental stability and self-confidence. He did not succeed very well in that, but what seemed to save him from disaster was his developing ability to play-act, dissimulate his distress and give an impression of being more normal, content and relaxed in life than he was in reality. He even managed to make one or two friends, albeit on a very superficial level, and he met a very pretty, bright, sociable and entertaining female student who accepted to go out with him and be his casual girlfriend during a few months.

Adrian was delighted and relieved by his success in the exams and the level of his marks in all four subjects, which, whilst not being the highest marks, were sufficiently good to enable him to send applications to several universities around the country to study Law. In actual fact, his initial desire was to study French language and literature, as he had always loved French from his early days at St Boniface's College.

However, Granny, Mummy, Uncle Patrick and a few other interlocutors persuaded him against French, as that subject would narrow down his choices of a career, and prevailed upon him to study Law, as this had a wide basis and greater appeal and would open many more doors and provide better opportunities for a career in many diverse fields.

As he accepted an offer to study Law at Exeter University, whose Faculty of Law had an excellent reputation, he started there in early September 1967, lodging with a fellow Law student with a family during the first year. Then he lived in the Catholic Chaplaincy on the campus during his second year and was given a bedroom in one of the university halls for his final year.

He encountered grave psychological and emotional difficulties during those three student years, for he met dozens of other students who were exceedingly bright, some very brilliant. Many of them possessed a great sense of humour and fun, an enormous self-confidence, cocky youthful arrogance, tremendous belief in their abilities and talents and an impressively ambitious and ruthless desire to become very successful in their fields and future careers. Adrian felt

very envious of all such qualities, as he was convinced that he did not possess any of them and his inferiority complex, lack of self-assurance, grave insecurity, deep sense of guilt about the breakdown of his family unit gnawed constantly at his psyche. His ingrained sense of worthlessness plagued him viciously, dragged him down and never gave him any respite.

Whilst Adrian did his very best to fit in and to make some friends, he was eaten up from his unhappy childhood by lack of confidence, the feeling of being greatly inferior and a deep fear of being disliked, rejected, betrayed and abandoned, which stultified, distorted and falsified his approach to others and made him act unnaturally, over-reach and over-react in his pathetic, overwhelming emotional need to please and gain the approval of other people, causing the opposite effect.

Many other students, most notably males, including some who studied with him in the Faculty of Law and saw him regularly, considered him somewhat abnormal, bizarre, maladjusted and very different from them with his hyper-sensitive attitudes, overly serious and anxious comportment and total lack of a sense of humour, taking everything at the first degree. Which caused them to treat him with a cruel contempt and a cold, standoffish manner and to mock and bully him on some occasions.

One day at lunchtime, after a period in the Law Faculty library followed by a lecture on Commercial Law attended by two dozen students, he latched onto, and followed like a pathetic lamb, two female and three male students walking to a pub in Exeter city centre, where they found a corner space and bought beer and sandwiches. He sat sheepishly and in silence and merely listened to the bubbly conversation and funny jokes and laughter exchanged between the others. However, the mood changed suddenly when one of the girls named Maureen told them, with tears streaming down her cheeks and her chest heaving in anguish, about a tragic accident a few days earlier in a suburb of London when a car driver lost control and careered into the bicycle of her elder sister, causing her to crash down onto the road and suffer severe head injuries. The other girl and the three boys merely exchanged very embarrassed looks, bowed their heads and said nothing. Then Adrian told Maureen he was terribly sad to hear this awful news, expressed deep sympathy for her anxiety and said that he hoped that her sister would soon recover fully from her injuries.

Maureen looked over at Adrian, wiped the tears from her eyes and cheeks and said to him in a feeble and sobbing voice, 'Thank you, Adrian, for those kind words and for caring, which I appreciate very much.'

'It is normal to care, Maureen; that is what friends are for,' Adrian replied as he held her gaze with his lovely blue eyes and smiled tenderly at her.

'You do not have any friends, you pathetic little worm!' screamed one of the boys at Adrian as he scowled at him with a contemptuous and harsh expression in his dark brown eyes.

Adrian felt a searing pain in his heart as if he had been struck by a long, sharp dagger. He stood up hesitatingly, nearly toppled over like a drunkard in an alcoholic haze, regained his balance shakily then rushed headlong across the

room. Struggled down the stairs to the basement and shut himself inside the farthest cubicle from the entrance in the men's toilets. Sagged down onto the floor and rocked his body from side to side, with his arms folded tightly across his chest, as he banged his head repeatedly against the hard wall and wept bitterly for several minutes as a pall of depression and sense of hopelessness gripped his entire being.

The pain caused by the boy's cruel and hostile jab was so intense and cutting that Adrian felt there was no hope for him. He would never be liked or loved by the other young people of his own age and he had no other choice but to push his head deep down into the toilet, flush it, drown in the gushing water and put an end to his damned and miserable life.

As he was contemplating this morbid, radical solution, he heard a fist banging on the door of the cubicle and the voice of his tormentor apologising and asking him to come out. However, the tone of voice was cold, completely insincere and false and Adrian felt convinced that the only reason for the boy's presence there was that Maureen must have admonished him and ordered him to come down and apologise to Adrian.

He waited slumped on the floor for some seconds, then hauled himself to his feet, wiped his eyes dry and opened the cubicle door. When he saw the other boy standing there with a sneering and cruel smile on his face, Adrian felt a red-hot rage mounting in his chest.

He bunched up his left fist, as he had more strength in his left arm being left-handed, smashed the fist hard into the middle of his face and shouted at him in great anger and frustration as he crashed to the floor with blood bursting from his broken nose, 'Fuck off, you horrible turd! Don't you ever dare say a nasty word to me again or I will pulverise you into pulp like a log of wood reduced to mash!'

Adrian ran up the stairs, glanced over his shoulder to see Maureen and the others still sitting in the corner, turned on his heels and rushed out of the pub. Whilst he gleaned a tiny momentary satisfaction from having punished the other boy for his nastiness, the cutting remark remained in the forefront of his mind and in his troubled and unsettled state he felt absolutely convinced that what the boy had said was true and that he did not have any friends and was completely unable to make any friends. He thought constantly of his two beloved brothers and he prayed and hoped that their personal situations were as good as humanly possible and that in the Royal Navy, where they both studied and worked albeit on two different ships, they were able to make some friends among the other seamen whom they frequented.

****

When Adrian was thirteen, Mummy had introduced him to Janet, one of her close childhood friends, her husband Francis, their son Michael and their daughter Susannah, when they came to Stenhill Cottage for lunch one day in July on their way down to Cornwall for a fortnight's summer holiday.

Since then, they had all met up again on one or two occasions together with Janet's sister Rose and her husband Chris, who lived in a small country village not far inland behind the seaside town of Exmouth in Devon. Adrian was almost the same age as Susannah whilst Michael was eighteen months younger than his sister.

Adrian liked Susannah and Michael but he did not think that Susannah was pretty. He thought that the most attractive feature was her shoulder-length reddish auburn hair, which she had no doubt inherited from her mother, who was tall and statuesque and had a magnificent head of flaming auburn hair with many tinges of red and copper, as well as a fiery, feisty, energetic and dynamic personality and a very artistic temperament, which had enabled her to attend an art school in London and become a successful commercial artist earning nearly as much income as her husband, who owned a boutique selling men's clothes and shoes in Central London, where they lived in a large and comfortable flat.

After Dad's untimely and tragic death, Adrian had only seen Michael, Susannah and their parents once more one Saturday in August when Adrian was fifteen. When Adrian started studying at Exeter University, he only came home on occasional weekends and was contented to play in rugby matches for the university team on most Saturday afternoons during each term. He came to live at home during each holiday and spent most of his time working at the local tile factory in order to earn some pocket money and enough money to put aside and use for buying some new clothes, a new bicycle and other necessary items, as he wanted to take any financial burden from Mummy and to help her, as she did not have much means and was having to work hard as a nurse at the Tiverton Hospital to earn a salary.

It was when Adrian was near the end of the autumn term of his first year at Exeter University that he began to sense that he found it much easier to develop human contacts with girls than with boys. Firstly, several of the female students appeared somehow to be attracted to him, for reasons that Adrian could not fathom out. For he had been so badly harmed by his childhood mishaps and traumas that he had no love or appreciation of himself, no recognition nor acceptance of any qualities in himself and a predominant feeling of being physically ugly, dreadfully inferior to any other human beings and really worthless and useless.

Secondly, after having been bullied by boys at school during several years and so cruelly and barbarically abused sexually by the teacher at St Boniface's College he had an instinctive and automatic wariness and fear of the male species and the male penis, that dagger-like weapon, as well as a strange sense that the male possessed ugly traits of nastiness, deviousness, cockiness, arrogance, thirst for domination, power and aggressiveness tending more towards hypocrisy, betrayal, starting conflict and war rather than searching for conciliation, friendship and peace.

On the contrary, the female seemed to be softer, gentler, kinder, more dependable, compassionate, conciliatory and easier to relate to on psychological and emotional levels. Thirdly, he started to wonder whether

some girls were in actual fact attracted by his enormous emotional fragility, awkwardness, humbleness and lack of confidence or pride, distinguishing him from many of the other male students, who strode around the campus with their backs straight like iron rods, their chins proudly jutted up and out, their chests thrust out like puffed up cockerels, so full of self-confidence, so sure of their primacy, wonderful abilities and qualities and so convinced that they were God's gift to women and that all the girls at the university were dying for them to take them to bed, then penetrate and possess them with their magical male daggers.

Bowed under as he was by the heavy weight of his complexes and the overall disastrous consequences and after effects of his unhappy childhood, which made him slump and hunch over his shoulders rather than straighten his back, it did not occur to Adrian for quite a long time that some girls found him physically attractive and appreciated his Welsh jet black hair combined with lovely blue eyes. His handsome face with regular features, and his slender and athletic frame with muscular arms and legs kept fit by regular sessions in the gym and frequent training and matches on the rugby field, as well as the physical work at the tile factory during his holidays, also attracted some girls.

When he was back at home for the Christmas holidays in December 1967 at the end of the first term of his first year at university, Margaret told Adrian that her close friends Francis and Janet and their children Susannah and Michael were coming to visit them and have a late lunch with them at the cottage on the Saturday before Christmas on their drive down from London to spend Christmas and the two weeks of Susannah's and Michael's Christmas holiday with their Uncle Chris and Aunt Rose at their charming village house. Adrian shrugged his shoulders and merely noted this information with apathy and lack of enthusiasm, as he had almost forgotten about these friends of Mummy since he had not seen them for four years.

As she heard the car pull into the driveway on the appointed Saturday, Mummy checked the lunch was cooking well, took off her apron, opened the kitchen door and rushed out to greet the visitors. She was followed by Granny, who had also been invited by Mummy and had driven over in her little blue snail on wheels from her flat in the nearly village of Willand.

Adrian ambled out of the cottage behind them in a nonchalant, apathetic mood and with a slow, lethargic step and saw Mummy hugging her dear friend Janet then Francis after they had closed the front doors of their large black car. Then the two back doors opened and Adrian had a double take as Michael and Susannah stepped out onto the driveway. Michael stood impressively tall, much taller than his medium-sized father and towering over his statuesque and elegant mother.

Adrian surmised rapidly that Michael's height was about halfway between the heights of his own brothers Justin and Neil. He noticed also, with a sense of envy, which brought his strong feeling of inferiority back to the forefront, that Michael had become quite ruggedly handsome and possessed the same dynamic and feisty look in his eyes as that of his mother.

When Adrian looked at Susannah as she started walking towards him, the shock was so great he felt a physical reaction in his solar plexus. They were both now nineteen years of age and the last time he had seen her four years ago he had found her plain and not at all pretty except for her magnificent and striking hair. Now as he gawked open-mouthed at her and could not prevent himself from studying her from her feet up to the top of her thick crown of flaming red hair, very similar to that of her mother, he had a first image in his mind of a former ugly duckling turned into a majestic swan then another, more appropriate, image of a drab, uninteresting caterpillar's chrysalis that had been transformed into a colourful, exotic, beautiful butterfly.

Susannah was almost unrecognisable except for that wonderful head of hair. Adrian stood transfixed and could not move for several seconds as he stared very impolitely at her gorgeous face, appealing brown eyes, sensuous lips, full breasts, provocatively rounded hips and long, shapely legs. She was strikingly beautiful, nearly as tall as him, and he was almost bowled over by her radiating sensuality and strong sex-appeal as she stood in front of him then planted a wet kiss on his right cheek and told him in a warm, deep, sensual voice that she was very pleased to see him again after those four long years. She stepped back then, slowly and deliberately, looked him up and down as well and her radiant smile seemed to indicate that she too appreciated the big physical change in Adrian since their last meeting.

The immediate mutual attraction was very forceful like two magnets being drawn strongly and inexorably to each other. During the lunch, Adrian and Susannah seemed to be in a world of their own. They replied politely when spoken to by the others but they could not stop gazing into each other's eyes across the table and smiling discreetly to one another and Adrian felt uplifted each time she seemed to be flirting with him through the amazing, magnetic, warm and appealing flashes of expression in those irresistible brown eyes.

When they all rose from the dining table after lunch and Francis looked at his watch, thanked Margaret for a wonderful lunch and said that they must continue their journey down to the house of Rose and Chris, Michael shook Adrian's hand and said he had been delighted to see him again.

Susannah then came up to Adrian, cupped her left hand over his right hand, caressed his hand with hers, gave his hand a firm squeeze and said to him, in a languorous and sensual manner as she looked deeply into his blue eyes with those warmly communicative brown eyes, 'You know, Adrian, it has been a pleasant surprise and a real pleasure to see you as you are now after all these years. I do hope that during these coming two weeks of my holiday we may have the chance to see one another again, just the two of us, and to start to get to know each other better.'

Adrian was so dumfounded and flattered that such a beautiful girl would say such kind, endearing and encouraging words to him that he was silent for a moment, as he lost himself in those irresistible brown eyes. Then he lowered his gaze to her lovely, full, perfectly shaped lips, which he felt sorely tempted to kiss, looked up again into her eyes, smiled sheepishly and stammered with a

soft voice that it would indeed be great if they could meet up again during her holiday.

Then he cupped his left hand over her right hand, caressed both her hands with his two hands, squeezed her hands with his, and finally pushed her lightly away while releasing her hands as he plucked up the courage to say with an awkward laugh, 'Go now, for if you do not disappear in the next minute I will want to keep you trapped here as my prisoner!'

'Oh my, you are quite the romantic!' Susannah gurgled, then she leaned forward, pressed her lips on his cheek and whispered, 'I think I would derive great pleasure from being your prisoner! See you again very soon, I hope!'

After the car had left the driveway, and Mummy and Adrian had finished washing the pots and pans, plates, cutlery and glasses and settled down with Granny on the sofas in the lounge for an afternoon rest, Mummy said she had observed that he and Susannah had seemed to hit it off very well together. And she was very pleased about that, as she considered Susannah, the daughter of her best childhood friend and her own god-daughter, to be a lovely girl with a good character and a very attractive personality. It would be a very positive development if Susannah were to become Adrian's steady girlfriend, especially as he had never yet had a steady girlfriend, since his short friendship with the girl he had met at Exeter Technical College a year earlier did not really count.

Adrian looked over at her in mild irritation at this parental intervention and matchmaking posture, but, realising that her intentions were good, he replied in as gentle a tone as possible, 'Well, Mummy, I must admit that I had never anticipated that Susannah would have grown into such a splendid and beautiful young woman. It would certainly be pleasant to see her again but let us just go slowly and see how things shape up.'

A few days after Christmas, Mummy replied to a telephone call in the dining room and, after chatting merrily for a minute with the person at the other end, shouted up to Adrian, who was reading a book on his bed.

She gave him the telephone with an expansive smile on her face as he came down into the room, then he whispered to her, as he was not expecting any call, 'Who is it?'

'Aha! You must find out for yourself!' Mummy shouted gleefully and deliberately loudly so that the person at the other end of the telephone would hear her.

Adrian felt weak at the knees and slightly giddy in the head as he heard the warm, deep and sensuous voice of Susannah.

After having asked him if he, Granny and Mummy had enjoyed a pleasant Christmas celebration, she continued in a lilting, pleasant manner, 'Have you heard about the new film called *The Graduate*? It is a comic drama made by an American filmmaker based on the novel of the same name written by Charles Webb and starring those great actors Dustin Hoffman, Anne Bancroft and Katharine Ross. It was released in a few countries a few days before Christmas and will be showing in three days' time at the cinema in Exeter. As I have my driving licence and can borrow my parents' car and you told me the other day

that you also have your licence and your own little second-hand car, would you fancy meeting at the Hole in the Wall restaurant in Exeter in the early evening for a bite of supper then going to see the film?'

Adrian felt ecstatic at this opportunity to see her again. He did not want to have to admit to her that he had not heard of the novel or the film, but even though he felt stupid and a humbled ignoramus the important thing was that they could spend some time alone together. The whole evening went very well and, while they were holding hands watching the film, Susannah suddenly leaned closer to Adrian, turned his head towards her with her free hand and kissed him passionately on the lips.

After that, there were a few holes in the plot for them as they missed some parts of certain scenes due to several moments of passionate and tender kissing and embracing. But as they left the cinema they hugged one another and decided that they could return another day to see the film again and watch the scenes they had missed and conduct some more kissing practice during other scenes they had just watched that evening!

They were indeed able to do that and they even managed to meet up a third time, before Susannah and her family had to drive back to their home in London, where Susannah was a student at university and Michael was undergoing an apprenticeship in the clothing industry, the "rag trade" as it was popularly called, with the aim to work in his father's boutique and take over its management one day.

The downside and worrying aspect for Adrian was that, having so little confidence in himself and no trust at all in other men, he could not help feeling anxious and disturbed by the fact that, each time he and Susannah walked together in the streets or were at a table in a restaurant, most of the men who saw them turned their heads, stared at Susannah and ogled her openly and showed in their demeanour that they were attracted by her beauty and sex appeal and fancied her physically.

However, he attempted to push such anxieties and worries to the back of his mind when he was at university again in the spring term.

Whilst they did not exchange letters, Adrian and Susannah managed to telephone one another on a few occasions during the term. Just before Adrian was preparing to return home for the Easter holidays, he received from Susannah an invitation over the telephone to spend a long weekend with her at her parents' home in London the weekend after Easter.

When he mentioned this to Granny and Mummy, they both expressed delight and on the designated Friday afternoon Mummy drove him in her little green snail on wheels to Exeter St David's railway station. Adrian slept during most of the train journey and Susannah met him in the evening on the platform at Paddington Station in central London. She took him for a most pleasant meal in one of the Chinese restaurants in Chinatown situated between Leicester Square and the Soho district, then they went to see a film at the Odeon Cinema in Leicester Square.

After they arrived in the late evening at Susannah's home after taking a metro train ride in the London Underground, Adrian was feeling extremely tired, so Susannah led him straightaway to one of the two small visitors' bedrooms in the flat with an en suite bathroom. He collapsed into bed and fell rapidly into a deep sleep, which was very rare for him as he still suffered regularly from disturbed and agitated nights and awful nightmares which had continued to pursue him over the years consequent upon the traumas of an unhappy childhood, especially that of a swirling vortex hurtling him down into a black abyss in the deep, dark bowels of the earth.

The following morning, when Adrian ambled into the well-appointed kitchen, Susannah was busy preparing their breakfast. As he asked where were her parents and Michael, she laughed loudly with her seductive deep-throated laugh and told him that her parents had gone away for a week's holiday in the Scilly Isles and Michael was enjoying a few days' break staying at the holiday home in the Cotswolds of one of his old school pals.

'So we have the run of the flat just for ourselves until you have to take the train back to Devon on Tuesday!' She gurgled as she danced around the kitchen table then turned to Adrian, wrapped her arms around him and gave him a long, passionate kiss on the lips.

After breakfast, Susannah took Adrian to visit an exhibition at the famous Victoria and Albert Museum, then they walked several miles seeing some of the great sights of London, stopped for a light lunch in an Indian restaurant, continued walking to see more sights. Finally, they walked all the way back to the flat, where they collapsed in exhaustion on the sofa in the lounge in the late afternoon. Everywhere they walked during the day, Adrian could not fail to notice with increasing anxiety and trepidation that most of the men they passed turned around to ogle Susannah, stared at her lasciviously and undressed her with their eyes as if she was merely a tasty morsel and desirous sex object. And, rather than being offended, she seemed to appreciate and relish the attention she received from all these obscene and horny males, which made Adrian's troubled and insecure state even worse.

After a moment sitting on the sofa, Susannah said that she was going to have a bath in one of the two bathrooms and so should he in the bathroom adjoining his bedroom. Some twenty-five minutes later, as he stood naked in the bathroom towelling himself down after a most relaxing hot bath, Susannah appeared in the doorway with a large towel wrapped around her and without saying a word beckoned to him with a wagging finger to follow her. As they walked down the corridor, Susannah stepped into her bedroom, a very feminine space with soft lilac wallpaper on the walls, large curtains in pastel tones matching the wallpaper and several large dolls dotted about on the chest of drawers, the table and a large chair.

When Adrian arrived in the doorway, Susannah stood facing him in the middle of the bedroom then she undid the towel and let it drop to the floor, revealing her splendid, full, curvaceous body and a small tuft of reddish ginger pubic hair as she parted her legs very slightly.

Adrian let out an involuntary gasp as he stared at this wonderful vision and he felt a strong stirring sensation down in his groin.

'My beloved, Adrian, I want you to deflower me!' Susannah exclaimed with a very seductive smile and a fiery come-on look in her brown eyes.

'Deflower you? What do you mean?' Adrian stuttered as he gulped for air and felt panic rising in his chest.

'I mean I want you to take my virginity. In the same way as you have no doubt taken the virginity of one or two other lucky girls.'

'But, but', Adrian stammered feeling like an idiot and going bright red in the face, 'I have never taken any girl's virginity. I am still a virgin myself.'

'Well, well, how surprising, but how wonderful! So, I will take your virginity and you will take my virginity, and you will be my first lover and I will be your first lover.'

As she said that, Susannah walked slowly to Adrian, undid his towel, threw it over onto a chair, kissed him on the lips with passionate desire and caressed his chest with both her hands, then his hips. She took his growing penis into a hand, rubbed gently back and forth and caressed it while he started caressing both her breasts and explored every inch of her body with his hands.

She led him to the bed with her hand, lay down on her back, spread her legs wide open and drew him down on top of her. With his total lack of experience, Adrian had no idea what to do, for he was completely ignorant about preliminaries and foreplay. As his fully erect penis was throbbing with desire like a red hot poker, he placed it immediately at the edge of her vagina and pushed into her and thrust forward as a wave of pleasure engulfed and consumed him.

He heard Susannah emit a piercing scream but he could not control himself, he was unable to stop his thrusting movement, despite the heart-rending screams pounding in his ear. He continued thrusting faster and faster as the pleasure became overwhelmingly acute until he was fully spent and collapsed in a confused and dazed state, pinning poor Susannah under his heavy, sweating body. The pathetic act was over in twenty seconds flat! When he gained some element of control of his wits, he rolled over, lay panting beside her and was appalled and wracked with guilt as he saw the tears rolling down her cheeks. He kissed the tears away, stroked her cheek and apologised profusely for having caused her pain rather than giving her pleasure.

'My dearest, there is no need to apologise. You have successfully deflowered me. You have broken my hymen, which I know has to happen the first time, and that is what caused the pain. From now onwards, making love together will give us both a lot of pleasure and there will be no further pain, so all is well, I assure you! We have taken each other's virginity and we are now lovers.'

Indeed, all went very well for some time from that moment onwards. During that exceptional and memorable weekend, they spent the days visiting further foremost sights of London and soaking up the atmospheres in Carnaby Street, Piccadilly, Regent Street and Oxford Street.

At night, they made slow, tender and sweet love then slept in each other's arms in Susannah's bed. When the ensuing summer holidays arrived, they managed to arrange to meet up alone either in London or in Devon and their love affair continued unabated.

However, on every occasion that they met, Adrian became increasing unsettled and unnerved by the brazen, animal attitudes and behaviour of almost every other man who caught sight of Susannah as well as her unabashed reactions and appreciation, bordering on enthusiasm, as her knowledge was confirmed that so many men found her very sexually attractive and lusted after her. Further, after Susannah exclaimed to him with astonishing enthusiasm on one outing during those summer holidays that she absolutely adored sex, he started to have worrying, nagging doubts about her fidelity to him and began to fear with panic and increasing pains in his heart that when she was in London away from him during term time she was going out with male students at her university or with other men and abandoning her irresistible body to various sexual adventures. He listened attentively when she said in no uncertain terms how attached she was to him and how much she wanted them to develop a long-term relationship.

However, he had never mentioned his unhappy childhood and other sad experiences to her and had decided not to burden her with such heavy subjects and to keep his secrets hidden deep down inside his being. Consequently, she was totally unaware of his deep-seated, overwhelming fears of being betrayed, rejected and abandoned again, his craving need to be loved but great horror at the sad perspective of a love relationship to which he committed failing and breaking up as his parents' marriage had, and his enormous difficulty to have trust and confidence in others.

During that autumn term at university, Adrian started to think very carefully about the nature of his relationship with Susannah and whether they could or should build a future together, a wish that she had ardently expressed.

After much painful soul searching and analysis causing him great mental and emotional strain and suffering, he seemed to hear little voices deep inside whispering to him that he should not make a commitment to this girl. That she was not the right partner in life for him and that he should tread very carefully, take his time and not act with any precipitation in forming any firm commitment to any woman, for with his dreadfully unhappy and scarred background and insecure and fragile psyche any failure of any such committed relationship would be wretched and undoubtedly destroy him.

So, after Adrian had returned home for the 1968 Christmas holidays, he did not telephone Susannah. When she called and asked if they could see each other one evening as she was staying with her uncle and aunt, so that they could celebrate together the first anniversary of their relationship, he was tempted in his initial cowardly reaction to say no and to write her a letter informing her that he was obliged to end the relationship. His guilty conscience gnawed at him and prevailed, so he agreed to meet her.

When they were together alone at her uncle's and aunt's house, as they had gone to a party at a friend's home, after Susannah started undressing and said merrily that she wanted them to make love her joy turned to bewilderment and confusion then anger and tearful anguish when he refused to be seduced by her. He explained to her, in as simple and quick a manner as possible without "beating about the bush", as he awkwardly and stupidly said, that he could not continue with the relationship and was obliged to say goodbye to her there and then, whilst wishing her all the best and declaring that she would no doubt find a much better and more suitable man than him with whom she could build a happy future.

After that evening, Adrian never saw Susannah again, but he felt extreme sadness and emotional pain bordering on depression for some time afterwards. However, he could not avoid hearing faint little voices inside him repeating, each time that he felt some regret over Susannah, that he was to be congratulated and had made the right decision for himself and his future life.

Over the next eighteen months until he left university, he had one or two casual flirtations and he met a girl on the campus and allowed himself to go out with her as her boyfriend for almost a year. However, when she told him that she loved him very much and wanted them to marry and be together forever, he automatically and uncontrollably suffered again the mental torture of fearing betrayal, rejection, abandonment, loss of her love in the future and a breakdown of their couple. He had to undergo the mentally exhausting exercise of analysing the situation and concluded that there were fundamental elements lacking in this girl and in their relationship. He applied his basic rule to be extremely careful and cautious before committing himself and found himself being nagged by his little inner voices insisting that a firm commitment to and a future with this girl would end in total disaster, which had to be avoided at all cost for his own survival in life.

Finally, he realised that he did not love her enough, in actual fact he did not love her at all, but merely liked her, and could not make a happy future with her, so he told her honestly that, in all fairness to her, he was obliged to put an end to their relationship. When she broke down and said that if he left her she would commit suicide, he was totally shocked and nearly buckled under a terrible surge of guilt.

However, he told himself that he had spent his whole life attempting unsuccessfully to fight against awful complexes and sensations of guilt relating to his family situation and to the sexual abuse he had endured, feeling that they were his fault, but there was no reason why he should feel any guilt concerning this girl.

So, he told her that he would not submit to her emotional blackmail and that she had to do what she felt she had to do and it would be none of his business. When he left university, he had only managed to make two male friends with whom he would keep casual contact over the ensuing years and one of them told him many years later, much to his relief, that he knew the girl

never committed suicide, had gotten over Adrian after some time and had gone on to develop a reasonably happy and satisfying life.

Throughout his three years at the university, Adrian was plagued by the dreadful guilt complex, inferiority complex, lack of confidence in himself, conviction that he was worthless, bouts of depression and thoughts of suicide and very grave difficulty to concentrate. He only managed to obtain a Third Class Degree in Law, which was the second worst level of pass in the Faculty of Law that year in summer 1970 and so much lower than the Upper Second Class which his lecturers and the Dean of the Faculty had hoped for him. Both Granny and Mummy made no attempt to hide their anger, disappointment and frustration at this poor result. Nobody could understand any reasons for this relative failure. This was logical, as Adrian had never divulged to anyone at university or anywhere else the horrors he had lived through as a child and at school and the adverse personal consequences.

As for Granny and Mummy, they just simply could not comprehend the mental, psychological and emotional problems and difficulties which pursued Adrian over the years since they continued to consider, in their naïve, warm-hearted and well-intentioned approach, that after he had been saved by them through adoption he should automatically be a normal, well-adjusted and reasonably contented person like the other young men and young women in the university environment. If only it were that easy and simple! Adrian kept his two beloved brothers constantly in the forefront of his thoughts and each evening, before getting into bed and attempting to sleep, he prayed for them both and hoped that they were not plagued by the same mental, psychological and emotional problems and difficulties in life that he was encountering.

A few months after leaving university, as he was living at home again with Mummy and he was undertaking a sabbatical year in order to reflect and analyse in what direction he should and wanted to go in his adult and professional life, Adrian accepted to accompany Mummy on a car drive one day to see Virginia, one of her lady friends who worked with her on certain projects within the Roman Catholic diocese englobing the counties of Cornwall, Devon, Somerset and Dorset. Virginia lived in the town of Bournemouth in Dorset, a Channel coastal town directly to the east of the Jurassic Coast, which, Mummy told him, stretches from Orcombe Point near Exmouth in Devon to Old Harry Rocks near Swanage in East Dorset, a distance of almost one hundred miles. She told him that the Jurassic Coast consists of Triassic, Jurassic and Cretaceous cliffs spanning one hundred and eighty million years of geological history.

Mummy did not tell Adrian but one of her motivations in inviting him to accompany her that day was to introduce him to Marigold, who was the goddaughter of Virginia and was staying with her for a few days, as Virginia had disclosed to Mummy during their recent telephone conversation.

Mummy, with her strong, assertive and domineering personality and good organisational skills, took her self-appointed match-making role very seriously and felt concerned for Adrian's love life and personal future as he was getting

older and remained detached without any serious female partner. Susannah was her own goddaughter, she had known Susannah since her birth and adored her and had felt very sad for her and extremely sorry when Adrian ended their relationship and broke Susannah's heart. She had not cared at all for his second girlfriend, the one he went out with at university, and she had breathed a big sigh of relief the day he told her that he had broken off with that one. She had met Marigold three times on her visits to see Virginia, as Marigold felt very close to her godmother and stayed with her as often as she could, and she had formed an excellent opinion of her and considered that she would make a very fine partner for Adrian.

Adrian and Marigold took well to one another as from the first meeting, especially on an intellectual level, as they both had a lot of intellectual curiosity and loved reading books, and on a human level as she was gentle, kind and caring and did not have one nasty streak in her. She was reasonably tall and slim with fair hair, large and gorgeous blue eyes, a very pleasant smile and a lovely sense of humour, fun and mischief. She had a pretty face but was by no means a classical beauty and her body was shapely in a normal way and was certainly not exceptional. It was a refreshing change from the exotic, flamboyant and man-eating Susannah, for Marigold did not have an obvious sex appeal or desire to attract other men and when they went out on dates together over the following twelve months Adrian never once suffered the anxiety and trepidation about other men that he had endured when with Susannah.

However, Adrian simply allowed the friendship to develop and expand like the growing course of a country stream then river flowing along peacefully and uninterrupted. He merely enjoyed Marigold's company each time they were together without thinking any further, without attempting to convert their friendship into a sexual love affair and without feeling for a moment that Marigold was the woman of his life. It came as a big surprise and a huge shock to his system when she told him, after fourteen months of seeing one another spasmodically, that for her he was the man of her life, she loved him deeply and wanted to marry him and have several children with him.

Automatically, his basic principle and defence mechanism of treading carefully, acting prudently and cautiously with avoidance of precipitation into a firm commitment with any woman took the upper hand. Marigold's mention of marriage and raising children together brought violently and persistently to the surface yet again his great fear of future betrayal, rejection, abandonment, loss of love and breakup of the marriage.

Finally, he realised that he had a deep affection for Marigold but did not really love her and he seemed to detect once more little inner voices warning him that this was not the woman of his life and a commitment in marriage with her would be a mistake and end up catastrophically.

Instinctively, he felt deep down once more that if he listened to the little voices and heeded their message he would avoid the risk of making errors. So, for the third successive time he made a clean and final break and put an end to

the relationship. Mummy was very sad and bewildered by his decision, which she had not anticipated, for she would have loved to have Marigold as her daughter-in-law. She began to ask herself what was wrong with her adopted son in his apparent lack of ability to make a firm and enduring commitment to a woman.

***

After he left university, Adrian turned against the generally accepted idea that he would continue the route towards becoming qualified as a Solicitor. He felt that the Law as he had been taught it at university was dry, arid, purely academic and theoretical and he could not imagine how he could put it into actual practice in a professional situation. He decided to take a sabbatical year, during which he alternated short term jobs as a labourer at the local tile factory then as a worker in a Mother's Pride bread factory in Exeter to earn some money with research and hands-on investigations into all the possible professional fields which might be open to a Law graduate, albeit one who had passed with a very poor grade.

As he realised that he had to remain open-minded, he arranged on two occasions to visit a Solicitors' firm in Tiverton then another Solicitors' firm in Exeter and was allowed to go to their offices for several days and watch the Solicitors in their daily work, discuss matters with them and glean an insight into the way they actually practiced the various legal subjects.

By end June 1971, he concluded that the actual practice of the Law was not dry and arid but very varied and most interesting and he decided that he would after all do the necessary to qualify as a Solicitor. He was able to arrange with the partners of the firm in Exeter that he had visited that he could undergo his two years of Articles of Clerkship in that firm and he started there in August 1971 and was amazed and flattered that he was given his own little office and the services of a secretary.

Adrian was impressed by and had always admired the energy, enthusiasm and dynamism with which Mummy threw herself into various activities as a volunteer in their catholic diocese. Including being on the board of the Diocesan Adoption Society and becoming the backbone, then the chairperson of the diocesan children's camps, which organised, in July of each year, a week's holiday, with full accommodation and meals, catechism classes, sporting events and various outings, in several towns throughout the diocese for catholic children and teenagers who did not attend catholic schools during term time. A priest was present at each camp and every camp was staffed by half a dozen volunteers. Adrian had been a volunteer at four camps in various places in Cornwall and Devon and thoroughly enjoyed his contact with the children.

His first year as an articled clerk seemed to go quite well but he was despondent at times because he was still plagued by all his complexes, overwhelming feeling of worthlessness and his continuing difficulties to concentrate. Further, he often felt submerged under waves of sorrow and

sadness due to having been unloved, rejected and abandoned by his parents and to being disconnected from his two brothers and he felt so far away from them and missed them desperately. However, he managed to develop his skills at play acting and pretence and to disguise his deep-seated anxieties, distrust and fears about other people as much as possible.

Mummy was delighted when Adrian offered to be a volunteer at a children's camp for a week in July 1972, during his two week summer holiday and break from the work at the Solicitors' firm. This camp took place at St Rita's Retreat and Conference Centre, a former convent, in the town of Honiton in Devon, just a few miles inland from the coastal town of Sidmouth. There were about twenty children at the camp with one priest and six volunteers of various ages.

One of the volunteers was Sandra, a brilliant, fairly pretty, well-built and sporting girl who was studying for a Mathematics Degree at Exeter University.

She took a shine to Adrian and did her best to be in the same places as him everywhere in the building and on the large sports field when they conducted various sports sessions and games with the children each day.

However, after his failed relationship with Marigold, Adrian did not feel inclined towards or interested in having a relationship with another female and he had not had a girlfriend since he broke up with Marigold. So he remained polite and civilised in his contacts with Sandra but rebuffed her obvious advances and ducked and weaved away one day when she followed him into the chapel, where he wanted to meditate and pray on his own, and attempted to pin him against one of the columns and kiss him on the lips. She was so annoyed and felt so insulted by his rebuff that she sneeringly asked him whether he preferred boys to girls in the sexual area!

He did not reply but as he walked away his blood started to boil as anger, turmoil and tears swelled up and he felt physically sick as the awful images of the terrible sexual abuse which his brother Neil had endured at the orphanage and his own ordeals of sexual abuse by the school teacher swirled in his mind and before his eyes. He felt relieved when he learned that Sandra had to leave the camp after supper on Friday evening due to some prior commitment the following day and as she waved goodbye to everyone he thought that it was a very good riddance.

On Saturday, the last day of the camp, a beautifully bright and sunny morning, all the children and the volunteers, as well as some parents and outside visitors, attended Mass celebrated in mid-morning by the priest in the chapel. At some moment just before the reading of the Gospel, Adrian, who was standing in a row behind the small children but ahead of many of the other members of the congregation, suddenly turned his ahead around, for some inexplicable reason as he knew it was impolite and frowned upon to turn around during Mass.

All of the heads in the rows behind him were a blur to him but his eyes compellingly and unavoidably singled out a young lady standing near the back whom he did not know and had never seen before. He drew in his breath

silently, as if he felt he had just seen a vision, and could not prevent himself from gazing at her for a few seconds as she stood out in this crowd. He was not sure whether she saw him staring at her. As he turned back facing the front his body trembled slightly, his mind was in a state of confusion and he felt very emotionally troubled.

During the rest of the Mass he could not pray and could not concentrate on the ceremony, which was totally unlike him, as he felt that he had the faith and he liked attending Mass. As he looked up at the priest and the altar boys then higher up at the Cross hanging high behind the altar, the image of the unknown girl's face and hair floated before his eyes and, as hard as he tried, he could not banish that image from his mind. Later on, as she passed his row on her way up to receive Holy Communion, he gasped as he looked at her and thought how lovely, unique and pure this girl looked.

After Mass, all the volunteers lined up in the convent's large library in order to greet and shake hands with all the parents and visitors, which had always been the custom on the last morning at each of these camps all over the diocese. Adrian nonchalantly said hello to and shook hands with many parents and some visitors who passed in front of him. Then he saw the unknown girl approaching and a tall, slim, fair-haired young man coming just behind her. As she stopped in front of him, his body trembled again, he felt a strange sensation and he could feel a weakness in his knees. She looked at him with the most beautiful, large, warm, engaging, velvety brown eyes, smiled at him with a uniquely wonderful smile and he almost panicked. When she stretched out her graceful right hand and he took it in his right hand, he felt a soft flash of electricity shooting up his arm but it was not painful or disagreeable but felt good and that first physical contact with her warmed his heart. He looked into her eyes for far too long and he held on to her hand for far too many seconds, which appeared to annoy the young man who almost shoved her with his shoulder as if telling her to move on to the next person. The young man towered over Adrian, making him feel very small, grimaced at Adrian with a cold expression in his light blue eyes and almost crushed his hand in a vice-like grip and Adrian told himself that he had upset the boyfriend in showing so obviously that he was under the girl's spell and charm.

During the day, the lovely girl and Adrian somehow seemed to bump into one another on several occasions and were able to make dribs and drabs of conversation. She told him her name was Yseult; she was Swiss and nearing the end of a year's stay in London as an au pair girl to improve her English. She said Yseult was pronounced "*Isolt*" and Adrian thought what a unique first name for a unique girl!

Adrian tried his best to hide his relief when she told him that the young man accompanying her, whose name was Colum, was an Irish student who she had met in her local Catholic parish in London and had become a casual friend. She added that they were there that day because Colum knew one of the elderly lady volunteers named Diana, who had told him by telephone that she would be at the camp and that if he felt like a change of air and getting out of London he

would be most welcome to come down to visit her. He had asked Yseult if she wished to come down with him, she had thought that it would be fun and a new experience and they had travelled down by train to Honiton railway station and were having to take a return train back to London in the early evening.

Adrian had a strange, new and mysterious feeling building up inside him as the afternoon wore on, and the time was approaching when Colum and Yseult would have to say goodbye to everyone. He had thoroughly enjoyed the company of this enchanting girl for the brief moment and he seemed to hear little voices deep down urging him forcefully not to lose contact with her. He managed to take an opportunity when he was alone with her, while Colum went off to say goodbye to Diana, to extract from her the family surname and her postal address at home in the Canton of the Valais in Switzerland. She told him that she and her friend Christiana, a French au pair girl sharing a rented flat with her in Earls Court in London, would be coming down soon to have a few days holiday in some parts of Devon before she had to fly back to Switzerland in a few weeks' time. And she knew already they would be spending one night at the Women's Youth Hostel in the town of Bridport, not very far to the east of Honiton. Adrian could barely disguise his delight and excitement. He gave her his home telephone number and they agreed that on a specific Saturday morning she would call him and tell him where to meet her near Bridport so that they could spend a part of the day together.

Adrian had managed to sell his old Austin A40 and had graduated to a second-hand, grey, convertible Triumph Herald with red seats and a canvas roof, which opened down in the fair weather. He loved the thought of taking this enchanting girl out for a long drive in it. However, consumed as he still was by his overwhelming inferiority complex and sense of worthlessness, Adrian felt convinced that this wonderful and special girl he had only met once would quickly forget him and would not telephone him for a second meeting. He dreamt of her in bed at night and saw in front of his eyes her long, exotic shoulder-length chestnut brown hair, reminding him somewhat of the look of Françoise Hardy, the young French singer who was having enormous success, not only in France but also in the United Kingdom. He saw as well her magnetic brown eyes with their lively, deep and velvety texture and expression, her very special high cheek bones and that radiant, most attractive and seductive smile. He kept wondering what had happened to him in just one short meeting with this girl. He was astonished that she had caused some stirring inner reactions in his being such as he had never felt with any other girl in the past. His little inner voices told him that, for the first time in his life, he had had a *"coup de foudre"*, to use the term in French, a unique experience of love at first sight, which, rather than make him rejoice, caused him to suffer a state of confusion and a dreadful panic.

He was terrified at the thought that he had fallen under her spell and wanted so very much to see her again but she would not allow it to happen, would reject him and would simply fly back to Switzerland and forget that they had ever met. So, his glee and appreciation were immense when the telephone rang

on that Saturday morning and Yseult told him, with her rich, musical, warm voice, to meet her and her friend Christiana in the afternoon at a specific roundabout just outside Bridport.

When he arrived in his sporty-looking grey car with the red seats and the roof down, as the weather was good, the two girls laughed and roared with approval and told him to drive them to the Youth Hostel near the harbour in Bridport, where they checked in and left their rucksacks. It had obviously been agreed beforehand between the two girls that Christiana would go off, see the surrounding sights and leave Yseult and Adrian to spend the evening together.

They walked around parts of Bridport for a while and did not stop talking about all sorts of subjects until they felt thirsty and hungry in the early evening. When they came across an attractive, old world pub with a large bar and spacious room they settled down on a corner bench and carried on chatting non-stop for nearly three hours as they drank and ate slowly and in a relaxed mood. They were amused to see a gorgeous, multi-coloured parrot with a large beak sitting in a cage not very far from them. But he was garrulous and squawky and managed to talk in English. So after a while, Adrian felt he wanted to wring his scraggy neck as he started repeating some phrases they uttered and Adrian certainly did not want the other people in the crowded bar to know from this damned parrot what he and Yseult were saying to one another!

After they left the pub and started walking back to the street where they had left the car, they decided that, as it was such a pleasant evening, it would be fun to drive down to the seafront, take a short stroll along the sandy beach and listen to the waves of the English Channel rolling in.

As they approached a tall red telephone box, Yseult said that she must go into it and call Christiana to tell her that she would arrive back at their dormitory in the Youth Hostel rather much later than she had anticipated. Instead of waiting politely outside, Adrian followed her into the telephone booth and studied her hair and her face with the high cheek bones from the side as she spoke to Christiana at the other end, feeling sorely tempted to caress her silky, chestnut brown, cascading hair with his hand but refraining from doing so.

When Yseult replaced the telephone on its hook and turned to face him fully, the space in the booth was so small and narrow that their heads were very close. Adrian looked deeply into her lovely brown eyes, feeling he could lose himself in them. His gaze lowered to take in those superb high cheeks then moved down to her mouth. He could not resist the temptation and he bent down and kissed her firmly on the lips.

Instead of reciprocating, she moved her head back abruptly, her eyes flashed with hot anger and her right hand whipped up sharply and slapped him hard on his left cheek. After a moment's shock, Adrian smiled sheepishly and apologised to her in a faint, humble voice like a chastised child who had been caught stealing a tasty sweet in a sweets store. It was true, he was guilty of stealing a sweet, tasty kiss!

As he looked at those amazing eyes with a vivid look of blazing fire in them, showing a strong and determined temperament, he thought secretly to himself that this was a girl to marry!

When Adrian dropped her off at the Youth Hostel after their walk along the beach, he thought that it would be interesting to try to kiss her once more and see whether the fiery thunderbolts shot out of her eyes and her hand again. However, he decided against it, not wishing her to have a bad opinion of him, and he merely shook her hand. As on that day when they had met for the first time, he held her hand for a fraction too long and felt the agreeable electric sensation rush up his arm. Having waved goodbye to her and started his return drive to Stenhill Cottage, he suddenly became very wistful and sad and tears filled his eyes so much that he was obliged to pull into the first layby he saw. He could not understand what was happening to him as he wept bitterly, his chest heaved and he said to himself that he was going to miss this extraordinary girl terribly, as she had made an unbelievable impact on him. He had no idea if he would ever see her again, but was fearful that she was far too good for him in all ways and would no doubt reject and forget him. He felt again that he had been smitten by a lightning bolt, that *"coup de foudre"*, and his little inner voices repeated again that he was a victim of love at first sight beyond his control and that there was nothing that he could do to fight against it.

As they had said on parting that they would keep in touch by correspondence, Adrian wrote a letter to Yseult a month later, giving her his news in as chatty, offhand and casual a style as possible, without giving her an inkling that he had been deeply smitten by her. He doubted very much whether she would bother to reply from her home in Switzerland. As he did not mention anything about this girl to Granny and Mummy, they were both curious and wondered what the matter was when the post arrived one Saturday morning some weeks later when Granny was visiting, as she did very frequently. Mummy handed an envelope to Adrian and, after studying it, he flew up the stairs two at a time and shut himself in his bedroom. He trembled as he held the envelope, double checked that the postage stamp was a Swiss one, opened the envelope gingerly and read the letter, admiring Yseult's fine and very attractive handwriting and her command of the English language.

If anyone had told Adrian that one could get to know a person's character traits and personality simply through an exchange of letters, without seeing the person, he would have laughed in their face and said they were talking nonsense. However, after nine months of writing letters to Yseult and receiving her letters Adrian felt obliged to revise his opinion. They had only met twice, for a brief while on each occasion, yet he felt that he had come to know Yseult well through the contents of her letters and he hoped that she felt she knew him through his letters. He sent her a recent photograph of himself and was delighted to receive two lovely photographs of her, which he kept safely in his wallet and pulled out frequently to gaze at and recall just how lovely she was. He had far deeper and warmer feelings for her and felt much more attracted to her in every way than he had ever done for any girl he had known earlier.

After the nine months separation, Adrian could not believe it when he received a further letter from Yseult, sent from Dusseldorf in Germany, where she had gone three months earlier to study the German language and work in a company, telling him that she missed him, wanted to see him again after all this time and asked if he would drive up to London to meet her if she came over to stay with a girlfriend in the near future. After having feared, through his deep complexes, lack of self-confidence and overwhelming feeling that he was devoid of any worth, that she would merely consider him a "pen friend" for the exercise of exchanging correspondence and leave it at that, he had to read this new letter three or four times until it sank into his pathetic mind that she wanted to see him again and to develop their friendship.

He was ecstatic at the prospect of seeing her again soon and wrote back immediately asking her to tell him on which day and at what place in London he should meet her. Her reply came back very quickly, so he divulged to Granny and Mummy the existence of this girl and he asked Mummy if she would mind if Yseult were to come back from London with him and stay with them for a holiday for a short while. As this meant that Yseult would have to sleep in Mummy's double bed beside her, as the cottage only had two bedrooms, and Adrian knew he could not contemplate her sleeping with him in his single bed and he knew anyway that Mummy would forbid it, he was very worried that Mummy would refuse to allow this unknown girl to share her bed. If she did, he would have to find a room for her in a Bed and Breakfast in the small nearby town of Uffculme and would have to pay the cost himself out of his meagre savings.

However, Granny sensed immediately in her great wisdom that something special had happened and he had very deep and true feelings for this girl and she persuaded Mummy that it would be interesting for them to meet her, so Mummy acquiesced and told Adrian that Yseult could come to stay at the cottage for a short holiday. In an excited state, Adrian sent a quick letter to Yseult in Dusseldorf inviting her for a holiday for as long as she wished at the cottage and was delighted when a reply came back saying she would be happy to stay with them for a few weeks.

Yseult travelled with her suitcase by train from Dusseldorf to Calais in France, then by ferry across the English Channel and by train again from Dover to King's Cross Station in London, where Adrian met her on the platform. They were very moved to meet again after those long nine months of physical separation, stood facing each other clasping their outstretched hands and gazing into each other's eyes, then she allowed him to hug her and give her a tender kiss on the cheek without slapping him with a forceful hand on his cheek. He smiled and said that was progress after the unforgettable slap and the volcanic look in her eyes in the telephone booth in Bridport! However, he did not dare to attempt to kiss her on the lips. They drove in his grey Triumph Herald to the rented flat of her girlfriend, who was able to accommodate them for the night.

They set off early in the car the next morning for the long drive down to Devon. As the weather was pleasant, Adrian was able to put the roof down and

as he drove and the wind ruffled their hair they chatted non-stop with great pleasure and felt totally at ease with each other. When they arrived at the cottage in the early evening, Mummy had made a superb supper and was intrigued to meet this girl about whom she knew virtually nothing, apart from one or two dribs and drabs that Adrian had accepted to mention to her. As Granny did not like to drive after dark, she was not present and she spent the evening at her own flat in Willand, but she drove over the following morning. After spending a few hours walking around the garden and in the nearby lanes, then sitting in the lounge with Adrian and Yseult, she felt a strong approval of and attraction to this girl. She told Mummy that she wondered whether their friendship would develop into a deeper and longer relationship or would fizzle out as Adrian's earlier relationships with girls had done. Mummy said little, kept her thoughts to herself and simply made Yseult's holiday with them as comfortable and pleasant as possible, whilst looking forward secretly to the day when she would leave and return to her own home in Switzerland and would hopefully cut off any further contact with Adrian, for she was undergoing big pangs of jealousy about this particular girl.

After several days and having spent every waking moment of each day with Yseult, sometimes in the company of Granny and Mummy but often alone together, especially on some evenings when he drove her to Cullompton for a meal in a local restaurant or to a favourite pub in a nearly village or to watch a film at the cinema in Exeter, Adrian started hearing little inner voices nagging at him, pulling at his heart strings and ringing small bells in his mind like holy angels transmitting insistently a very important message.

He had felt on several occasions over the past years that if he listened to his little inner voices and heeded their messages and acted upon them, he was never wrong and never made a mistake in his decisions. When he was alone in bed at night, sensing her presence in the other room just across the corridor, he analysed his feelings for Yseult as objectively as possible and his firm conclusion each time he thought about her was that he really loved this girl, in a way he had never been able to love earlier girlfriends, and he had met the woman of his life. The soul-mate with whom he wanted to live for the rest of his earthly existence.

Adrian felt shocked and bewildered as he threw out of the window recklessly his fundamental principle of proceeding very slowly and cautiously and taking his time with great prudence before accepting to make a commitment to a women, in order to avoid making a mistake and having a marriage end up in the dreadful and disastrous way that his parents' marriage had done.

He had only met this Swiss girl on a few occasions, but, with their nine month exchange of letters and the wonderful days he had spent with her since her arrival in England again, he felt uniquely, strangely and utterly sure about his deep feelings and love for her and his desire to be with her forever. If he was taking a big risk, it was a risk that he felt he was obliged to take as his love for this girl and his desire to commit himself for life to trying to ensure her

happiness were so immense and compelling and beyond his control in actual fact.

However, did she have the same feelings towards him and would she have him living with her, walking beside her and accompanying her for the rest of their lives? Due to his overwhelming inferiority complex, insecurities, anxieties and other mental and emotional problems linked to feeling worthless, Adrian automatically started feeling grave doubts on that score. He tried to battle within himself against such negative thoughts and to develop more positive and hopeful vibrations. He listened very carefully to his little inner voices and was overwhelmed with joy and felt blessed when they told him steadfastly and repeatedly what he should do. As he thought about it over and over again, the image in the chapel at Honiton all those months ago flashed again in his mind. A strong conviction filled his mind and heart that it was the Holy Spirit which had made him turn his head during that Mass and single out that girl with his eyes and had told him silently that this was his future wife.

Knowing that Yseult would only be staying at the cottage for a few weeks, Adrian started to explain to her, during their times alone walking down the country lanes and across the fields or sitting in a local pub enjoying a drink, the dreadful conflicts between his parents and the breakdown of their marriage, causing such an unhappy childhood for him and his beloved brothers. Then the loss of Anita who he would have loved to become his substitute mother, followed by his four dreadful years at the two orphanages, and the tragic loss of his adoptive father at the age of fourteen. He omitted to mention to her the unspeakable sexual sodomies and abuse endured by big brother Neil at The Grange and by himself at St Boniface's College, for the emotional pains and scars were so deep and difficult to cope with that he just could not talk about those subjects and had to keep those dark secrets buried inside his tortured psyche.

He was delighted to learn from Yseult that her parents were very happily married, living together in their small house in a pleasant country village in the Canton of the Valais in Switzerland, and she was one of five children, having two elder sisters, one elder brother and a younger brother, who all lived near one another in the Valais. She said that she still lived together with her parents when she was back in Switzerland.

One day, she told Adrian that, as she had been away from home for a few months, firstly in Germany and now staying with him and Mummy at Stenhill Cottage, she was going to have to return to Switzerland in a week's time. Adrian nearly panicked at this news and, after dithering and mulling the situation over and over in his swirling thoughts, and after heeding his little inner voices which had been hammering at him for the umpteenth time, he took his courage in both hands when they were standing alone together in the lounge while Mummy was busy in the kitchen preparing their lunch and Granny was not there as she was busy tending her own garden in Willand.

He bent down on one knee, being an incurable romantic at heart, took Yseult's right hand tenderly in both of his hands, looked up into her gorgeous

brown eyes with his adoring blue eyes and said, 'My darling Yseult, I know that I love you and care for you very deeply, so much so that I want to spend the rest of my life with you. I will do my very best to make you happy. Please will you marry me and be my wife and share the journey through life with me?'

She looked down at him and the expression in her eyes showed clearly that she was very surprised by this outburst and this gesture and had not expected it at all. She held his gaze for a long moment and he prayed silently that she would see not only the loving expression in his eyes but look beyond those eyes right into his heart and detect how his heart and his entire being were burning with true love for her.

Then, whilst continuing to look him steadfastly in the eyes, her eyes slowly changed from an expression of surprise to one of pleasure and a velvety warmth and she replied with that deep, musical voice that he had come to love so much, 'Adrian, I must admit that I did not expect this and certainly not so soon, but I thank you for your proposal of marriage and I am very pleased to tell you that I accept it!'

Adrian stood up, let out a cry of joy, embraced Yseult in what must have seemed to her like a crushing bear-hug. Kissed her lovingly on the lips for what must have seemed to her like an eternity. Then twirled her around the room in what must have seemed to her to resemble a very clumsy waltz whilst treading on her toes several times and apologising profusely like a dumb idiot.

Then he released her, told her to wait there a moment, rushed out to the kitchen and told Mummy with an excited and gushing voice, 'I have just asked Yseult to marry me and she has said yes!'

Mummy looked at him in astonishment and was so bowled over by this news that she almost let drop the hot pan containing roast potatoes that she had just extracted from the oven with her thick oven gloves. She just managed to place the pan on the top of her Rayburn cooker then turned to Adrian and said she was very happy for him.

However, the look in her eyes and the expression on her face indicated immediately to him that she was not at all happy for herself to hear this news. Adrian told her to take the gloves off her hands and to follow him into the lounge where Yseult was waiting. When Mummy saw her, she gave her a cursory hug, a perfunctory peck on the cheek and a short word of congratulations. Yseult glanced over to Adrian with a look in her eyes showing that she understood well that his adoptive mother and her future mother-in-law was not very enthralled at all by this development.

The atmosphere in the cottage over the next few days until Yseult's departure for Switzerland was rather tense between Mummy and Yseult. But when Granny visited and was told the news, she reacted with a genuine happiness for both Adrian and his future bride. She told Adrian when they had a moment alone together that she thought Yseult was a marvellous person and she congratulated him warmly on having asked her to be his wife and said she was sure he would never regret this all-important, life-changing decision.

During the weeks when Yseult was back with her family in Switzerland, Adrian felt very miserable and he missed her terribly, but they did manage to speak together over the telephone on a few occasions and he also spoke to Yseult's elder sister in French, which gave him immense pleasure as it was his favourite language. When they were reunited after Yseult was able to return to Stenhill Cottage, she told him that she had sobbed continuously on the aeroplane during the flight from Gatwick to Geneva airport, as his marriage proposal had come as a real shock, perhaps rather too soon, and her emotions were in a mixed up and really pitiful state.

However, she reassured him that she did want to marry him and live the rest of her life together with him, through thick and thin and for better or for worse, *"pour le meilleur ou pour le pire",* as she quoted the proverbial term in French. Having suffered the worst at the hands of his parents and a few others, Adrian prayed that their life together would definitely be for the best.

As it was necessary for Adrian to attend the Solicitors' Qualifying Course at the College of Law at Lancaster Gate in West London from August 1973 to February 1974, they lived in lodgings in South Kensington during that time. While Adrian studied extremely hard for the qualifying examinations, Yseult managed to obtain a reasonably well-paid job in a boutique selling off-the-peg clothes for women, which she enjoyed very much, demonstrating a talent for business and acquiring skills in marketing and sales. Mummy had hoped very much that they would return to Stenhill Cottage for a few days around Christmas, but felt very disappointed, bitter, jealous and despondent when Adrian told her that he had accepted an invitation from Yseult's parents to spend the Christmas and New Year break with them in the Swiss canton of Valais and to meet all of Yseult's brother and sisters and other members of their large family.

During their stay in Switzerland with Yseult's family at their home in a small village and up in their mountain chalet in a charming and unspoilt mountain village and ski resort, Adrian started to feel happier and began to relax more than he had ever done. He had fallen deeply in love with this very special and remarkable girl. Now he also fell in love with her wonderful father and mother, her two sisters and two brothers, the glorious high mountains in the Valais, the delightful small chalet, with its red window shutters and spectacular views and the typical charming Swiss mountain village, as well as the many friends of Yseult, among them several being friends she had kept from childhood and during her teenage years.

Meeting such good long-standing friends of hers had a profound effect on Adrian, as he had not been able to gain any friends at all from his rotten, dysfunctional, abnormal and miserable childhood and teenage years. He was so impressed and pleased to see just how normal, well-adjusted, sensible and emotionally secure and stable Yseult was after having been brought up by loving, caring and united parents together with her siblings in a truly happy family environment.

He was especially touched and proud when Yseult introduced him to her various friends as her future husband, *"mon futur époux"*, as she said in her charming local Valais accent. When they were alone together on a few occasions, he begged her to say *"mon futur époux"* over and over again and he gurgled with a boyish joy and an expansive smile each time that she repeated the very welcome phrase.

They decided that they wished to be married in the Catholic Church in the mountain village. As Yseult explained to him, the Valais was a Catholic canton and all the churches in the various villages and towns were Catholic, as were all of the members of her family. When they discussed arrangements for the wedding with her parents, they all thought that it would be lovely to have the wedding on a Saturday at the beginning of May, which was a very pleasant month with many colourful flowers and various trees in full bud or bearing flowers.

In the immediate future after the marvellous Christmas and New Year break, Adrian had to return to London to continue attending the courses at the College of Law in preparation for the very difficult examinations in February. Yseult accompanied him and carried on working at the boutique during the following weeks. The Solicitors' Final Qualifying examinations took place in mid-February in an enormous hall at the gigantic Crystal Palace.

When Adrian walked into the hall on the first morning to sit the first exam and saw the hundreds of desks and chairs lined up in long and wide rows throughout the hall, making him imagine a small army of tin soldiers in battle formation, his first reaction was one of blind panic and he almost turned around and fled away from the place.

He was overwhelmed by fear and an instantaneous feeling that with his worthlessness he could not possibly cope with this situation and sit amongst the hundreds of other candidates who were undoubtedly brilliant and much more intelligent and capable than he could ever be.

During the past six months of constant and intense courses and study, he had continued to be pursued by his acute difficulties to concentrate and the overpowering feeling of inadequacy. As he watched whilst the throng of men and women poured into the hall and took their places in readiness for this first exam, he was submerged by a lack of confidence and almost caved in to his terror and the desire to throw in the towel and avoid sitting all the exams over the ensuing few days.

However, after a visit to the men's toilets and a brisk walk up and down the corridor near the huge hall, and after hearing suddenly little inner voices admonishing him for his cowardice and telling him that he could do this and survive this testing experience, he tried to calm his nerves, walked back into the now almost full hall, sat down in his designated place, took several deep breaths and knuckled down to answering to the best of his ability all the questions on the exam sheets on the desk.

At the end of the very difficult three-hour written exam, Adrian was mentally exhausted and he walked out of the hall and away from Crystal Palace

without looking at or speaking with anyone and made his way back to his lodgings. It was the same pattern each day over the following several days until he had finished the last exam and could finally relax and drink a cool beer in a charming London pub, the first occasion on which he had had the spare time to enter a pub during the six month period of very intensely pressurised and gruelling studies.

After Adrian had accomplished the task of enduring all the exams and Yseult had left her temporary job, they returned to stay for a while with Mummy at Stenhill Cottage and were delighted to see the beautiful Devon countryside, breathe in the pure air, enjoy the calm and the musical singing of the birds again and revel in the sight of the black and white cows in the fields of the local farm after the huge buildings, crowded roads and pavements, noisy hustle and bustle and pollution of London.

In their discussions about future plans, Adrian had divulged to Yseult that Mummy had made it clear to him that she would be delighted if, after qualifying, he became a salaried solicitor then a partner in the excellent firm where he had undertaken his Articles of Clerkship in Exeter, play golf and become a proud member of the old and reputable Exeter Golf and Country Club, own a yacht moored somewhere along the River Exe on the outskirts of Exeter, live in a lovely detached house with a large garden near Exeter and be able to visit her and Granny on frequent occasions.

He told Yseult that he did not want to become a country solicitor but, before meeting her, had harboured dreams of emigrating to Canada and seeking a job as an employed solicitor in the Legal Department of a multinational company in a part of Canada where he could work both in English and French, as he loved the French language and desired to be able to work in both languages.

When Yseult mentioned that there were several multinational companies established in Geneva, Lausanne and other parts of Suisse Romande, the French speaking part of Switzerland, Adrian felt that, as he loved her family, the Swiss mountains and the glorious scenery around Lake Geneva, which they had seen briefly during their recent stay in Switzerland, the best plan would be for him to find a job as an employed solicitor in one of those multinationals and for them to settle down in Switzerland.

Yseult had made it clear earlier on that, if he did wish to work as a solicitor in England and live somewhere in southern England, she would gladly follow him as his wife and adjust to a new life in the town or city of his choice. But she was naturally delighted with his desire to work and live in Switzerland. So, they decided in a meeting of the minds and by mutual agreement that they would make their married life in the French speaking part of Switzerland.

A few days later, when they were sitting in the lounge with Mummy at the cottage, Adrian told her that they were going to be married in the Catholic Church in the Swiss mountain village and they were going to live and work in Switzerland. The fact that they would marry in a Catholic Church naturally delighted Mummy, who was an ardent practising catholic.

However, their decision to live and work in Switzerland hit Mummy like an unexpected bombshell, destroying all her dreams of an idyllic future for her adopted son very near her. She fell silent for a few minutes, attempting to take in and digest this disastrous development, but her attitude towards Yseult thereafter changed radically and became somewhat cold and distant.

When she had an opportunity to be alone with Adrian, she told him in a forceful, aggressive and bitter manner that this foreign girl was trying to take him away from his country and his fellow countrymen and, if he went along with her bad scheme, she would cause him to be a traitor to his country! Adrian was shocked and dumfounded by such a horrible tirade and ridiculous accusation against his fiancée. He defended her, explaining to Mummy in as gentle a way as possible, for he understood well her emotional and psychological feelings and her jealous reaction against Yseult, that it was his decision to live and work in the French speaking part of Switzerland and his desire to be able to work both in English and French. He managed to calm her down a little, but as from then she was quite unpleasant and very cool and distant with Yseult and their relationship became very strained, which was embarrassing and awkward as Yseult was having to share the same bedroom with her future mother-in-law.

In mid-March, Adrian and Yseult returned to Switzerland and occupied the small spare bedroom in her parents' home. Before leaving England, they made it clear to Granny and Mummy that they were naturally invited to their wedding, but Granny declined the invitation, saying that she was now becoming too old and frail to undertake such a journey. As Adrian unfortunately did not have any friends of his own that he could invite to his wedding, he agreed with Mummy that they would invite a few of her good friends to accompany her on a ten day trip and holiday to the Swiss mountain village on dates around and including the wedding.

As Adrian dreamt with deep emotion of having his two brothers with him at the wedding, he telephoned Aunt Clotilda from Stenhill Cottage and asked if she knew of any address where he could get in touch with Neil and Justin. She told him that she had not had any direct contact with Justin for some time, but she had an idea from a postcard which Justin had recently sent her that they were both on two separate frigates on a tour of duty and naval exercises somewhere in the Indian Ocean. She suggested that Adrian could send a letter to each of them with the words "PLEASE FORWARD TO HIS SHIP" marked in capital letters on each envelope and post each envelope to the central headquarters of the Royal Navy in London. Adrian followed this advice, but he never received any replies to his two letters and invitations to his wedding and never knew whether they had in actual fact been delivered to the two brothers. It was an enormously sad disappointment that he would remain cut off from his beloved brothers and could not have them beside him as he celebrated his wedding.

Together with the willing and happy assistance of her father and mother, her two brothers and two sisters and a few close friends, Yseult threw herself

with great energy and enthusiasm into planning and organising the wedding mass at the church. The drinks party took place afterwards in the large barn behind the chalet owned by one of her aunts in the central square of the mountain village. Adrian was deeply moved when he saw both the Swiss flag and the Union Jack, which Yseult's brothers had strung up on a beam beside each other, and listened to several of her friends singing songs loudly in English in his honour in their amusing Valaisan accents. The evening reception with a superb dinner and dance and various party games in a lovely and very charming restaurant built in a deep and high grotto on the shore of a small lake on the outskirts of a small town was a great success.

Adrian was content to follow along and was again very impressed and happy to witness the loving, caring and united relationships and constant good humour between the members of this delightful family into which he was entering with immense joy and deep gratitude to destiny. The civil wedding took place at the small local registry office in Yseult's home village on May 2nd 1974 and the religious wedding was held in the lovely mountain church on May 4th 1974. Altogether, there were about forty guests, including Yseult's family members, her closest and dearest friends, Mummy and three of her best friends and another couple of her friends who made the journey over from England.

Later on, in some of the photographs that had been taken that day, Adrian and Yseult were highly amused to see how Mummy made sure she was standing beside Adrian on the other side from Yseult and hung onto his arm with a vice-like grip as if indicating she did not want to let go of her adopted son and give him to this foreign woman! Yseult chuckled as she told him she wondered what sort of future relationship she was going to have with her very jealous battle-ax of a mother-in-law!

The morning of his wedding day had started very badly for Adrian. He had asked the College of Law in London to post his exam results to the home of Yseult's parents. When her father handed him the envelope with an English stamp that morning a couple of hours before they were to drive up to the church in the mountain village, he rushed into the bedroom he and Yseult occupied and opened the envelope with trembling hands.

After reading the results for each exam and the overall score for all the exams, he emitted a loud and painful groan, slumped down on the bed and wept bitterly and started rocking his body furiously from side to side in the same way he had done as a miserable child in the orphanage.

All of his red hot emotional feelings of being a total failure, a subnormal, inadequate and entirely worthless person and the other inferiority complexes caused by his wretchedly unhappy childhood rushed automatically, uncontrollably and violently up to the surface like the deep boiling lava of a volcano explosively erupting to the top and smothered him as he lay prostrate on the bed with his hands over his eyes feeling suddenly and utterly depressed.

When Yseult ran into the room, she was very shocked when she saw Adrian in this pitiful state. She had not before experienced the sight of seeing

him like this. Her elder brother Gabriel, who had been in the lounge speaking with their mother, followed her into the bedroom and they both asked Adrian what was the matter. He blurted out tearfully and shamefully in uncontrollable anguish that he had failed his qualifying exams by just a few points and was extremely disappointed and downhearted as he had studied so hard and relentlessly. But he saw the negative results showed just what an inferior and inadequate being he was and he was not worthy of such a magnificent girl as Yseult. They did not understand and felt confused for they could not comprehend or be aware of the deep-seated mental and emotional problems inside Adrian and the appalling and destructive consequences caused to his fragile and insecure psyche by his awful childhood. All they could do was to comfort him, assure him that it was not shameful to fail some exams and tell him he could sit the exams again and would undoubtedly succeed the second time around. They managed to calm him down and when Adrian asked Yseult in a pathetically feeble and humble voice if she still wanted to marry such a miserable, worthless failure she playfully mocked him for his stupidity and reassured him that in two hours' time in the church she would be saying "Yes" to that question! She begged him to regain his composure, to put the failure of the exams behind him for the time being and to wash and start putting on his fresh white shirt, smart new blue suit and matching blue bow-tie for their wedding mass up at the church in the mountains.

This he obediently did like an adoring puppy dog and when he saw his future bride later on approaching him up the aisle on the arm of her beloved father in her splendid white wedding dress and he looked deeply into those wonderful brown eyes with their warm, loving, velvety expression and at her uniquely engaging, marvellous and irresistible smile he felt he saw the vision of a beautiful angel before him.

During the mass, whilst they knelt side by side in front of the altar and the priest, he thanked Divine Providence silently for having brought this lovely, superb woman into his life. And he swore that he would never betray, reject or abandon her the way his goddamn father had betrayed, rejected and abandoned his mother and he would love, care for and cherish her forever and would seek continuously to ensure her happiness to the best of his ability.

Chapter 8
Reunifications with Brothers

When Adrian commenced his new life together with Yseult in Switzerland and undertook searches for a first employment, he had the misfortune to be looking for a job in the middle of the first Arab Oil Crisis of 1973 and 1974, which affected the economies of all countries around the world and caused an important global recession.

Try as hard as he could, he was just not able to find an employment and was informed by some multinational groups that they were having to down size and reduce the numbers of their employees because of the negative financial impact of the Arab Oil Crisis. Like many other people, Adrian was astonished to learn that the members of the Organisation of Arab Petroleum Exporting Countries (OAPEC) had proclaimed an oil embargo as from October 1973 on several Western states, in retaliation to the involvement of the United States of America in the 1973 Yom Kippur War.

In effect, six days after Egypt and Syria launched a surprise military campaign against Israel, the Americans supplied Israel with large quantities of arms. In response, OAPEC announced an oil embargo and raised the price of oil produced by them by seventy percent and started to cut production of oil thereby causing oil prices to quadruple during 1974, stock markets to crash around the world and a severe economic recession to set in in several important countries.

Upon the suggestion of Yseult's elder brother Gabriel, who worked in a Swiss bank, Adrian contacted top management of the bank at its important offices in Geneva asking whether they might have a position for him in their Legal Department. They replied that the work in their Legal Department was mainly local and based on Swiss law, whereas he would naturally want a job with an important international element as he was trained in the Anglo-Saxon common law system.

However, they told him that they were very pleased to have university graduates in any subject among their future top management members and would be pleased to offer him the opportunity to follow the bank's annual general banking training course which would start that August of 1974 for a year until the following August. When Adrian mentioned this to Gabriel, Yseult and their parents, they all considered that this would be a fine opportunity and a smart move giving him a further training and some activity and experience until the economic situation improved and he could obtain a

real employment. Consequently, Adrian thanked the bank for its kind offer and told them that he accepted it gratefully; he felt at any rate that beggars cannot be choosers in such a volatile and unstable economic environment.

When Adrian and Yseult moved from the Valais to the city of Geneva, they lived at first in a one-room studio with a tiny kitchenette and very small bathroom, as anything bigger was beyond their financial means, in a very old, cheap looking and somewhat neglected and rundown building in the historic and picturesque commune of Carouge in the southern outskirts of Geneva which was linked to the centre of the city by an old tramway or by bus.

During the first three months, Adrian followed training courses and worked in the bank's payments department and other services in the bank's building in the area of Acacias next to Carouge. Yseult was able to obtain a job working in the Human Resources Department of a large American multinational conglomerate which by good chance had the offices of its European Headquarters in another part of the Acacias area.

As to Adrian's astonishment and delight, the bank paid him a small salary for his efforts at the end of each month and Yseult received a reasonable salary in her employment, they were very careful with their money, saving up as much as they could. And were able, after six months spent in the tiny old studio, to upgrade by renting a two-bedroom brand new flat in a pleasant street in the commune of Grand-Lancy also in the suburbs of Geneva.

They made the acquaintance of a lovely couple who lived in the other flat across the hall on the same floor. He was Anglo-French and was named Ernest. She was a black American and her name was Charlotte. They were both Doctors in Maths and brilliant, as well as very cultured and great fun.

Adrian and Yseult became very friendly with them and, with his enormous inferiority complex and low self-esteem, Adrian felt convinced that Ernest and Charlotte only wanted to be friends with them because they so liked Yseult. He attempted to mask his lack of confidence in himself by using his play-acting ability as much as possible and was gratified to see that the friendship grew stronger as time wore on.

Adrian and Yseult also managed to purchase out of their savings a small second-hand car, a NSU Prinz, made by the subsidiary of the Audi German car manufacturer. They loved going for short drives at weekends in this feisty car with its sporty engine and garish, bright-orange colour, which ensured that other car drivers saw their car from quite a distance as they explored other suburbs of the city and some of the surrounding countryside.

After the first three months learning and working in the bank's Acacias building, Adrian spent the next nine months attending further training courses in all aspects of the banking industry at the bank's training centre in the Eaux-Vives sector of the city, staffed by excellent and very professional tutors, and working successively in each of the bank's departments in their large building situated in the long Rue du Rhône, the rich street of gold in the city centre where many banks, other financial institutions, jewellers, watch and clock

manufacturers and other flourishing businesses, clothing boutiques and retail shops had installed their premises.

Due to his invasive mental and emotional problems, especially his lack of self-esteem, predominant inferiority complex and difficulties to concentrate, Adrian found training beside and working alongside other bright and well-applied trainees and employees at the bank very arduous and stressing and he returned home to the flat feeling very mentally and physically exhausted on many evenings. However, he found the year's management course to be very positive and intellectually interesting and stimulating and he had no regrets at having undertaken this experience.

Sometimes at weekends, Adrian and Yseult took the tram or a bus from Grand-Lancy to the city centre. They enjoyed ambling along all the streets, walking around the lovely old town and ogling at all the superb antiques, with prices way beyond their meagre means, in the many antiques shops and admiring the paintings, statues and ceramics on display in some of the art galleries which were established in the longest street of the old town called Grand'Rue, or sipping cups of coffee, tea or fruit juices in some of the charming *bistrots*.

However, the atmosphere became tense between them on several occasions during those months when they caught the sight of various couples of men walking along the streets holding hands tenderly, putting their arms around one another with evident affection or blatantly kissing each other on the lips whilst caressing each other's body in a show of strong sexual desire and mutual attraction.

Each time, Adrian had an automatic, visceral, aggressive and clearly upset reaction to seeing such homosexuals, with their openly sexual conduct, and he displayed a very harsh and negative attitude towards them that Yseult could not understand and found wrong and very distasteful. On each occasion that such encounters occurred, she admonished Adrian and criticised him forcefully, saying that he should have an open, tolerant, compassionate and understanding approach towards homosexuals and should accept them as they were.

Adrian just gritted his teeth and clammed up, failing to defend or explain his attitude, and indeed it was impossible for him to do so, for he could not divulge to his wife the appalling mental and physical sufferings that his elder brother Neil and he had endured at the cruel hands and penises of males and his inevitable, consequential loathing and fear of sexual activity between males.

This dark, infamous and degrading secret had to remain deeply buried. Whilst he wanted very much to share as many things as possible with his wonderful wife, whom he loved, admired and respected enormously, it was simply and absolutely impossible for him to share that ignominious and frightful secret with her or, for that matter, with any other living human being.

At night after each such occasion when they had seen couples of homosexuals together, Adrian lay in bed with his back turned to Yseult, whilst she slept peacefully in a welcome slumber. He curled his body into the foetus position, clenched his fists tightly and wept bitterly as the awful, nightmarish

images invaded his fragile mind and haunted him yet again of big brother Neil being sexually abused by those brutal bully boys at the orphanage and himself being painfully sodomised, destroyed and humiliated by that vicious male teacher at St Boniface's College.

He feared that these appalling memories and recurring nightmares would drive him mad, especially as he could not talk about those dreadful experiences with anyone at all. But he repeated to himself that he had to have a very strong character, accept as best he could what had happened and live with it and cope with it to the utmost extreme of his ability, albeit being dragged down sometimes by bouts of great sadness and abject feelings of deep depression and nihilistic despair.

The only other alternative was suicide, but he knew instinctively in his head and his heart that ending it all was no option to be entertained, for several good and positive reasons, the best of them being the joy of having Yseult in his life.

After having already been tempted by and refused suicide on several occasions over the past years, most notably during some dark, friendless, hostile and wretchedly unhappy experiences at university, he concluded irrevocably that suicide was a coward's way out of life's difficulties. He would not lower himself to being a coward but would face up to all the horrible dirt that life had thrown at him since his early childhood.

He had to try to cope with all the psychological and emotional pain, suffering and bitterness and seek some possible ways to repair a part of the overall damage which had warped and distorted his entire being and caused overwhelming anxieties, insecurities, concentration difficulties, feelings of inferiority, low self-esteem and a profound sense of being abnormal, subnormal and devoid of any worth or value.

* * *

After Adrian had successfully completed the one-year management course at the bank in August 1975 and had been given a fine looking certificate attesting to this achievement, he was offered a post as an assistant manager in the bank's Institutional Clients Department in which he had trained and worked in the last three months of his training course.

Whilst he was very appreciative and grateful to be given this full employment with a true salary in a department where the work was most interesting and inspiring, including contacts with managers of very rich and powerful pension funds and various other institutions, he told his colleagues after a few months that he still harboured the desire to find a job as a solicitor in the Legal Department of a multinational company.

Whilst regretting his decision, the head of the department told Adrian that he and the other members in the team understood fully his wish to pursue a career as a solicitor and said that Adrian could take his time, with no pressure, to seek a suitable situation and should simply inform him when he had found one and should give him his letter of resignation.

As the economic environment was still somewhat negative and depressed due to the consequences of the Arab Oil Crisis, the search undertaken by Adrian for a new job remained sterile and fruitless by that Christmas. As the Law Society of England and Wales had informed him that he could decide in his own good time when he wished to take all the Solicitors' Qualifying Examinations again, with the agreement of his boss at the bank he started studying again and refreshing his knowledge in all the legal subjects at home in the evenings after work and at weekends. He flew over to London and sat all the exams again in that huge and intimidating hall at Crystal Palace in February 1976. When he returned to Geneva and waited to receive the results of the exams, he continued his frustrating search for a new employment.

One evening, as she perused the scant offers of jobs in the employment section of the local newspaper *Tribune de Genève,* Yseult suddenly said to Adrian in a gleeful and excited voice, 'Hey, come and look at this job advert. The large Swiss group Nestlé are looking for a young solicitor who must be trained in the English common law system. This ought to be a perfect opportunity for you!'

As Adrian looked at her, his eyes misted over as if a dark cloud had passed causing a deep shadow. His inferiority complex, lack of confidence in himself and very low self-esteem rushed up to the surface, in a manner entirely beyond his control yet again, and he became overwhelmed by a state of blind panic.

Over the past year, he had heard all about Nestlé from various sources and contacts and he knew that this group was the largest food, powder milk and baby food products manufacturer in Switzerland and was ranked as the number one multinational worldwide in its field of activities. On a few occasions, as they drove in their little orange NSU Prinz to spend weekends with Yseult's family in the Valais, they had left the motorway above Vevey and had driven down and across through the lakeside towns of Vevey, Montreux and Villeneuve to see the sights before regaining the motorway just after Villeneuve. They had driven right past the huge, imposing and unmistakeable metal and glass building which was the world headquarters of this enormous multinational group and Adrian had learnt that two thousand employees worked in that building alone.

Adrian tried desperately to regain some composure. But, as he said to himself that the Legal Department at Nestlé's world headquarters in Vevey must be staffed by many brilliant and highly efficient lawyers, his fear that he was not intelligent or capable enough to succeed to obtain and hold onto a job in such a professionally high-powered environment submerged him like an enormous, crashing ocean wave.

In attempting to overcome his sense of panic by putting into practice yet again his play-acting abilities to cover up his negative inner emotions to some extent, he croaked embarrassingly, spluttered a nervous cough, cleared his voice then replied to Yseult in as flippant and casual a manner as he could muster, 'Oh, you know, I am not sure that such a job would be very interesting for me. I must say that it does not fill me with much enthusiasm. I think that I

must carry on my search and find an employment which is more suitable for me.'

Yseult stared back at Adrian with a total lack of comprehension at his negative reaction. She had already shown on several occasions that she had a very strong character and an energetic, lively and dynamic personality. Adrian cowered under her stare as he saw anger welling up in her facial expression and a look of red-hot volcanic fire dominating her eyes.

She stood up and, with her hands on her hips, she almost spat at him as she spluttered angrily, 'What a ridiculous thing to say! You would be an absolute fool if you did not apply for this job! You may not get as good an opportunity as this again, especially in the prevailing sombre economic environment. For God's sake, what is wrong with you? I insist that you stop being stupid and you reply to this advert and apply for this position straightaway!'

Adrian slumped his shoulders and felt very crestfallen and weary. This was the first time that Yseult had actually asked him what was wrong with him. Unknown to her, there were many things that were wrong with him.

Although he had told her about certain aspects of his unhappy childhood, he had not felt capable of explaining properly and fully to her all the mental, psychological and emotional anxieties, insecurities and complexes which continued to plague him and poison his existence and the frequent state of exhaustion which battling against such invisible but very real problems caused to his system, so he had said little or nothing about them.

However, Adrian, who was hyper-sensitive and overly anxious about many things, had already seen that he had married a young woman who had an excellent natural intelligence, good practical sense, a down to earth attitude and a high dose of wisdom. He sensed, after having observed her father and mother closely, that she had inherited these fine qualities from both her parents, but more especially from her father, who was very practical, down to earth and a fountain of wisdom. He knew that what she had just said was absolutely correct, so he apologised humbly for having been negative, followed her sound advice and made the application for the job, albeit feeling certain in the secret recesses of his being that the Nestlé management would not take even one look at him.

In the space of a few weeks, Adrian received good news on two counts. Firstly, the envelope from the Law Society arrived. And he was extremely relieved and pleased to read that he had passed all the exams this time round and was going to be enrolled as a Solicitor and would be receiving soon an official certificate stating he had been enrolled on the Roll of Solicitors, bearing the original signature of the Master of the Rolls Lord Denning, who had led an illustrious and highly successful career as a High Court judge, then President of the Court of Appeals, Lord Chancellor and Master of the Rolls.

Secondly, a letter arrived from the Human Resources Department of Nestlé in Vevey inviting Adrian for an interview at the famous metal and glass world headquarters situated on the shores of Lake Geneva or *Lac Léman*, as it was also named. When Yseult jumped up and down with joy, wrapped her arms

around him and gave him a smacking kiss as a congratulatory reward for obtaining an interview, Adrian smiled sheepishly and said sardonically as he slumped his shoulders like a worker carrying a heavy weight, 'But I have not yet obtained the job and most probably will not do so, for there must be dozens of excellent candidates for the post who are much brighter than me and have much better credentials than me and I have not yet worked as a lawyer in any multinational company, so my chances must be extremely slim.'

'And you are extremely exasperating with your negativity!' Yseult exploded. 'Just go for the interview with a confident attitude and we will see.'

Adrian informed his superior at the bank that he was obliged to take a day off to drive to Vevey for the interview, but, as he sped along the motorway in his sporty orange NSU Prinz on the appointed day, he felt increasingly more petrified as the car gobbled up the kilometres.

After he had parked the car in the Nestlé visitors' car park and started walking towards the high and wide door at the building's entrance, he became filled with terror and overwhelmed by his lack of confidence and low self-esteem and he felt a painful lump in his throat and a constriction in his chest causing great difficulty to breathe.

He stopped in his tracks, told himself he could not face the interviewer and almost turned on his heels and fled back to his car. Then he thought of his darling Yseult and how ashamed of him and bitterly angry against him she would be if he behaved like a coward and failed to undergo the interview. He told himself that, not only he did not want to have to face the red-hot volcanic fire in her eyes, also he must not be a coward and must put a brave front on the situation and exercise his ability to play act so as to disguise his nervousness and lack of confidence.

Once he felt resolved to do that and had managed to calm down somewhat, the interviews with the head of personnel and a senior lawyer in the Legal Department went far better than he had anticipated. He was amazed when he was called back for more interviews a few weeks later and he simply could not believe it when he received a letter, signed by both the head of personnel and the head of the Legal Department, offering him the post of International Corporate Lawyer.

Adrian and Yseult both resigned from their positions in Geneva, terminated the lease on the flat and managed to find another flat in Chernex, a small village nestled high on the hillside above Montreux, which had a reasonably large balcony and a stunning one hundred and eighty degree view stretching over the marvellous, long, croissant shaped Lake Geneva. And, to the left-hand side behind the lake, the incredibly impressive and beautiful seven summits of the mountain range named *Les Dents-du-Midi*, all lined up like seven large teeth pointing skywards and culminating at over three thousand metres. Over to the much lower mountain on the right-hand side called *Les Plaiades,* which was studded with many villas and chalets and became illuminated at night as the numerous lights in the windows glistened like a thousand twinkling stars. Adrian started his new employment at Nestlé on July 1st 1976. Yseult was

delighted to find a very interesting post with an advertising agency based in Lausanne.

Adrian was amazed, intrigued and confused when he received on August 25th 1976 an envelope bearing a couple of colourful stamps of New Zealand. He showed it to Yseult, saying that he did not know anyone in that country and he had to admit that he barely knew where New Zealand was on the globe! He opened the envelope standing in the lounge and was astonished to have in his hand a letter dated August 18th 1976 from the Trust Department of a company called The New Zealand Insurance Company Limited based in the city of Auckland in New Zealand.

He was completely flabbergasted and bowled over when he read silently the opening paragraph of the letter, signed by a Trust Officer, informing him:

It is with regret that I have to advise you of the death of your mother in Auckland on 15th July 1976. This Company is the executor of the late Mrs Rosamund Walton-Mornick's Will and I enclose for your information a copy dated 28th July 1965. You will note that you and your two brothers are to share her estate equally.

As he could not take in what he had just read, Adrian read the paragraph a second time. His hand suddenly started trembling so much that he let the letter and its annex drop. He clasped his hand over his mouth to stifle a painful moan and then pushed the hand slowly up to each eye attempting to wipe away the hot, wet tears which started welling and cascading down his cheeks. As the emotional anguish which began to submerge him became rapidly so great his head started spinning and he crashed down onto the floor with a thud like a heavy sack of potatoes. Yseult cried out, asking him what the matter was.

As he continued to sob and tried to wipe away the gushing tears, whilst feeling a searing pain in his heart, he raised up an arm towards Yseult and wagged a finger at her as a sign that she had to leave him alone for a moment.

After a minute or so, with his eyes smarting from the bitter tears, he managed to sit upright on the floor, picked up the annex to the letter and read his mother's two-page will. His chest heaved with deep emotion as he read the names of his brothers Neil and Justin and his own name set out in capital letters and underlined as their mother's three heirs in equal parts. He read the two-page will three times with the best concentration that he could muster then shook his head violently from side to side whilst taking several short, deep breaths of air and read the will yet again as if he needed to ensure himself that he was not dreaming.

He scooped up the letter from the floor with his free hand, stood up very unsteadily and gave both documents to Yseult to read.

She read them twice, also started to sob and to shake her head, then handed them back to him as she said, 'This is an incredible development! I just do not know what to say!'

'It is absolutely unbelievable!' Adrian replied with a feeble voice as he waved the documents gripped in his left hand and shook his head yet again. He took her left hand in his right hand and they both sat side by side on the sofa as he perused the letter and the will one more time.

'Can you imagine?' He stuttered as his whole body started trembling. 'During all these years since I was six years old I have suffered deep down inside me from enormous and indescribable hurt, pain, guilt, bitter resentment and even hatred against my mother for having betrayed, rejected and abandoned me and my brothers when she put us on that aeroplane at Nairobi Airport in early 1955.'

'As I have never been able to understand why she turned her back on us and have had awful difficulty in believing or accepting the pretext that she gave us at that time for sending us over to our father, I have always had to try to cope with the dreadful suffering caused by my conviction that my mother did not love us. This suffering was compounded by the terrible betrayal, rejection and abandonment by our father a short while later in 1955 showing that he did not love us either.'

'However, I discover just today that our mother made a will, leaving everything she had to her three sons, in July 1965, ten and a half years after she said goodbye to us for the last time at Nairobi Airport. This huge discovery seems to indicate that, contrary to what I have always felt during these past twenty-one years, our mother did love us and must have continued to think about us during all those years. Why then did she not attempt to create some contact with us in all those intervening years?'

'Surely, she could have sent a telegram to our Aunt Clotilda, who was after all her sister-in-law whose address in Dickleborough she must have known, asking if she had any news of us or could give her an address for each of us? Whilst I feel very guilty right now for having believed all these years that my mother did not love us, I cannot help feeling at the same time that she did not love us enough. For she did not re-establish any contact with us, and she probably made a will in our favour as a way to assuage her conscience as she felt guilty about betraying, rejecting and abandoning us.'

'I am hopelessly mind-boggled, mixed up and muddled about all of this. I feel extremely sad that my mother has just died a few weeks ago without having any of her sons with her or at some place nearby. Also, over the years I have often thought about how very different and so much better, happier and emotionally secure and stable the childhoods and adult lives of Neil, Justin and myself would have been if our mother had kept us with her and had raised us in Mombasa, albeit alone, without our father, in the pleasant and united environment the three of us enjoyed for we were together and would have grown up together. This sudden news of her death is inevitably stirring up all sorts of emotions inside me, including the difficulties I have gone through as to knowing who I really am and what is my true identity since my mother put me on that aeroplane and I became an orphan after being abandoned by my father, then was separated from my beloved brothers, then was later taken in and

adopted by other people who changed my name. Further, this makes me think that if I had remained and lived all those years in Kenya with my mother and brothers I would never have met you, my darling! As I am babbling away tearfully like a blubbing baby you must truly think what a mixed up, crazy, emotionally unstable and weird person I am, so let us just stop talking about my mother for now!'

That night, Adrian could not sleep and had to endure recurring nightmares and deep emotional turmoil and, having just learned of his mother's death on the other side of the globe in New Zealand, he could not prevent himself from wondering where his father was in the world, what he had been getting up to, how many more woman he had been gallivanting around with after Anita left him and how many other children he may have sired in his debauchery and Casanova-like adventures over the past years, as well as whether he was in fact still alive.

The next time he read his mother's will again, he was intrigued to note, with a solicitor's attention to detail, that on the second line of the will his mother was described as a "Married Woman". He deduced from this that she and his father had remained separated but had never divorced, probably because his devious, calculating and self-centred father wished to avoid having to pay her any alimony or maintenance or any other financial settlement which she could have claimed against him in any divorce proceedings. His feelings of resentment, bitterness and hatred against his father seemed to increase somewhat but he found that such feelings against his mother were suddenly decreasing a little. And he was able to think about her with a small degree of tenderness and even compassion, as well as sad regret and the innermost sense of guilt which had always pursued him and would not go away.

Adrian wrote a letter of acknowledgement on August 29th 1976 to the Trust Officer named in the letter he had received and asked several questions, such as how he had known Adrian's address, if he could give him some explanations about how long his deceased mother had lived in New Zealand, as she wrote her will in that country in July 1965, from which country she had arrived in New Zealand, where she lived in Auckland and any other possible details shedding light on her life there.

A reply dated September 9th 1976, just two days after his twenty-eighth birthday, informed him, as to his first question, that his brother Justin had written a letter in 1959, when he was thirteen years old, from Aunt Clotilda's house address in Dickleborough to their mother at the address of the house where they had last lived with her in Mombasa and their mother had obviously received and kept this old letter as it was found in her personal effects after her death.

The executor then sent a telegram to Aunt Clotilda who was able to give them the addresses of Justin and Adrian but did not know of an address for Neil. It appeared logical to Adrian that Aunt Clotilda was able to give his address to the executor as Adrian had sent a postcard to Aunt Clotilda each time he and Yseult had changed address and on it had asked her to pass on his

new address to each of his brothers if possible, as he wished very much to regain some contact with each of them.

As to Adrian's questions concerning their mother's life in New Zealand, the reply letter stated:

Justin has already been in contact with us, asking for much the same information as you requested and, as we did not really have any contact with your mother during her lifetime, we referred him to your mother's solicitor in Auckland who knew her for most of her period in New Zealand. On speaking with that solicitor recently, he advised me that Justin has been in touch with him and he has replied to Justin giving him the information he required. No doubt, Justin will be getting in touch with you shortly.

Adrian suddenly recalled that in his first letter dated August 18th 1976 the Trust Officer had written in the last paragraph on the second page,

We tried to locate your brother Neil and any information you may have regarding his movements since leaving the Royal Navy would be appreciated.

Adrian rushed into the kitchen where his wife was preparing supper for them both and he blurted out in a loud voice and a tone which indicated to her that he was in a very emotionally agitated state, 'Yseult, it is essential for me to be able to see my two brothers again as urgently as possible! Over all the past years, I have had to keep as my priority my attempts to cope with all my psychological, mental and emotional problems and difficulties resulting from my unhappy childhood and to survive in this life. So I have only tried to keep in contact with my brothers by writing them letters and postcards occasionally, whilst not even knowing if they received them as they were anywhere in the world on Royal Navy frigates.'

'However, with this sudden and totally unexpected news concerning our mother, I feel an imperative need to be re-united with Neil and Justin. It is clear from the Trust Officer's letters that Aunt Clotilda was not able to give them an address for Neil but must have become aware, probably through Justin, that Neil has left the Royal Navy. Aunt Clotilda must surely know the whereabouts of Justin and whether or not he has also left the Royal Navy. If you do not mind, I would like to telephone Aunt Clotilda sometime tomorrow and ask if she can give me some news about Justin and perhaps an address or telephone number where I can contact him. Then Justin may be able to give me some contact details of Neil. Is it all right with you if I telephone Aunt Clotilda tomorrow evening? My mind is feeling too tired to do so this evening.'

Yseult smiled at him, with her radiant, seductive smile that made him go weak at the knees each time.

And he could detect a tender compassion in those lovely brown eyes as she replied with that warm, musical voice that he loved so much, 'Of course, I do not mind. I have the good fortune and joy to be in regular contact with my two

182

brothers and two sisters. What happened to you and your brothers when you were children is appalling and abominable and it is so sad that you have been separated from them for so many years. I can promise you that I will do all I can to help you regain contact with Neil and Justin.'

Before he went to bed, Adrian decided on an impulse to read again the last paragraph on the first page of the first letter received from the executor. He became deeply saddened as he read,

The estate of your maternal grandfather Mr C.E. Stewart-Price is being administered by solicitors in South Africa and the current situation is that his widow, your maternal grandmother, receives a life interest in the income but we understand that on her death your mother's estate will share in any remainder of that estate. However, we are unsure at this stage as to the exact amount, if any, that might be left on her death for you and your two brothers.

As his mind flittered back to his early childhood years in Nairobi, then at the farmhouse near Nyeri followed by the period living in the small house in Mombasa, Adrian recalled that he knew almost nothing about his maternal grandparents, for his mother had hardly ever talked to her sons about them. Except he did remember her mentioning on one occasion that they lived down in Cape Town in South Africa.

They had never come up to Kenya to visit their daughter and meet their three grandsons and they had not once sent any cards or telegrams for birthdays, Christmas, Easter or other festive occasions to any of their grandsons. It suddenly seemed to Adrian that those grandparents had not had any interest whatsoever in nor any love or consideration for their grandsons. Adrian now realised more than ever with profound sadness, regret and bitterness that, not only he and his brothers had suffered dreadfully from lack of love by their parents, they had not received either any love at all from those grandparents.

Also, in learning now of his mother's recent death he had discovered that his maternal grandfather had died a little while before her. This thought brought him to dwell a moment as well on his father's parents. He remembered that when his father took the three sons to meet their paternal grandmother he told them that their paternal grandfather had died many years earlier. His meeting with his paternal grandmother had been disastrous and he had found her a very cold fish and a somewhat stern, unloving and frightening old battle axe. He concluded ruefully that he and his brothers had not only lost out catastrophically as to their parents but also as to both sets of grandparents!

Adrian looked at the three signatures at the end of his mother's will. Firstly, he noted how stylish, neat, attractive and easy to read her signature was. Then he scrutinised the signatures of the two witnesses. The person having signed lower down on the right had written "Solicitor" just below and Adrian surmised that this person must have been his mother's solicitor in New Zealand.

On the left, the second witness had signed clearly "P.M. Reynal (Retired)" and had written his or her address in Auckland just below the signature. Adrian guessed that this person was probably a male or female friend of his mother.

***

Three days later, Adrian had the immense joy of speaking with Justin and hearing his strong, deep and warm voice over the telephone, having already called Aunt Clotilda, who had told him that Justin had married a marvellous Yorkshire lass named Maureen, had come out of the Royal Navy and was living with Maureen and their two little daughters Lydia and Lynette in Bradford, a large town in West Yorkshire in the foothills of the Pennines about eight miles west of the city of Leeds, a populous urban centre.

Aunt Clotilda was able to give Adrian the home telephone number of Justin but did not have any contact number for Neil. She said that Justin hardly ever wrote to her and only telephoned her once in a blue moon with very scant titbits of news. However, she had understood from a conversation with him that Neil's situation was not good at all and she was sure that Justin could give Adrian some details on that score.

In effect, after Justin told Adrian about his own family situation and his work in Bradford as an engineer, he explained that Neil seemed sadly to be taking somewhat after their father and committing some of the same sins as the father, as it were. Soon after leaving the Royal Navy, he met and married a delightful Irish catholic girl named Sheila, the wedding was very small, Justin and Maureen were the main guests and Justin was his brother's best man.

Neil and Sheila had two sons together, the elder being named Neil after his father and the younger was named Peter. They lived in a small, charming detached house in Poole, a large coastal town and seaport in Dorset on the south coast, not very far away from the town of Bournemouth. Neil managed to obtain an employment as an engineer with a medium-sized company just behind the port.

All seemed to be going well, but, when Neil and Peter were still very small, Sheila discovered somehow to her horror, probably through local gossip, that her husband had been having affairs with a succession of women in and around the town and did not seem to have any love for her and his two sons. Poor Sheila was a sorely wronged wife and she could not bring herself to forgive Neil for his lack of love, his betrayal and his emotional rejection and abandonment of his wife and children, so she divorced Neil and took their two sons with her to Londonderry in Northern Ireland to live near her mother.

As Justin related this to Adrian over the telephone and told him that Neil had not tried once to see his two sons again since the separation and divorce, he could not prevent himself from sobbing. Adrian started sobbing too and felt heartbroken that his beloved eldest brother had ruined his marriage and caused so much pain and suffering to his wife and two sons. As he tried to regain his composure, he thought sadly of the axiom that says the sins of a father are often

repeated by his offspring and the fact that the axiom applied unfortunately to his brother Neil.

When he had managed to stop sobbing, Justin explained to Adrian that after his divorce and the departure of Sheila and their two sons, Neil decided to look for a new employment, move away from Poole and make a new life for himself elsewhere.

As the economic situation in the country was not good, he found it impossible to obtain a new job as an engineer and after searching for some months, he accepted a lowly paid manual job with a rubber tyre manufacturing company in Corsham, a historic market town in the county of Wiltshire.

He rented a small one-bedroom flat in the town and after a while met a young woman named Miriam, who was also a divorcee and had a ten-year old son named Jeremy. He went out with her for a short period then they decided to live together in a small, terraced house that she was already occupying with her son. Justin added that he and Maureen had driven down on a Saturday to visit Neil and had met Miriam and Jeremy and were not favourably impressed at all by Miriam and were worried that she was not good for Neil. However, Justin concluded that Neil had made a choice to live with this woman and would have to bear the consequences of his choice. He had a telephone number for Neil and gave it to Adrian, who said he would contact Neil to arrange a suitable period for Adrian and Yseult to make a visit and would let Justin know. When Adrian and Yseult were with Neil, Miriam and Jeremy, Justin and Maureen could try to drive down one day to see them and the three brothers could be reunited again.

When Adrian dialled the telephone number that Justin had given him and heard the male voice answer at the other end, he felt a painful lump in his throat and a heaviness in his heart, for Neil's voice sounded like that of a very sad, pathetic and weary old man. They chatted for a few minutes and whilst they were both overjoyed to hear one another Adrian sensed with apprehension that there seemed to be something very wrong with his eldest brother. They agreed that Adrian and Yseult would come over to England for a few days during the Easter holidays in 1977, would stay at a bed and breakfast house which Neil promised to find for them in the centre of Corsham then would go down to see Granny and Mummy in Devon. It was difficult for Adrian and Yseult to get away at Christmas time as they were expected up at her parents' chalet in the mountains where it had already been arranged they would celebrate Christmas with her parents and some of her brothers and sisters.

After having taken an early flight from Geneva airport to Heathrow airport and driven in a hire car to Corsham a few days before Easter, Adrian and Yseult parked the car in the late morning in front of a small, drab and dirty looking terraced house in a long street of poky terraced houses in a rundown council estate on the outskirts of the town. Adrian had been told by Justin when he had visited him at the house in Dickleborough when Adrian was fourteen years old that the three brothers were descended from a long-standing, rich, upper class and privileged aristocratic family.

As he stepped now out of the car and looked around him at the decidedly poor, lower class and underprivileged surroundings, he could not prevent himself from shuddering as he felt the enormous contrast with his family's roots and feeling very sad that his eldest brother Neil had not been capable or in a position to do better for himself. He felt the apprehension welling up again concerning his beloved brother and was suddenly worried about what he would discover the other side of the black front door that he was looking at. Yseult saw the fear, concern and hesitation in his blue eyes and rushed over to him, put one arm around a shoulder and clasped his hand in her free hand and murmured words of encouragement to him as she pushed him gently towards the front door.

When Adrian had pressed the bell and the front door opened, he stood transfixed and stared in undisguised shock at the apparition of the man who stood before him. He had an involuntary double take and had difficulty in recognising Neil, whom he had not seen since their reunion at the house in Dickleborough nearly fifteen years earlier at the respective ages of eighteen and fourteen. His handsome face, so similar to that of their father, had lost a lot of its handsomeness and looked haggard, his beautiful blue eyes had no lustre nor any vivid sense of life in them and appeared somewhat sad and tired. He looked so much older than his real age of thirty-three, his shoulders were slouched and he did not appear to be well.

After staring at one another for a moment, the two brothers fell into each other's arms without saying a word and hung on to one another, locked in a warm embrace and kissing one another repeatedly on the cheeks, for what seemed to Yseult like an eternity. Then Adrian introduced his wife to Neil, who took Adrian's hand and led them both into a very small and cluttered living room where Miriam and Jeremy were nervously waiting to meet them. Images flashed on the screen of a television in one corner of the room and the sound of voices coming from the box was quite loud. Adrian began to feel irritated and to find it difficult to concentrate on what Neil was saying as he did not make any attempt to turn off the television, which Adrian considered to be very impolite and a sign of lack of education.

Neither Adrian nor Yseult were able to take to Miriam with any warmth or affection, despite their efforts and good intentions. She was not pretty and had a rather plain face with very dark brown eyes emitting a discomforting coldness and hardness, a thick pile of jet-black hair contrasting starkly with her milky white skin, and a somewhat strange, gauche and disconcerting manner and way of speaking.

Each time she struck up any conversation, she demonstrated that the centre of her interests was the accumulation of various material objects, whether large or small, which she was bent on collecting and placing around the cluttered house.

After a light lunch and a short rest, Neil proposed a visit to Corsham Court, a hugely imposing and grand country house with a very long driveway and an enormous landscaped park very near the centre of the town of Corsham. When

they arrived and began the tour of the house and its grounds, Neil told Adrian and Yseult that he, Miriam and Jeremy had visited the property on a couple of occasions and were very pleased to show it to them, as it was extremely impressive and one of the grandest and most reputed country houses in the whole of England with a fascinating history.

He explained that Corsham Court had been a royal manor in the early days of the Saxon kings, then after William the Conqueror it continued to be passed down through the generations in the royal family, forming part of the dowry of the Queens of England during the late 14th and early 15th centuries. During the 16th century, the estate had belonged to two of the wives of King Henry VIII, Catherine of Aragon until 1536, and Katherine Parr until 1548.

However, during the reign of Queen Elizabeth I, the estate passed out of the royal family and much later in 1745, it was bought by Sir Paul Methuen for his cousin who had the same name, whose grandson became Baron Methuen and Corsham Court continued to remain the seat of the Methuen family.

After finishing these explanations, Neil seized the opportunity with a smug smile and an evident sense of pride to inform Adrian and Yseult that he had learned many years earlier from Aunt Clotilda that their own family, the Walton-Mornick family, had counted several Sirs, Barons, Counts and even Bishops in their ranks over the centuries and had possessed various estates and houses, although none as grand and on such a large scale as Corsham Court.

Whilst they were walking in the park after visiting the huge house, Neil explained briefly that the very famous landscape architect and gardener Lancelot 'Capability' Brown had been commissioned in about 1761 by the Methuen family to redesign and enlarge the house and landscape the park, which was his most important commission after his work at the gigantic Blenheim Palace. Then in 1796, the equally famous John Nash had been commissioned to remodel the north façade of the house and further embellish other areas of Brown's external building works and reorganise the internal layout of the house to form a grand hall and a large library.

As they walked and admired the huge park, Neil and Adrian began to slow their pace and let Yseult, Miriam and Jeremy walk on ahead of them. They chatted for a while, catching up on each other's news, and demonstrated in a public show of warm affection, holding hands, placing an arm on a shoulder or simply linking arms, just how happy and grateful they were to be together again after such a long and painful separation over all those years.

However, when Neil told Adrian sheepishly and humbly that he seemed to have inherited the weaknesses and the bad traits of character of their father, Adrian could not prevent himself from reprimanding his eldest brother and admonishing him by saying that it was not a valid explanation and excuse for his bad behaviour towards his wife Sheila and his two sons Neil and Peter.

'Neil, much as I love you, I must say that I do not understand how you could betray, reject and abandon your wife and your sons. You have done to them just what our father did to us! Whilst it might be conceivably acceptable that you simply ceased to love your wife, as you may have made a bad choice

of partner, how could you turn your back on your two sons and break off all contact with them? When you recall all the pain, suffering and unhappiness which the absence of our father caused each of us, surely you can imagine how much pain, suffering and misery Neil and Peter are enduring due to the lack of love, the rejection and the abandonment on the part of their father?'

'I am not worthy of them, Adrian. They are much better off without me being in their life. I am a nothing, a worthless and inferior being and I would only be a negative element in their life. It is much better for them to be brought up by their mother, who loves them dearly and looks after them very well. At least they will not be orphans like we were. I do not deserve or merit forming a part of their existence. I am wracked and broken by guilt and my deep conviction that I am entirely unworthy of being with them. It is simply impossible for me to have contact with them!'

Adrian stopped in his tracks and stared at his beloved brother as hot tears filled his eyes. Neil's mention of unworthiness, nothingness, inferiority, negativity, lack of merit and guilt shook him to the core, for it mirrored and reflected fully all those dreadful feelings that had been festering inside his own being all these years. Not only were they brothers by blood, they were also brothers in pain and suffering.

As Neil looked back at him and started weeping as well, Adrian threw both his arms around him and hugged him in a warm embrace for a long moment, kissed him lovingly on both cheeks then released him, looked tenderly into those beautiful, sad blue eyes and said in a soft voice filled with compassion, 'I understand now. I do understand you. I promise that I am not going to judge you. Let us both do our utmost to survive in this life in the best way possible after all the horrible things we have both been through.'

The next day, Justin arrived with his family in mid-morning, having all risen and started driving from Bradford very early. The reunion between the three brothers was exceedingly warm and joyful, not having been the three of them all together since that wonderful meeting in Dickleborough fifteen years earlier. Adrian and Yseult took to Maureen immediately. She was a down-to-earth, direct and straightforward Yorkshire lass, with a lovely, open and smiling face, large, round, warm brown eyes, a strong chin denoting a strong character not to be messed with, a very deep and lovely voice, a glorious sense of humour and fun, an expansive smile and an infectious laugh. As for Justin's and Maureen's two daughters, Lydia and Lynette, they were both very pretty, with blond hair, magnificent eyes, superb smiles, great sense of fun and a very polite and pleasant manner. In short, they were both delightful and Adrian and Yseult loved their two nieces straightaway.

The rest of the day flew by in a blur, as they all revelled joyfully in each other's company, but Justin, Maureen and the girls were obliged to drive back to Bradford during the evening as they had some other social event the next day in their locality. During the supper before their departure, Justin told them all what their mother's solicitor in Auckland had told him in a letter about the elements of their mother's life of which he was aware.

'Apparently, after putting the three of us on that goddamned aeroplane at Nairobi airport in early 1955, our mother continued to live at the house in Mombasa but decided in 1960 to leave Mombasa and return to live with her father and mother down in Cape Town. About a year later, she met a man in a nightclub in downtown Cape Town. He was an Irishman whose name was Peter Reynal and he had been living and working in South Africa for a few years. He was many years older than our mother but they fell in love and she left her parent's house and moved in with him.'

Adrian perked up and interrupted Justin by exclaiming in an excited voice, 'Peter Reynal, you say? I recall very well having seen the signature of a P.M. Reynal who witnessed our mother's will in July 1965. That person wrote "retired" beside the signature. I have been wondering who this person was and whether it was a man or a woman. Was the witness this Peter Reynal you are talking about?'

'How observant of you, my dear little brother! I imagine your training as a solicitor taught you to pay close attention to detail. Yes, that witness was the Peter Reynal that our mother became involved with. When he came up for an early retirement in 1963 he suggested to our mother that they move to New Zealand and make a new life there. She agreed and they travelled by sea on a large liner to Auckland on a cruise which took several weeks. They found a small house for sale in Beresford Street in the Bayswater area of Auckland, bought it and settled down to their new life there. They were still living together in that house when our mother died on July 15th last year. They lived together as an unmarried couple for our mother was still married to our father as they never divorced legally and were merely separated so she could not marry any other man. Her solicitor told me that she contacted him in the late spring of 1965, saying that she wanted him to draw up her will in which she was leaving all her meagre assets to her three sons in equal shares. Peter Reynal fully understood and agreed with this and would be one of the two witnesses of her signature on her will. Her solicitor also mentioned in his letter that our mother appeared to have a real gift for creating crosswords and during the years that she lived in Auckland she was able to earn some money through royalties on crosswords that she succeeded in selling to some newspapers in New Zealand. That was all he was able to tell me about her life in Auckland.'

After leaving Corsham, Adrian and Yseult drove down to Devon and spent a couple of days with Granny and Mummy before flying back to Switzerland. When they arrived back at their flat in Chernex and started to consult their post, Adrian discovered an envelope with New Zealand stamps. He found inside a letter from the executor, a statement of account setting out figures in the administration of his mother's estate and a bank draft in Swiss Francs to his order issued by a New Zealand bank.

The statement of account indicated that each of the three brothers was to receive just 5,000 New Zealand dollars, as the size of the estate was not very large. With the conversion into Swiss Francs, the bank draft stated that Adrian's portion was twelve thousand Swiss Francs. He telephoned Neil and

Justin respectively and each confirmed to him that he had received a similar letter, a statement of account and a bank draft for an amount in pounds sterling. Although his part of the inheritance was not very substantial, Adrian found that he had just the right amount to buy a brand new silver grey VW Golf car. He and Yseult managed to sell their orange NSU Prinz for a small sum and every time he sat in their new Golf Adrian became very emotional and sentimental, thought wistfully about his late mother and thanked her in a silent prayer for this unexpected and treasured gesture of her love and affection for her sons, which amounted to a consolation in a small measure for all the pain and suffering caused by their separation from her and her absence from their life.

During the next year, Neil, Justin, Adrian and their little families were able to meet up again in England in the summer holidays and they all looked forward to having reunions as frequently as possible in the coming years. However, Adrian was dumfounded and terribly shaken when he received a letter in the spring of 1979 from Justin explaining that he, Maureen, Lydia and Lynette were leaving England in a few months' time and were emigrating to New Zealand and that he would telephone Adrian when he had a free moment in the very near future to give him more information about the situation. When the telephone rang a few evenings later, Yseult let Adrian take the call and his heart missed a beat when he heard the voice of Justin at the other end.

'Hi there, little brother! I trust that you have received my letter and I can understand that it must have come as a huge shock to you. The situation is that Maureen and I have become increasingly concerned and worried about the increase in violence and insecurity in England's inner cities and the risks for the safety of our two young daughters, which are becoming greater. We wish to bring them up in a much more favourable environment.'

'When I spoke about the subject to a fellow engineer in Leeds, he told me that engineers are very much in demand in New Zealand, he was confident I could find a good job there with no difficulty and life in the cities and towns of New Zealand is very secure, safe, friendly and pleasant. He suggested that I made enquiries at New Zealand House in central London. When I did so, they invited me to go down for interviews, which I did on three occasions.'

'Within two weeks after the last interview, I received a letter containing the offer of a good job as an engineer with a boat-building company in Auckland. I just could not believe it! I returned to New Zealand House for a further meeting and the signature of my employment contract. We will be leaving England in early August, my new employer will pay for us to stay at a hotel until we find a suitable house in the suburbs of Auckland and the girls will start attending a primary school in the vicinity in early September. Is there a chance that you and Yseult could take a few days off work in July to come over here to see us before we leave? You could also take the opportunity to visit Neil, Miriam and Jeremy.'

When Adrian had finished his conversation with Justin, he replaced the receiver on the hook and collapsed in a flood of tears on the floor. He had

managed to be reunified again with both brothers after so many long years of separation, but he was now going to lose Justin again!

Whilst he understood the concerns of Justin and Maureen and their decision to make a new life in New Zealand for themselves and their daughters, he felt terribly destabilised, disheartened and despondent at this new twist of fate. He was very worried that he and Yseult might not be in a position to see them again for many years, since New Zealand was so far away on the other side of the globe. And it would be very expensive for them to fly all that way down under and even more expensive for Justin, Maureen, Lydia and Lynette to make the journey all four of them back to England to visit family and friends. This sad news was an enormous blow to Adrian; he felt down and depressed for many weeks before managing to shake off his spleen, pull himself out of his low state of mind, come to terms with this new reality and accept that what was going to happen was no doubt in the best interests of Justin, his wife and his daughters.

In July, Adrian and Yseult flew over to England and were able to meet up with Justin, Maureen and the girls at the house in Dickleborough and to see Uncle Henry, Aunt Clotilda and their son James again. After saying very tearful and emotionally charged goodbyes, they drove over to Corsham and were able to see Neil, Miriam and her son Jeremy again before driving down to Devon to stay with Granny and Mummy before having to fly back to Geneva. When Neil and Adrian found a moment to leave Yseult, Miriam and Jeremy at the house and to take a walk alone together, Neil divulged to Adrian that they had a half-sister named Philippa, who was born in June 1955 some weeks after Anita had left their father for the final time.

'When Anita told us all that she could not continue her relationship with our father and was leaving him, and us as well unfortunately, I managed to speak alone with her in secret behind the back of our father. As our father had mentioned to us a little while earlier that our Uncle Henry and Aunt Clotilda lived in Dickleborough in Norfolk and that he would take us up there on a holiday trip to meet them sometime during the summer, I was able to obtain their postal address by telephoning the directory enquiries discreetly. I gave the address to Anita and begged her to write to me after the birth of her baby, addressing the envelope to my attention at the house in Dickleborough, telling me where she was and whether the baby was a boy or a girl and the name she had given to our half-brother or half-sister.'

'I always knew you were clever and smart!' Adrian interjected excitedly with a look of admiration and hero worship as he gazed up at his taller brother. 'I shall never forget how, when our father met us at Heathrow airport and told us the young lady accompanying him was our aunt, you whispered to Justin and me that you could tell she was not our aunt but his mistress! That was very smart! So was obtaining the address of Aunt Clotilda and giving it to Anita!'

'Well, thanks for the compliment' Neil replied as he blushed. 'When we were taken to Dickleborough by our father on that fateful and life-changing trip, Aunt Clotilda gave me an envelope addressed to me which she said had

arrived just a few days earlier. It contained a short letter from Anita informing me that she had given birth to a baby girl and had given her the name of Philippa. She also mentioned a postal address where she was staying with our half-sister and that I could write to her if I so desired.'

'However, after the terrible shock of being dumped by our father with Aunt Clotilda then being completely betrayed, rejected and abandoned by him, followed by those ghastly experiences in those two orphanages, it was all that I could do simply to survive and try to cope with all the suffering and unhappiness. So Anita and Philippa went out of my mind for all the time that we were enduring life in the orphanages. When I started my new life in the Royal Navy, I read Anita's letter again, wrote to her and received a reply. I maintained some correspondence with her for a while, but after my last letter was returned as she was no longer at that address, and I did not receive any more letters from her, I was not able to maintain any further contact with her. It is amazing and very sad to think that we have a half-sister living somewhere but we have no way of knowing how to get in contact with her. We do not know whether Anita may have even gone to live abroad and taken Philippa with her, or may have married a man and changed her surname to his. I have tried to search for Philippa under the surname of her mother that Anita had given me but have drawn a complete blank. It is naturally possible that she has married some man and has taken on his surname.'

'Naturally, as you say. It does indeed seem bizarre and somewhat unfortunate and unjust that we know we have a half-sister called Philippa but have no way of finding her. However, remembering the passionate loins and extremely strong sexual drive of our rampant bloody father, one cannot help but wonder whether we may have one or two other half-brothers or half-sisters floating about somewhere out there in the universe!'

Neil and Adrian looked at each other as Adrian made this remark and they both burst out laughing, but it was a laugh tinged with bitterness, anger and resentment against a father who had not been capable of faithfulness towards their mother nor of love, loyalty or responsibility towards his three sons.

As they started walking back to the house, Neil suddenly told Adrian that he was in a fix financially and he wondered whether he could ask Adrian to lend him five hundred pounds.

'I feel very bad to have to ask you this. I have had some financial problems twice before since moving in with Miriam, who is very demanding on several fronts, and Justin has helped me out by lending me some money on both occasions. However, I feel I cannot ask him to help me this time as he and his family are preparing to emigrate to New Zealand and naturally will need all the money they have got. I need five hundred pounds right now because I am being bullied, harassed and pressurised by Miriam and her ghastly, pushy mother who insist that I buy a new fridge and washing machine to replace the very old and unreliable ones at our house.'

Adrian thought to himself that he commiserated with his brother, for he too knew very well what it was to be bullied and harassed, having suffered greatly

on that score from mean, nasty, bad faith and ill-intentioned boys, male students and men over the years.

He had already sensed a long time ago that such persons can feel your inferiority complex, lack of self-confidence, emotional insecurities and great vulnerability and they play on that to bully, harass and dominate you, treat you badly and humiliate you. He imagined that this was also the case with this Miriam and her mother, whom Neil had already told him he did not like at all. Adrian told Neil that, whilst he was prepared personally to lend him the five hundred pounds, he would have to consult Yseult and ask her if she was agreeable to him doing so.

When they arrived back at the house, Adrian asked Yseult to come out into the back garden with him. He put the question to her, explaining his own sentiments on the unfortunate and difficult situation that his brother found himself in with these two grabbing, domineering and vulture-like women taking full advantage of his weaknesses. Whilst she was quite shocked by her brother-in-law's request, she was very shrewd as to human psychology and a very humane, loving and good-heartened person. She sensed also how important it was emotionally for her husband to help his brother whom she knew he loved very deeply. She said she had no objection so Adrian went ahead and lent Neil the requested five hundred pounds, which Neil promised him he would reimburse as soon as he was able to do so.

One evening near the end of that July, Justin telephoned Adrian and they talked for a while and told each other how much they loved and appreciated one another and were going to miss each other but would do their best to maintain some contact through exchanges of letters until they would be able to meet up again.

In early December 1979, Adrian was very excited to receive an envelope bearing New Zealand stamps on the front and Justin's name and an address in Auckland on the back. He tore the envelope open with great impatience and was astounded by what he read in the letter written in Justin's small, slanting handwriting.

You will have difficulty in believing what has happened! As soon as we all arrived in Auckland, we were put up in two large and comfortable bedrooms in a pleasant hotel near the centre of the city. I started my new job at the boat-building company and Lydia and Lynette started their first year at their new school in a part of Auckland not too far from the hotel and were taken there by bus each morning and driven back by bus in the mid-afternoon. As I was busy working hard, Maureen undertook the task of searching for a suitable house for us to buy, for we had saved up some money in England and the cost of houses here in New Zealand is much lower than in England. It took some time but in the end, she showed me a house in the Bayswater area of Auckland which seemed to meet all our requirements and had quite a large and pleasant garden and a lovely view over the entire area looking towards the sea. After comparing it with one or two other properties and haggling with the sellers over the price, we bought that house and moved in. Lydia and Lynette each

have their own little bedroom, Maureen and I occupy the largest bedroom and we use the fourth bedroom as an office.

At weekends, we have all explored together the entire city of Auckland and all the surrounding suburbs by driving around in the car. On one Saturday morning, whilst both the girls were at volleyball training at a nearby sports centre, for they are both quite tall, taking after me I suppose, and are very sporting and athletic, Maureen and I set out on a leisurely walk from our house.

After walking the length of our long street, we found ourselves in the next street directly in front of ours. As we started ambling along it, we saw a sign almost lost in a high hedge indicating that this was Beresford Street. I halted, had a double take, stared at the sign again and a light flashed on and off behind my eyes and bells clanged inside my ears. I seized Maureen's hand and dragged her back to our house, saying that I had to check out something. I rushed up to the office, pulled out the file containing our mother's will, looked at the second page and there it was! I had completely forgotten beforehand but had suddenly recalled on the walk when I saw that sign that, as the witness Peter Reynal had written on the will and her solicitor had told me in his letter, our mother had lived with him in Beresford Street in the Bayswater area. I looked again and saw that the exact address was number 79 Beresford Street.

As I was not sure whether there might be a second Beresford Street somewhere, I asked Maureen if she was game to go back and check out number 79 in the Beresford Street directly in front of our street. She concurred, we drove back in the car this time and, when we had arrived at number 79, we saw clearly the name Peter Reynal in faded capital letters on the letterbox. I trembled in trepidation but took my courage in both hands and pressed on the doorbell.

When the door opened after a few seconds a tall, very elderly man stood there and asked me what I wanted in a slight Irish accent tinged with a Kiwi brogue. I told him my story as concisely as possible and, as shocked as he was, he confirmed that he was the Peter Reynal who had loved our mother and had lived there in that house with her until she died! He invited us in for a cup of coffee, we have visited him several time since and he has given me one or two photos of our mother. Enclosed is a copy which I have had made of a photo of her sitting in her armchair in the sitting room of that house which Peter took about six months before her fatal illness. Can you imagine it! Our mother lived from 1963 until her death in 1976 in a house in the street directly in front of the street where I am now living! Maureen and I still have difficulty believing it and find it an incredible twist of fate!!

Adrian became highly emotional as he read Justin's letter again and looked at the photo of his mother several times. In that photo, her face was bloated, her body was round and fat and her eyes seemed heavy with sadness. He thought back to those early days in Kenya when she was young, full of life, attractive to look at and sexually desired by many men. He imagined to himself that she had been living all these years with much regret, great guilt and enormously

pathetic nostalgia for the days long gone by of joy and happiness when she was young.

He started sobbing as he looked again at her face, not having seen an image of her since early 1955, when at the tender age of six he caressed and kissed her cheeks for the last time and screamed in anguish and hopelessness after her when he was torn away from her to board that horrible aeroplane. He whispered to her that, despite all his pain, suffering, anger, resentment and guilt, he had never stopped loving her, had missed her dreadfully and had never got over being separated forever from her as a small child, but was dearly grateful to her for not having forgotten her three sons and for her demonstration through her will that she did love them after all despite everything.

He wrote a letter swiftly back to Justin, agreeing with him and Maureen that it seemed an incredible and almost unbelievable twist of fate that their mother had been living in the street next to the one where Justin had settled. He added that he was pleased to imagine that it was possible that the soul of their mother, which he had faith was enjoying redemption and happiness in Heaven, had guided Justin and Maureen when they arrived in New Zealand to find a house in that particular street and become acquainted in the neighbouring street with the last man whom she had loved and lived with in her earthly life and who had known of the existence of her three sons and had been a witness to her will leaving all her earthly assets to them.

He concluded that he was delighted for Justin that he had found in Peter a real link and connection to their mother and that Peter could share with Justin in a tangible manner all the love and fond memories of their mother that he harboured in his heart and mind.

However, Adrian did not have the luxury of much time to dwell on those matters as he and Yseult were on the threshold of certain major events which were going to have an important and long-lasting impact on their lives.

Chapter 9
Suicidal Catastrophe

In spite of Adrian's emotional and psychological problems and difficulty to concentrate, he managed to do well in his job as an in-house corporate lawyer with Nestlé and his developing ability to play act and disguise his complexes and lack of self-esteem and self-confidence stood him in good stead.

He and Yseult made a certain number of friends in the area around Vevey and Montreux and, in particular, they became closely friendly with an English colleague of Adrian at Nestlé named Albert who had a senior position in the group's Internal Audit Department. Like their continued friendship with Ernest and Charlotte, who remained in Geneva, their friendship with Albert was one that would become a life-long and important relationship in their lives.

Adrian still could not believe that he was actually able to make a few friends and he continued to be convinced, with his lack of self-esteem and sense of personal unworthiness, that their various friendships were due mainly to the lovely and attaching personality, charms, natural intelligence, great sense of humour, irony and sarcasm and overall qualities and merits of his wonderful wife.

Due to the emotional anxieties, inferiority complex, insecurities and nervous tensions which still plagued him, Adrian found some solace, comfort, strength and emotional relaxation each time he indulged in drinking beer, wine, champagne and Rémy Martin cognac either by himself or in the company of others when they invited people to their flat or were invited to parties or other social functions. His penchant for and need of such alcoholic beverages to calm his tensions and relax his system was a source of constant concern and worry for Yseult and caused friction and rows between them on several occasions.

Another difficult and constant problem was Adrian's jealousy, an automatic, unfortunate and uncontrollable consequence of all his complexes, insecurities and low self-esteem. He had married a woman who, while not being what could be termed as classically beautiful, was very attractive to men, with her irresistible velvety eyes, natural charm and seductive manner, lovely smile and infectious laugh, superb figure, perfectly shaped legs and an engaging, intelligent, dynamic personality and strong character.

On several occasions, Adrian endured an acute pang of jealousy when other men paid what he considered an inordinate amount of attention to his wife and he thought that she had responded to such attention with too much alacrity and an increased effusion of her considerable charm. There was no doubt that she

had a high degree of success with men and he was very fearful that she would not remain faithful to him. His highly emotionally charged reactions to situations due to his uncontrollable jealousy caused quite a lot of friction, tenseness and arguments in their couple. He felt sure that she would not put up with him for a very long time and would walk out on him with some other man someday. He fought the best he could against his inner anguishes and deep-seated insecurity and emotional problems, but it would be many long years before he would manage to reduce and get over all such difficulties.

Adrian found certain contradictions inside himself, one being that, whilst he had a very low self-esteem, an inordinate lack of self-confidence and an insidious quivering mass of insecurities, he began to realise through his professional work at Nestlé that he was not stupid and indeed appeared to be quite intelligent and very capable as a lawyer, when his difficulty to concentrate did not draw him back and hamper him.

He did not have much interest in money for money's sake, but he found that he had a certain ambition inside him, which was to push his intellectual capacities and professional abilities to the highest degree possible. After three and a half years at Nestlé and having worked on various interesting and complex projects, he sensed that he was hankering after a change and wanted to take up new professional challenges. He wrote to a few head-hunters in Geneva with whom he had maintained a casual contact asking them to let him know if any interesting prospects arose.

In the autumn of 1979, one of them informed him of a great opportunity to become a European Attorney in the Legal Department at the European Headquarters in Brussels of Baxter Travenol Laboratories, the world's number one medical care products group whose world headquarters were based in the town of Deerfield very near the windy city of Chicago.

When he mentioned this to Yseult, she was somewhat surprised, as, being a true Swiss, she had imagined that he would continue developing his career in the Nestlé group until retirement. However, she did agree with him that it would be an interesting professional challenge for him, enabling him to work in the heart of Europe and learn and practice European Law, and would constitute a fresh change for them and a new experience living in the city of Brussels. He told the head-hunter he was very interested by the opportunity, was called to Brussels then to Deerfield for several interviews and was given the job. This was a major event in their lives and they started feeling both apprehensive and excited about the forthcoming change and the move to Brussels, which was scheduled for end January 1980.

A second major event intervened in early December 1979, when Yseult divulged to Adrian that she was pregnant with their first baby. He was over the moon with joy, as he had already told her at the time of their wedding that he would like them to have several children, at least three, as he was one of three, but not five, like her and her siblings, as that might be too much to cope with, so why not the good compromise of four children!

So, she was expecting the baby when they moved to a rented individual villa with a small garden in the pleasant residential Brussels suburb of Rhodes-Saint-Genèse. They told the gynaecologist in Brussels that they did not want to know the baby's sex until the delivery, which took place at the Edith Cavell Hospital in Brussels in late August 1980. Yseult gave birth to a superb, robust baby boy and they named him Steven.

Adrian threw himself into his new activity as from March 1st 1980 as a European Attorney for Baxter in Brussels with great enthusiasm, but he became somewhat disappointed and disillusioned quite rapidly, due to the boss. This man was one of the hardest, harshest, most unpleasant and unlikeable men that Adrian had ever met. He was overpowering, domineering, insensitive, calculating, lazy and a true bully of the nastiest kind. There was another European Attorney, a Belgian lawyer named Jean-Philippe, who had been working there for three years before Adrian's arrival.

He was very brilliant, an excellent lawyer, had a very good, honest and morally upright character and a charming and most attractive personality, with a great sense of humour, and a very sensitive and kind manner and attitude towards other people. He was married to a Belgian woman and they had two young daughters. Adrian and Jean-Philippe hit it off well from the beginning and they introduced one another to their other halves and the two couples became firm and close friends.

Jean-Philippe had been working under the orders of the unpleasant superior for the past three years and, although he became rattled by and angry at the other man's awful attitudes and bullying behaviour on a few occasions, he seemed to manage to cope with the difficult situation and stand up to the bullying boss.

Adrian guessed with envy that Jean-Philippe was able to remain strong, combative and positive because he had had a normal, stable, loving and confident upbringing in a close-knit family, together with his brother and sister. With a father who was very brilliant and had been, before his death, one of the best and most reputed independent lawyers in Belgium with a thriving practice. And with a wonderful, very loving mother who was still living in a village near Brussels next to the one where Jean-Philippe and his family owned a house.

For Adrian, the situation was very different. Even though he had succeeded in obtaining this employment, he continued to be bowed down under the negative and damaging consequences of his unhappy childhood, with little self-assurance, hampering insecurities, guilt, hyper-sensitive reactions and a level of self-esteem which was still very low.

During his first year there, the boss increased his workload continuously, made him take on more and more responsibility for various projects, ordered him to go on ever increasing and very tiring business trips to several European countries and generally oppressed him, bullied him and treated him like a slaving workhorse with insensitivity and a great contempt as if playing deliberately and sadistically on his weaknesses and vulnerability.

Adrian obtained a short reprieve from the awful treatment meted out by the boss when in the summer of 1981 he, Yseult and little Stephen returned to Switzerland for a welcome three-week holiday and were able to drive in their beloved silver grey Golf from Brussels through the Ardennes, Luxembourg, part of France then into Switzerland to the Valais where they stayed with Yseult's parents for several days.

During that holiday, Adrian paid for Neil, Miriam and Jeremy to fly over to Switzerland and come up to the chalet in the mountain village to spend a week with Adrian, Yseult and little Steven. Neil complained of a bad back problem and other aches and pains and when he went for a gentle walk with Adrian above the village Adrian realised quickly from some of Neil's remarks that the bad back and the other pains were psycho-symptomatic of and a physical manifestation of Neil's deep mental and emotional problems stemming from their unhappy childhood, as well as great difficulties he was enduring in his personal relationship with Miriam and due to all the bullying, harassment and pressures as to material and financial matters that he was suffering at the hands of Miriam and her dislikeable, dragon-like mother.

Adrian commiserated and gave Neil as much moral support as he could and repeated that the two of them had to do their utmost to survive in this life in the best way possible. He refrained from telling him about the bullying and the harassment he was enduring from his boss as he did not want to burden Neil with that since it seemed clear to him that his beloved brother had enough problems and worries of his own to have to contend with.

On a two-day business trip to Stockholm after roughly eighteen months in the job, all seemed to be going well as Adrian attended meetings with local distributors of Baxter products, local Swedish lawyers and other business contacts then participated during the second evening in a dinner with all of the management and staff of Baxter's subsidiary based in Stockholm in a four-star hotel where he was staying in the centre of the city.

Whilst he had been listening to the conversation between the colleagues at his table and had added some snippets of his own remarks as they waited for the dessert to be served, he felt all of a sudden a brutal pressure and pain in his throat and chest, as if a giant metal vice had been clamped there, causing a difficulty to breath, and a severe ache in the head, as well as a strange and unpleasant sensation in his shoulders. He managed to remain at the table but could not utter another word due to the pain and discomfort.

As soon as the meal was finished, he muttered goodnight to the colleagues and rushed up in the lift to his room on the sixth floor. Barely had he closed the door that he felt very bizarre sensations inside his head and through his body, then he started shaking and trembling furiously, fearing he was having an epileptic fit. He started to feel panicky then an enormous feeling of depression swept over him and engulfed him like an oppressive, black storm cloud. He began to suffer extremely negative and suicidal thoughts and when he threw himself onto the bed without having undressed, he could not sleep at all during the night but was pursued by ghastly nightmares and plagued by the same

swirling vortex which was hurling him down in rapid circles deep into the black bowels of the earth that had haunted him so many times many years earlier when he lived in the orphanages, then at Stenhill Cottage, St Boniface's College and Exeter University.

The suffering and despair caused by the depression and the nightmares became so intense and unbearable that he thought he was really going mad. He rose from the bed at some point in the night, staggered like a drunkard over to the open window, looked out then down and almost clambered over the window sill to throw himself down to a certain death and liberation on the concrete path six floors below.

He started praying feverishly for help to his deceased mother, then images seemed to float miraculously before his eyes in the open window space of his beloved wife Yseult, his gorgeous one-year old son Steven and his two brothers. This calmed him a little, but in spite of his efforts to fight against it he was in the grip of a very severe depression and as soon as he returned home the next day, he explained in desperation to Yseult that he needed very urgent professional help from a psychiatric specialist.

Yseult managed to find a lady through urgent enquiries over the telephone who was qualified and experienced in assisting persons who had suffered traumas and great unhappiness in their childhood causing all sorts of negative psychological, mental and emotional problems and frailties in their adult lives. When Yseult gave her a concise description by telephone of what she understood Adrian had endured as a child, the bullying treatment of his present boss and the terrible depression which had just overwhelmed him, the specialist agreed to see Adrian at her office immediately that evening to determine what form of therapy might be possible and useful. She made him tell her in full detail everything that had happened to him and his brothers over the years and, after listening very attentively without interrupting him, she told him that it appeared clear his case was very bad. She said it seemed evident that the oppression and bullying meted out by his present boss had pushed him over the precipice and plunged him into this depression but that had been able to occur because the root cause of his extreme hyper-sensitivity, mental frailty and emotional vulnerability was the unhappy marriage and frequent fights and hostility between his parents, the lack of love, the betrayal, rejection and abandonment, his overpowering sense of guilt and the absence of both his parents as he grew up.

'As a consequence of all that suffering and unhappiness, you have undoubtedly some lacks and some needs on the psychological, mental and emotional levels. Lack of a strong psyche, lack of a love of yourself, lack of a sense of identity about who you truly are, lack of self-esteem and belief in yourself, lack of mental and emotional stability and security. Need of love, which is huge, need of approval by others, need of consideration and admiration, need of respect from others, need of self-esteem, need to feel on the same level as others and not inferior and without any worth or value, need to

overcome and kill your great sense of guilt, which can be extremely difficult as guilt can poison a person's life for years or decades.'

Adrian attended several intense sessions with this specialist over the coming weeks and with her help by following a commencement of a basic therapy he managed to rid himself of the grave depression after approximately six weeks and to go back to work. She gave him certain psychological tools which permitted him to say to himself that he would never again allow this brutish boss or any other person to bully, oppress or attempt to destroy him and would be strong mentally and stand up to them in the way that his colleague and friend Jean-Philippe stood up to their boss, although he realised this was much easier to say than to do.

Indeed, the specialist warned him that he was a severely damaged and fragile person and he would never be able to recover fully from all the deep internal wounds that had been inflicted on him by that unhappy childhood but would have to try to reinforce his psyche and mental and emotional state as best he could.

Finally, she warned him also that, as neither she nor he could predict what lay ahead for him in the future, it was certainly possible that some events or incidents in his future life might well give him some further hard knocks to his system and cause those wounds to open and bleed again.

Within the next month and after much thought and soul-searching, Adrian told Yseult that he wanted to look for a new employment back in Geneva and leave Baxter. Firstly because he just could not continue working with his impossible boss and, secondly, because he really missed Switzerland, her large and lovely family, the glorious mountains, the majestic Lake Geneva and the city of Geneva itself.

She was disappointed, as she enjoyed her life in Brussels and appreciated the pleasant social life which they had been able to develop and her friendships with one or two other young mothers whom she met at the baby club with little Steven. However, she told him that she understood how he felt and he should be free to look for another professional situation in Geneva if that was what he wanted and she would simply follow the movement. She added the wonderful news that she was pregnant with their second child and laughed as she said that it might well be that she would return from Brussels to Geneva expecting their second baby in the same way that she had left Geneva for Brussels expecting their first baby.

Bolstered morally and emotionally by this most happy anticipation of their second child, Adrian contacted the same head-hunter in Geneva who had proposed the job at Baxter and asked if he could find him a suitable position in a group in Geneva. The head-hunter came back quite rapidly with a suggestion of a situation as the International Lawyer with a new financial group setting up its world headquarters in Geneva. Adrian took a few days off work to fly to Geneva, underwent a series of interviews within the new financial group, was offered the position and accepted it with alacrity, concluding that being accepted for this job, being able to resign from Baxter and contemplating the

forthcoming birth of their second child were extremely exciting and positive developments.

Adrian, the very heavily pregnant and exceedingly tired Yseult and little son Steven all returned to Geneva and moved into a brand new rented flat in the Malagnou area of Geneva. Adrian started his new job on July 1st 1982 and Yseult gave birth to a beautiful baby girl in late July 1982 at a clinic in Geneva. They gave her the name of Tatiana and they both thought that Tatiana Tunnington sounded most lyrical and musical.

Whilst Yseult was kept very busy looking after two-year-old Steven and tiny baby Tatiana, Adrian settled into his new professional activity and found it most stimulating and gratifying to participate in all the work involved in establishing and developing a new multinational financial group headquartered in Geneva. He was not bullied or mistreated by anyone and his direct superior was a highly competent lawyer with Egyptian origins who was one of the kindest, most considerate, gentle and softly-spoken men that he had ever met, who reminded him somewhat, with his humane qualities and mild manner, of his late adoptive father Keith whom he still missed very much. This most likeable superior with his respectful, collegial, positive and helpful attitudes and disposition enabled Adrian to begin to have a little more faith and confidence in men.

However, Adrian's improving mental and emotional state became extremely perturbed, disturbed and destabilised after he read a handwritten letter from Neil, which arrived near end November 1982 together with a Christmas card. The contents were dark, negative and full of bitter recriminations against their father and mother, especially their father, Miriam and her awful, predatory mother and mankind in general. Neil appeared sore, raw and raging. Adrian was so disconcerted by what Neil wrote that he did not know how to handle the situation and he was so worried about Neil's mental health that he could not sleep for several nights. After a few days, he sent a Christmas card and a brief letter in which he expressed his compassion and solidarity and exhorted Neil to put on a brave front, confront all his problems and difficulties in life with courage, and he reiterated what he had said during their walks together in Corsham and above the mountain chalet that they both had to do their utmost to survive in this life in the best way possible.

Life continued and Yseult seemed to become more and more attractive, charming, mentally strong and sensible and was a very loving and attentive mother. Steven and Tatiana became bigger, stronger and absolutely delightful. Adrian carried on with his various tasks and activities in the financial group, involving a few interesting and fruitful business trips abroad, including memorable experiences in Denmark, Saudi Arabia and Morocco.

One Friday evening near end June 1983, Adrian and Yseult held a dinner party for a few friends at their flat, asking all the guests not to talk and laugh too loudly so as not to wake Steven and Tatiana, who were sleeping peacefully in their respective bedrooms down the corridor from the living room. The guests seemed to be having a very enjoyable evening and the last one left at

two o'clock in the morning. As they cleared away some items and put dishes and glasses into the dishwasher, Adrian and Yseult said to one another that it had been a most pleasant party and they retired to bed feeling in a very good and contented mood.

About a half hour later, when each was still trying to fall asleep after the excitement of the successful dinner party, Adrian heard the telephone ring several times in the living room. He ambled down the corridor emitting an unsuccessfully stifled yawn and wondered who on earth could be calling at nearly three o'clock in the morning.

'Is that Mr Adrian Tunnington?' a female voice asked when he picked up the receiver.

'Yes, I am Adrian Tunnington. Who is speaking please?'

'I am a nurse at the hospital in Reading near London in England. I am extremely sorry to have to tell you that there is dreadful news about your brother Neil. I think I should let his partner Miriam tell you. She is here beside me and I will pass the telephone to her.'

'Adrian, this is Miriam,' a soft voice cracked by emotion mumbled at the other end, so soft that Adrian had to strain his ears to hear her at all.

'Hello, Miriam, what is happening?' Adrian asked in trepidation and with great apprehension.

'It is so terrible! It is absolutely horrible! I do not know how to tell you!' Miriam's voice rose by several decibels as she screeched and burst into a flood of tears.

'Calm down, Miriam. Try to calm down and just tell me what this is about.'

'The worst possible thing has happened. Neil has committed suicide! He is dead, Adrian! He is dead!' Miriam screamed as the sound of her sobbing became much louder.

'Oh my God, no! Oh my God!' Adrian mumbled down the receiver and he almost let it drop as his legs started to buckle beneath him and Yseult arrived just in time to support him under his arms. His tears cascaded down his cheeks and onto his pyjama top as he tried to encase the shock and recover his wits.

'Miriam, this is absolutely appalling. It is so horrific. I am so sorry. I am so sorry for you and Jeremy. Do you feel capable of telling me what happened?'

'He disappeared from home three days ago. He simply disappeared after leaving the house in the early morning to go to work as usual. He has never disappeared before. He did not come back home in the evening or during the night, so I called the police and asked them to conduct a search.'

'I took a recent photo of him to the local police station and they diffused it to police stations around the country as they do in a search for a missing person. He was found unconscious in the morning yesterday, lying face down on a bed in a poky bedroom in a tiny, shabby hotel in a small town near Reading. The police told me there was an empty bottle of whisky and an almost empty bottle of aspirin pills lying on the floor and a long handwritten letter was placed on the bedside table addressed to me. I have now read the letter and its contents are terrible. I will show it to you when it is possible. He was

transported by ambulance to this hospital and they tried to pump out his inside but it was too late and he died before I was able to reach the hospital. It is all so ghastly! I just cannot believe that he has gone!'

'This is the nurse speaking again,' the first female voice said as she took the telephone from Miriam. 'Please may I express my deepest sympathy and condolences for your sad loss. Unfortunately, we now have to speak about practical aspects of the situation. Your brother's body is down in the morgue in the basement of this hospital. Miriam here has identified his body but, as you are his brother and his closest next of kin, it is essential that you come over here to identify the body yourself as rapidly as possible. Then the arrangements for his funeral will have to be made.'

'My wife and I will fly over as quickly as we can. Please tell Miriam that I am prepared to make the arrangements for the funeral with my wife's help and to pay for the expenses once my wife and I are in England. If you will give me your full name and telephone number I will ring you as soon as I can tell you when my wife and I expect to arrive at the hospital.'

After Yseult took the receiver from him and put it back on its hook, Adrian slumped slowly like a zombie in a daze over to a chair at the dining room table and wept his heart out with his hands clamped over both eyes. This was worse than the worst nightmare he had ever suffered. Yseult came to him, wrapped her loving arms around him and emitted a few soothing, calming words.

When he felt capable to speak again, he told her, 'My darling, this is unbelievably horrible! Over the years I have nurtured fears that this might happen but I never really thought that Neil would do it! I just cannot cope with this without your support. Please, will you ask your parents to come and stay here with Steven and Tatiana while we go over to the hospital in Reading, have the body driven down to Corsham and arrange for Neil's funeral down there?'

Yseult concurred readily and, as they were both exhausted, they went back to their bedroom. But as they lay on the bed neither could fall asleep and Adrian suffered recurring nightmares again when he shut his eyes so he remained lying on his back with his eyes open until it was time to get up as Steven and Tatiana had awoken. Adrian just could not possibly go to the office and he spoke by telephone with his boss, who told him compassionately to take as many days off work as was necessary and not to come back to the office until he felt he could face it.

After the arrival of Yseult's parents and their tearful goodbyes to them and the two children, Adrian and Yseult flew to Heathrow airport then took a taxi to Reading hospital. Miriam had naturally returned by train to her house in Corsham the same day after she telephoned Adrian with the nurse. When they met the nurse and she told Adrian he should follow her down to the morgue, Yseult asked to accompany them, but Adrian told her to stay in the waiting room.

'I have to do this, my darling. I do not want you to see his face in this appalling situation, but I must do the identification. I have to do it and I can do

it. My heart is already broken by his death and it will not break any more from seeing his face. Please wait for us here.'

The act of looking at his beloved brother's waxen, lifeless face and body was the hardest thing that Adrian had ever had to do. As he gazed down and told Neil silently how much he loved him he wept more tears than he thought it was humanly possible to weep. The nurse took his arm and supported him as they took the lift back up to the ground floor.

When Adrian and Yseult arrived by hire car in Corsham, they went with Miriam to the local undertakers, who arranged with the hospital for Neil's body to be brought down to their premises. After they had prepared the body and dressed him in a lovely shirt, tie and suit selected by Miriam, the body was placed in the wooden coffin, with the lid left off.

Adrian sat beside the coffin for a long time and was overwhelmed by immense grief, sadness and regrets. Adrian felt firmly that Neil had not had the strength to cope with all the dreadful impact and bad consequences of the unhappy childhood. He felt also a deep anger and resentment against Miriam and her mother and felt convinced that all their bullying, harassing and pressurising bitchiness had made Neil even more vulnerable and unstable and had pushed him over the edge. He could not prevent himself from blaming them in some part, as well as blaming his father and mother in a greater part, for his beloved brother's death in a suicidal catastrophe.

Later, the hearse transported the coffin to the local church in Corsham, where it lay overnight, and Adrian and Yseult sat in one of the pews near the coffin for quite some time praying silently for the repose of poor Neil's soul. The funeral service, followed by the cremation of the body at the local crematorium, took place the next morning with just Miriam, Jeremy, Miriam's parents, her sister and her husband, Adrian and Yseult in attendance. After they all returned to the house of Miriam's sister and were having a much needed alcoholic drink, Adrian told Miriam that he would take it upon himself to call Neil's ex-wife Sheila and inform her of Neil's death.

'That bitch! Why should you call that bitch? I do not agree that you should call her for she left Neil's life some years ago!'

'Who is the bitch?!' Adrian rounded on her in an explosive anger. 'How dare you call her a bitch and how dare you tell me I should not call her! She is the mother of Neil's two sons Neil and Peter, who are my nephews. She has a perfect right to be told of Neil's death and to inform his sons that their father has died!'

As he said this, Adrian saw in a flash a gruesome image of his brother's dead face and he felt not only a keen anger but a degree of hatred against Miriam welling up inside him.

'Adrian, you are quite right! I agree entirely with you. Miriam, you should be ashamed of yourself!' Miriam's sister blurted out. 'Adrian, if you wish you can use my telephone and call Sheila from here in a little while.'

Adrian thanked her profusely and when he did make the call Sheila took it and was completely shocked to hear of her ex-husband's death. Adrian asked

her not to tell their two sons that their father had committed suicide but to say that he had died of a fatal illness of some sort, for he wished to spare them the further anguish that the mention of suicide would inevitably cause. Sheila was grateful for his sensitive advice and assured him that she would follow it.

After the return of Adrian and Yseult to Switzerland, the delayed shock of the full impact of Neil's suicide, at the young age of thirty-nine years, hit Adrian with a terrible force and nearly destroyed him. He struggled under a heavy pall of sadness and had to use a lot of mental and emotional strength to avoid falling into a deep depression. He pulled out Neil's last letter that Miriam had given to him and when he read it rapidly a first time then read it again more slowly, the sadness and anguish which engulfed him were terribly deep and became rapidly accompanied by an enormous sense of guilt.

He told Yseult that he now realised with hindsight that the last letter which Neil had sent him in late November was a cry for help from his brother and he had done nothing to go to Neil's succour and had not helped him in any way at all. Adrian said that if he had reacted better he may have been able to assist him and Neil's suicide could have been avoided. Yseult told him to stop thinking that, for Neil's suicide could not have been avoided, as his despair of this life must have been so extreme that once he decided to end it all no one at all would have been able to dissuade him. An excessively difficult task for Adrian was to have to telephone his brother Justin in Auckland and tell him about the terrible and tragic suicide of Neil.

It was impossible for Adrian to rid himself of his overwhelming sadness, grief and pain over the death of Neil and his oppressive sense of guilt concerning his death, on top of the long existing guilt about the breakdown of his family unit. He was bowed down under a very heavy weight of invisible depression and it took him more than five years to get over his grief and accept the loss of the brother whom he had loved, hero-worshipped and cherished with such ardour.

Whilst his normal, day-to-day life continued and his love of his wife and children increased and he derived much pleasure and happiness from his family life and watching his children develop and grow up, there was a gaping wound in his heart, which bled frequently, from the terrible loss of his brother. His mind would wander off and he would sometimes be mentally absent, even in the company of others. He suffered greater problems of concentration than ever and huge difficulty to appreciate simply each day and the present, for his troubled mind and grieving and guilty emotions would travel back inexorably into the past, despite his feeble efforts to avoid such.

During the first few months after Neil's death, Adrian felt constantly disturbed and perturbed about his violent and tragic suicide, which he considered had been caused for the greatest part by the awful consequences which he could not cope with of his unhappy childhood pursuant notably to the betrayal, rejection and abandonment by their father. In realising that he knew so little about their father, he asked Yseult if she would mind if he contacted Aunt Clotilda and requested if he could go over alone to stay with her for a few

days to ask her various questions about his father's family and his father in particular. As Yseult had no objection and hoped that such a move might help Adrian to overcome somewhat his enormous grief over the loss of Neil, Adrian telephoned Aunt Clotilda's number one evening and was told by a female voice at the other end that, as both Uncle Henry and James had died, Aunt Clotilda had sold the Dickleborough house to her and her husband and had bought a small bungalow in the town of Pulham Market situated about halfway between Dickleborough and Diss.

As this lady gave Adrian Aunt Clotilda's new telephone number, he called, spoke with his aunt, told her about Neil's suicide, and agreed with her the date on which he would come to stay with her for a few days during a holiday.

When Adrian arrived at his aunt's bungalow in a taxi from Diss railway station, she gave him a warm welcome and one of the bungalow's three bedrooms for his use during his stay. They sat and chatted in her small living room and he was amused to see how many filthy, smelly Gauloise cigarettes she managed to smoke, obliging him to open a window before he choked to death, and how many tots of neat Scottish malt whisky she was able to consume before they went to bed.

The following day, he invited her to have lunch at Pulham Market's one local pub on one corner of the most pleasant and charming village green just a few minutes' walk up the road from her bungalow with its small garden. She was now completely white-haired, elderly, very thin and frail and leaned heavily on his arm as they ambled slowly up to the pub.

Over a lunch, which lasted two hours and included several glasses of white then red wine followed by a couple of tots of whisky, as well as several filthy cigarettes smoked by Aunt Clotilda, she listened carefully as he asked her various questions about her family and his father. She divulged again that her family was an aristocratic Welsh family, with some Scottish blood as well, going back many centuries and, while it had contained many illustrious and successful members over time, it had also contained some members who were cranky, odd, dysfunctional or dishonest rascals to say the least, including her own mother.

She said that her father, Adrian's paternal grandfather, had returned from the First World War completely shell shocked and after some time her mother had him sent away to a lunatic asylum in London and never saw him again. She said that she, her two sisters and her one brother, Adrian's father, had suffered greatly from this lack of the presence of their father and had also endured great difficulties and emotional upsets as each was carted off by their mother to a boarding school over several years and treated by her with a certain lack of love and affection.

Aunt Clotilda made it clear to Adrian in her attitude and remarks that she adored his father and he was her favourite sibling. Certain things she said to Adrian showed clearly that she wished to protect and defend his father and excuse him to a certain extent for what he had done to his three sons since he had had a somewhat unhappy and traumatic childhood himself.

During his few days' stay with Aunt Clotilda, Adrian was also able to meet his Cousin Roberta again. She was married and lived in Cambridge with her husband and their three children, two boys and a girl. He had not seen her for so many years that he did not recognise her at first when she arrived in her little car at Aunt Clotilda's bungalow. She was tall, very slim, with a lovely face and superb greyish blue eyes, a magnificent crown of silver grey hair and a very aristocratic bearing and manner.

Adrian liked her very much and before she had to leave them and drive back to Cambridge she was able to provide him, showing a great sense of humour and delicious sense of irony, with a few snippets of information about their weird and warped family. She told him that she was continuing to undergo research about the past history of the family, especially in Wales, and she promised to send him further information as and when she was able to obtain anything interesting, revealing and useful.

When Adrian and Aunt Clotilda were alone again, she told him on his last day that, after his father had abandoned him and his two brothers in July 1955, during the next few years he ran up considerable debts with his high living and expensive entertainment of various female conquests and had spent some months in a prison after having been condemned for embezzling and stealing money from some victims of his charming, deceitful and calculating manoeuvres.

Further, he had broken the law, with the connivance of dishonest Trustees and solicitors, by selling during the second part of 1955 a lovely, five-bedroomed house in Marlow, a town within the Wycombe district in south Buckinghamshire located on the River Thames a few miles to the southwest of High Wycombe and to the northwest of Maidenhead and about thirty miles west of central London.

Aunt Clotilda explained that the house was a superb and comfortable secondary residence with a pleasant garden going right down to the bank of the River Thames, which had been bought by her grandfather and where members of the family, including herself, her two sisters and Adrian's father, spent many happy holidays when they were young. Their grandfather had put this property into a Trust, with the binding legal provision in the Trust Deed that it was entailed, must not be sold out of the family and would become owned by each successive eldest son in each generation and kept in the family down the generations.

As Adrian's father was the only son of his generation, he became the legal owner of the house upon the death of his own father and should have kept it so that it would devolve down to his eldest son Neil after his death. Instead, as he needed some money to upkeep his expensive lifestyle he broke the entail and sold the property illegally with the assistance of the dishonest and corrupt Trustees and solicitors to whom he must have paid some inducement money. She said that she had had no further contact with her brother over the past many years, did not even know if he was still alive, but she begged Adrian to

be indulgent towards him and to try to forgive him for having rejected and abandoned his three sons.

On the flight back to Switzerland, Adrian reflected on all that his aunt had said and, whilst he felt that his anger and resentment against and hatred of his father seemed to diminish a fraction, he concluded that it was presently impossible for him to forgive his father's sins and misdeeds against his wife and his three sons causing so much misery, unhappiness, insecurity and instability and causing in great part the tragic fact that Neil took his own life.

Chapter 10
Tragic Loss of Second Brother

Adrian had felt as a very young lad in Kenya the disturbing sensation that death was stalking him like a dark, ominous cloud after the appalling, violent and hideous deaths of the white farmer Ray, the six *Mau Mau* warriors, the young black teenager Jomo, lovely Shelia the Kikuyu maidservant and the two Alsatian dogs Romulus and Remus.

As a young man he felt again the stalking, ugly presence of death after the untimely, cruel illness and death of his adoptive father Keith, the discovery that his birthmother Rosamund had died, the terrible suicide of his much loved and sad brother Neil and the death, nine months after Neil's disappearance, of Granny, his adoptive grandmother whom he had come to love and cherish very dearly.

Two years earlier, in 1982, she had moved from the flat she rented in the small village of Willand into a flat in sheltered accommodation in the town of Cullompton, where Mummy could visit her frequently and take her to mass at the local Catholic church. She contracted some form of cancer about a year before her death and when it became evident to Mummy and the doctor that there was very little time left for Granny to live, Mummy telephoned Adrian and he took some time off work to fly over and spend her last week beside Granny who had become extremely weak and just lay in her bed in her flat all the time. Adrian had not been permitted by Granny and Mummy to be at Keith's bedside in his final hours as they felt he should be protected at the young age of fourteen and should not have to witness such a gruesome death. He told Mummy that he wanted to be with her and Granny during the last week of Granny's earthly existence and Mummy said it was entirely normal and she was very grateful to him for leaving his wife and two young children to be with her and Granny.

On the last day, Mummy, a very close friend of Granny and Mummy named Catherine and Adrian sat on chairs on both sides of Granny's bed. Mummy and Adrian each took one of her hands in theirs and they watched in silent prayer as she seemed to be asleep with her eyes closed, then emitted a sound like a soft rattle in her throat and exhaled her last breath in one long whoosh and departed with what appeared to be a contented smile on her face. It was so peaceful and Granny appeared to be so serene, which Mummy and Adrian considered to be wonderful and normal as, with her deep faith, she had already told them some time earlier that she was confident that at her death her

soul would find happiness in Heaven. She died on April 7th 1984, one day before her ninetieth birthday. A lovely funeral mass was held for her in the Catholic church in Cullompton and she was buried in a tomb very near that of her son-in-law Keith in the Cullompton cemetery.

Adrian missed Granny immensely and he meditated often on how Divine Providence must have intervened and allowed him when he was just seven years old to meet this marvellous and generous lady who had taken him under her wing and had arranged for him to be able to leave the hellish orphanage at eleven years of age and start a new life with her, her daughter and her son-in-law.

He owed so much to her, had spent so many happy and contented moments in her kind and loving company and had also suffered alongside her when he had witnessed some less pleasant times when Mummy had appeared to treat her harshly and unkindly and to dominate, pressurise and bully her with her forceful and domineering character and manner.

However, as he had grown older he had realised that Mummy loved her mother very much and had done so many things to ensure her mother's comfort, well-being and happiness with immense generosity and goodness of heart. He became aware that Mummy, just like him, missed Granny every day and prayed constantly for the repose of her soul and its happiness in Heaven.

After Adrian had left Nestlé, he and Yseult maintained their friendship with Albert, the former colleague of Adrian at Nestlé, and were delighted when Albert came to Brussels to stay with them in their rented house when Steven was a small baby and had come laden with lovely gifts of clothes and toys for the little fellow. When they returned to Switzerland and lived in the rented flat in Malagnou in Geneva, they were able to see Albert again on various social occasions.

Adrian was very pleased when Albert telephoned him a few days before Easter in March 1984 telling him that his brother Arthur and his sister-in-law Lilian, who lived in a village not far from Tunbridge Wells in the County of Kent in England, were coming over in their car with their two children to stay with him for Easter and he would like to be able to drive to Geneva with them one day during their stay to show them the sites and to visit Adrian, Yseult, Steven and Tatiana so that they could meet these members of his family. They agreed upon a day for the visit, which turned out to be two days before Adrian had to fly over to England to spend Granny's last week with her.

When the doorbell rang during the afternoon on that day, Adrian opened the front door to allow the five visitors to enter and he and Yseult were very happy to see Albert again and to meet Arthur, Lilian, their young son and even younger daughter. After a first cup of tea, whilst the children were playing together with little Steven and Tatiana in Steven's bedroom, the adults sat and chatted in the lounge. Adrian went into the kitchen at one point to make some more tea and he felt suddenly a presence just behind him. As he turned, he saw Lilian standing there and she looked steadfastly at him with her beautiful, large

brown eyes and as he gazed back at her he felt an extraordinary depth and wisdom in her eyes.

She continued to look hard at him for a few seconds, with a puzzling, quizzical look on her face, then her look softened, her eyes seemed to become illuminated and she smiled gently as she said to him, 'Adrian, I have a message for you. It is from your brother, who died last year in very tragic circumstances. The message is from his soul, which says that he loves you very deeply, he is terribly sorry for hurting you badly by what he did, and he accepts his punishment for his terrible act of suicide by staying and suffering in Purgatory for quite some time. But he is confident that his soul will one day be admitted by God into the joy and happiness of eternal life in Heaven.'

Adrian was so flabbergasted and shocked by her words that he very nearly let drop the large teapot which he was holding. Shaking his head, he just managed to put the teapot down on the kitchen table then he looked again into her eyes with a piercing and questioning look as if he could not believe what she had just said.

Sensing immediately his incredulity, Lilian repeated again what she had just said but more forcefully and convincingly than the first time and a strong white light seemed to shine in her eyes. She watched tenderly as tears welled up in his eyes and cascaded down his cheeks, which turned bright red, and his body started to tremble. She stepped forward, wrapped both her arms around him and caressed the back of his head as he slumped on to her shoulder and wept pitifully.

After a long moment, he seemed to recuperate his self-control somewhat, placed both his hands on her shoulders, pushed her back away from him and said to her in a hoarse whisper, 'How on earth can you say such things to me? I do not know you. We have never met before and today is the first time that we have ever seen one another! Has Albert told you about the death of my brother?'

'No, he has not mentioned it to me. Whether he has told my husband about your tragic loss, I do not know, but he has never mentioned it to me. The fact is that I am a very religious and spiritual person and I have certain gifts and capabilities on a psychic and spiritual level. You could say that I am a medium and the spirit world sometimes uses me as a means of communication of messages that the souls of people who have died wish to transmit to their loved ones left in this earthly life with whom I come into contact. It was after I came into your flat and saw you for the first time that I received suddenly in my inner being the message from the soul of your brother requesting me to relay it to you.'

'Please believe me, Adrian, when I tell you that I know that it was the soul of your brother which sent me the message, which I do hope will give you some comfort and consolation as your brother's soul is very aware of how much you have suffered since his death.'

Adrian looked into Lilian's eyes, saw again the incredible depth, genuineness and strength in them, then he cupped both her hands in his and

told her softly that he was completely astounded by all this but, due to his own spiritual faith, did believe that what she said was the truth and he was immensely grateful to her for telling him.

'You know, I pray for the repose of my beloved brother Neil's soul every day, but have always been terribly worried that his soul has been condemned to suffer in Hell for eternity, for I am a Roman Catholic and our church has always promulgated that suicide is a mortal sin and condemns the person's soul to damnation in Hell. What you have said seems to indicate that this is not so.'

Lilian continued to allow Adrian's hands to be cupped over hers and, with a very tender and warm look in her eyes, she said to him very gently, 'Adrian, do not believe everything that is served up to you by the leaders of the church. They are only men, flesh and blood and human beings like the rest of us. What you should believe is that God is a loving and forgiving God who only banishes to Hell the souls of men and women who have turned their backs on Him and do not want to be with Him. It appears clear that your brother's soul has repented and has begged forgiveness for that dreadful act of suicide by the earthly body of Neil and has made it clear to God that it wishes to be in Heaven with him as soon as this is possible. His soul will gain the light and happiness of Heaven after enduring the necessary intermediary state in Purgatory for a period of time.'

Adrian thanked her profusely and warmly for these encouraging words of hope, then told her that they should go back into the lounge to be with the others, lest her husband and his wife should think that they were doing something very naughty together in the kitchen!

After they all left in the early evening and Steven and Tatiana had been put to bed, Adrian told Yseult about the extraordinary encounter with Lilian and said that he did procure much hope from the message that Neil's soul would be permitted entry to Heaven at some point in time. He continued to think fondly about Neil every single day, for his heart ached so much as he missed him dreadfully, and to pray for the peace of his soul and its joyful admission one day into the light and happiness of Heaven.

Two other major events occurred for Adrian, Yseult and their children during the year 1984. Firstly, Adrian and Yseult had used all their savings during 1983 to purchase a plot of land of about one third of an acre in a residential street in a lovely commune in the Canton of Vaud. They had a four-bedroom villa in the classical "Vaudois" style built on the plot and were able to leave the flat in Malagnou and move into their new villa in the early summer of 1984.

Secondly, Adrian was given the opportunity to leave the financial group and take up a new challenge as the International Legal Adviser in the Legal Department of the Swiss subsidiary in Geneva of a large international bank, again being able to work in both English and French. He commenced this new professional activity on October 1st 1984 and was very soon thrown into a fascinating and hard-working environment in a bank with thriving activities, clients and projects in many countries around the world.

Two years later, a very happy event occurred when a second son was born in early July 1986. After Yseult had divulged to him that she was pregnant, Adrian told her that, if the baby was a boy, as they put into practise again their principle of not wanting to know the sex before the baby's birth, he wanted very much to name him Justin after his beloved, sole surviving brother. She acquiesced immediately and joyfully, telling him that Justin was a name which she liked immensely and she also liked his brother Justin very much.

When Adrian wrote a letter to Justin and Maureen, informing them of the birth of this second son and his name, he received back a postcard written by Justin telling him how happy and honoured he felt that this nephew had been named after him. He added that he hoped sincerely that Adrian and/or Yseult might one day be able to make a trip down to New Zealand to stay with them in their house in the suburbs of Auckland.

To Adrian's great surprise and jubilation, an opportunity for him to make such a trip arose unexpectedly in October 1987. One of the bank's corporate clients was a large privately owned company manufacturing and selling various metallurgical products, which was based in the city of Sydney in Australia. Adrian had worked on several occasions with members of the bank's important Trade Finance Department and Letters of Credit Department on the complex legal aspects for the structuring of financing granted by the bank through issuance of letters of credits and bank guarantees for large amounts of money in favour of this corporate client. This involved obligatorily the cooperation on the other side of some of Australia's big banks in order to allow the corporate client to finalise trade deals with many of its suppliers of various raw materials required to manufacture its products.

In the process of these financing projects, Adrian had had direct exchanges of letters, telefaxes and e-mails with the man who was the major shareholder and the Managing Director of this company. One day, he was amazed to receive a long letter from this businessman, explaining that his company had decided to sue, in an important litigation, two of Australia's largest banks which had behaved badly and negligently and had hampered the company's business through malpractice with regards to some of the letters of credit and bank guarantees issued by Adrian's bank in Geneva.

He wrote that, in the preparation and the filing of the court case in the civil courts in Sydney, the company's solicitors and barristers had told him that it would be very favourable to and advantageous in the company's lawsuit if a person from Adrian's bank who was proficient in letters of credit and bank guarantee matters could act as an expert witness for the company and go down to Sydney to provide his expert testimony in the case before the court. He concluded from his various exchanges with Adrian that the latter would be the perfect expert witness, if he and his employer would agree, and, if so, the company would pay the price of his aeroplane tickets to and from Sydney, the cost of his room at a good hotel in Sydney for three nights and all his meals and any other sundry expenses during his trip.

Adrian submitted the request to his direct superior who was the bank's General Manager. The latter said that this company was a long-standing and faithful client of the bank, whose financing to further the company's various projects generated good fees for the bank, and he agreed that Adrian should make the business trip down under and be the expert witness for the company's case in accordance with its Managing Director's request. In an excited state, Adrian telephoned his brother Justin in Auckland and it was arranged that Adrian would take a few days holiday after the trip to Sydney and would fly over from Sydney to Auckland to spend a few days with Justin, Maureen and their two daughters.

Adrian was very fortunate and spoiled to be able to fly first-class in a jumbo jet of Japan Airlines to Anchorage in Alaska, where the aeroplane was refuelled, then all the way down over the Pacific Ocean to Sydney airport, where he was met by the company's Managing Director in person and driven by him to a four-star hotel in the centre of the thriving and bustling city of Sydney. During the first two days, he was allowed to rest and do some light sightseeing, in order to recuperate from the jet-lag, then he accompanied the Managing Director and the company's solicitor and barrister to the court-house to give his testimony as an expert witness before the three judges of the High Court.

In the first place, the company's barrister asked him several questions in a very polite and respectful way and in his oral replies he gave his expert advice and testimony on the various technical aspects to the best of his professional ability. Then, he was cross-examined, firstly by the mild-mannered barrister for one of the two Australian banks who were the defendants in the matter, secondly by the barrister of the other bank, which Adrian knew was a much larger bank. This barrister was tall and imposing, with a most superior, arrogant and supremely confident attitude and a highly aggressive manner.

Whilst it had seemed evident to Adrian in studying the facts and the law in preparation for his testimony that the bank represented by this barrister had committed the faults and failings reproached by the company, the barrister started twisting, distorting and spinning elements right from the start in the questions he put to Adrian. And, when Adrian began to object to and disagree with his remarks, the barrister began to bully, bamboozle and break him with an extreme oral nastiness and overpowering attitude. Adrian's deep-seated inferiority complex, lack of self-assurance and feelings of being valueless and worthless rushed swiftly to the surface and he almost panicked under the barrage.

Then he recalled his determination, after recovering from the dreadful depression caused by his horrible boss in Brussels a few years earlier, that he would never again allow someone to bully and browbeat him and act with unjust attitudes and behaviour. He shook his head vehemently, stared back at the barrister with a steely look in his blue eyes, opposed him and stood up against his incorrect, untruthful and unjust remarks in his cross-examining

tactics. The barrister turned to the principal judge and told him the witness was not properly answering his question.

The judge called out to Adrian in a harsh tone, 'Mr Tunnington, you must answer the question just put to you or I may be obliged to have you charged with contempt of court, which could mean you will have to pay a heavy fine or even go to prison for a certain number of days!'

Adrian stared back in shock and trepidation at this tirade. The thought suddenly hit him in a flash that, as the two defendants were two of Australia's largest and best-known banks, this judge was being favourable to or was even in connivance with the barristers for the banks and did not want to make a judgement against such large and powerful financial institutions.

As Adrian could not stomach the prospect of such injustice against the plaintiff company, he felt indignation rising up inside him and stood up to the judge and retorted firmly, 'Your Honour, you can see clearly, and everyone in this courtroom can also see, that the barrister for the bank is attempting to bully and bamboozle me and make me say the words which he and his client want me to say but which I cannot possibly say because they would not correspond to the true situation in this matter. Since it is your legal and moral duty as a judge to act with fairness and impartiality towards both sides in this litigation, I humbly and respectfully request you to order the barrister to reformulate his question in the correct manner.'

A pall of heavy silence fell over the courtroom for a few seconds, then the judge smiled condescendingly, nodded his head, lifted up a hand, pointed to the barrister and told him that he had to reformulate his question and act with a more respectful attitude towards the expert witness.

Adrian was then able to answer the rest of his questions successfully with no further incident and no more threats of being in contempt of court.

At the end of the session, Adrian, the Managing Director, the barrister and the solicitor of the company left the building rapidly and tumbled into a nearby bar, where they each swigged down a soothing glass of cool Foster beer with a big sigh of relief that the unpleasant barrister of the bank had not succeeded in prevailing over Adrian with his nasty and twisted tactic. The litigation dragged on for many months and was finally settled out of court with a reasonable financial compensation being paid to the company by both banks.

When Adrian arrived at Auckland airport after the three-hour flight across the sea from Sydney, he was absolutely overjoyed to see his tall, broad-shouldered, handsome, blue-eyed brother Justin standing in the arrival area beside Maureen. The two brothers embraced one another in a long, warm hug for such a long time that Maureen joked, with her lovely, deep voice and sensuous laugh, that she felt very jealous as her husband had never hugged her for as long as that!

Soon after they had driven Adrian back to their house, the two daughters arrived home from school by bus and they all sat down together for a cup of tea and some cake and a wonderful, cheerful period catching up on news. It was marvellous for Adrian to see again his two blonde and very pretty nieces Lydia

and Lynette, who were now bubbly, happy and very sportive teenagers and as tall as him, evidently taking after their father and paternal grandfather as to height.

Justin told Adrian that it was sadly not possible to introduce him to Peter Reynal, as he had died of an illness almost a year earlier and the house where he and their mother had lived together had been sold. However, on a walk on the following day, they ambled down Beresford Street and Adrian and Justin stood side by side with their arms wrapped around one another as they gazed wistfully and nostalgically at the house and neat garden where their mother had lived for almost thirteen years and recalled fond memories of happy times with Neil and their mother back in Kenya when they were very young boys.

As they talked about Neil, Justin said to Adrian in an emotional moment, 'I was extremely angry at Neil for what he did and I still cannot get over my anger and grief! Why on earth did he end it all?'

Adrian replied tearfully that he had told Neil on one or two occasions when they were together that they had to survive in this life in the best way possible, but life had proved too difficult for poor Neil and he just could not cope. He then told Justin in detail about the letter he had received from Neil before Christmas the year before the death and the horrendous suicide note which Neil had left in the small hotel room and how the guilt he felt that he had not done more to help Neil still weighed heavily on his heart.

The following morning after breakfast, as they waved goodbye to Lydia and Lynette who were walking away to catch the school bus, Justin suggested to Maureen and Adrian that they could take a drive over to the crematorium where their mother's cremation had taken place and where Peter Reynal had taken them a few days after they had made his acquaintance soon after moving into their house one street away from his.

Peter had had a memorial plaque placed on a long wall at the crematorium in honour of their mother among the many other such plaques placed by the families of other deceased persons whose bodies had been cremated.

When they arrived at the particular part of the wall, Adrian gazed at the specific plaque and held Justin's hand as he felt renewed grief about their mother and started to weep. The dark brown metal plaque was inscribed with large white capital letters and numbers reading: "IN LOVING MEMORY OF ROSAMUND JOAN REYNAL BORN ON 14 OCTOBER 1919 DIED 15 JULY 1976".

Whilst attempting to regain his composure, he said to Justin with a trace of deep emotion in his voice, 'Her surname is mentioned as Reynal and not our family name of Walton-Mornick. I feel disturbed about that, for I have always thought that she and our father never divorced.'

'That is correct, little brother, they were never divorced. However, Peter Reynal told us that, as they had lived together for about thirteen years before her death, he felt that she had become his common law wife and he wanted this memorial plaque to reflect that by using his surname.'

'Well, as a solicitor I can understand that he felt she was his common law wife. I just feel a bit upset that our family name, which really was the surname she bore, does not figure on this plaque as if she has lost her true family identity. However, I suppose it is futile for me to say any more on that subject, for I too have lost my true identity as my adoptive parents changed my surname to theirs. At least Aunt Clotilda and Uncle Henry did not change yours to his surname and you still bear the family surname of Walton-Mornick!'

After the somewhat morbid visit to the crematorium, they drove along the North Shore coast and showed Adrian some of the really lovely beauty spots. When they arrived at one gorgeous beach, Justin suggested a swim in the sea and Maureen told them to go together whilst she had a welcome rest on the beach. Justin was such a strong swimmer that Adrian had some difficulty keeping up with him. As they started swimming back towards the shore side by side, they reminisced about those many times when they had swum together with their father and Neil in the crashing waves of the Indian Ocean at Diani Beach, other beaches and in the cool water of the swimming pool at the Muthaiga Club.

In the afternoon, Justin drove Maureen and Adrian into the city of Auckland and as they sped along Adrian was amused as Justin showed off his good knowledge of some of the history of New Zealand and facts about Auckland as he assumed the manner and voice of an experienced tourist guide.

'New Zealand was first discovered about seven hundred years ago by Polynesians from Eastern Polynesia who set up a distinct Maori culture. The first European explorer sighted New Zealand in the year 1642. From the eighteenth century the two islands of the country were regularly visited by explorers, sailors, missionaries, traders and various other adventurers. New Zealand was brought into the British Empire by the signature in 1840 of the Treaty of Waitangi between the British Crown and some Maori chieftains at Waitangi in the Bay of Islands. Wellington in South Island is the country's capital but Auckland here in North Island is its most populous city with over one million inhabitants in the whole area, being about one-third of the country's overall population.'

Justin paused to draw on the cigarette that he was smoking then he continued, 'Auckland's name in Maori is *Tamaki Makaurau* or *Akarama*, meaning *maiden sought by a hundred lovers* due to its natural scenic beauty. Auckland's trade has always depended on its harbours and it is the largest port in New Zealand. The city lies on and around an isthmus between Mangere Inlet and Tamaki River. Two harbours in the Auckland urban area surround this isthmus, Waitemata to the north and Manukai to the south opening west to the Tasman Sea. There is also an inland port with terminals without a direct maritime access located in Wiri in south Auckland. I work at the present time as the Chief Engineer at the Wiri Oil Terminal. I became bored and frustrated working at the boat-building company and find the work much more challenging and satisfying in my present situation.'

'You are indeed a clever smart arse, my dear husband!' interjected Maureen as she clapped her hands in mock congratulations.

Justin drew on the rest of his cigarette, turned to look at her in the seat beside him and puffed the smoke into her face then laughed like a cheeky little boy.

Sitting in the back of the car, Adrian was delighted as he thought to himself that his beloved brother and his wife had a truly loving, pleasant and easy-going relationship.

Maureen then said, as she rubbed her husband's shoulder affectionately with one hand, 'Now it is my turn to play the tourist guide. You will see Adrian that we are approaching the arched Auckland Harbour Bridge which crosses Waitemata Harbour. You will see in a minute or so the spectacular view that you have all around you as the car crosses the bridge. Once we reach the city, we will park the car and do some walking around. Auckland has an interesting and bustling city centre and it also has several lovely parks, the Auckland Domain being the largest. We will not have the time to walk around it, but there are two other places we want to show you. The first is Mount Eden or Maungawhau in Maori, which is a volcanic cone with a grassy crater, is the highest natural point in Auckland, offering a three hundred and sixty degree view of Auckland and is the most favourite tourist outlook. The other is One Tree Hill, which also provides spectacular views. There was once a lone tree at the top of the hill but it is no longer there and has been replaced by a tall stone monument. You will see that both Mount Eden and One Tree Hill are well worth the visit and the effort of walking to them.'

Adrian felt exhausted but exhilarated as they returned later to the house and a very welcome and lovely supper with his two nieces. He was able to stay with them for two more days, during which they showed him more sights, visited a few other wonderful beaches, held a very pleasant party on the last evening in their garden with several of their local Kiwi friends and offered a magnificent barbecue in Adrian's honour. The following day, after saying goodbye to his two lovely nieces, he was driven by Justin and Maureen to Auckland Airport. Before he left them, he and Justin exchanged loving, brotherly words and hugged each again for a very long time, causing Maureen to stomp her foot playfully and say jokingly that she was feeling very jealous again.

After hugging Maureen and kissing her goodbye Adrian said gently to her, loudly enough for Justin to hear, 'My wonderful, dearest sister-in-law, please look after him for me, won't you?'

She wiped away the tears in his eyes tenderly with her hand, planted a loving kiss on his cheek, said affectionately that she knew just how much Justin meant to him, even more so since the death of Neil, and she promised him that she would continue to look after Justin for him.

In any case, Justin was very tall, broad-shouldered, muscular and athletic and Adrian thought proudly of him as a giant, indestructible oak and felt certain that he would live to be one hundred years old or even more!

***

Adrian and Yseult felt very privileged to have their lovely villa and garden and spent many happy moments living there with their three children Steven, Tatiana and Justin.

However, they had a great interest in the architecture and general culture of Spain and the south of France, notably the area of Provence in the south-east of France. In July 1988 they were able to spend a marvellous three-week summer holiday renting a very pleasant Spanish-style villa in a private park with a mere one hundred metre walk down to the glorious, long sandy beach and the Mediterranean sea just three miles south of the coastal town of Salou on the Costa Blanca coast in Spain. They were able to look at many beautiful villas with their superb Spanish architecture during the holiday.

Also, Adrian had already taught Steven and Tatiana, now eight and six years old, to swim in previous years in various swimming pools in Geneva and in the one just outside the town of Nyon with its magnificent view over Lake Geneva, as well as the large pool in Divonne in neighbouring France just the other side of the border from Switzerland a few kilometres behind their villa.

During this wonderful three-week holiday in Spain, he spent long moments teaching two year old Justin to overcome any fear of water and to swim in the sea buoyed up by his inflated orange wings on both arms. When he then sat on the shore relaxing beside Yseult, he looked at his three children with great pride as they swam and played in the water and his mind was thrown back nostalgically to those great times when he swam in the waves of the Indian Ocean with his two elder brothers all those many years ago as a very small boy.

The following summer, the whole family were able to enjoy another holiday down in the south of France in the Camargue area and to swim in the Mediterranean Sea on the beach at Sainte-Marie-de-la-Mer, a picturesque and very historic town right down on the coast with a splendid beach stretching for several kilometres to the east and to the west.

Adrian and Yseult continued to study the Provencal style of architecture and their love of this architecture continued to grow. Adrian worked very hard in his job at the bank and he was given an important promotion to the position as Director of International Legal Affairs of the bank, with an appreciable increase in his annual salary and bonus.

After the appalling and unhappy childhood and other wretchedly negative experiences, the horrifying nightmares which had so tortured him and the dreadful loss of his brother Neil, which continued to affect him badly and cause deep pain, anxiety and grief, he had an imperative necessity to harbour positive dreams and projects in his mind. He found that the dream of building a Provencal style of villa for his family was beginning to germ in the back of his mind and it rapidly came to the forefront and dominated his thoughts. Whilst he loved the "Vaudois" villa in which they lived, there were hundreds of other, very similar villas throughout the area and he said to himself that this was not

the villa of his dreams and he really wanted to build the villa of his dreams for the benefit of his family and himself.

When he spoke of his dream to Yseult, who was very practical and down to earth and very careful with money, she said he was crazy and it was an impractical, pie-in-the-sky dream. But he persisted in his argument by saying that he was doing well professionally and continued to have good prospects and he asked for her support in maintaining this dream and to seize any opportunity that occurred to fulfil it. She did not say no but she felt very sceptical about any prospect of such an opportunity coming their way.

The following year, a person they knew mentioned to them that an elderly couple living in a house near the top of a pleasant cul-de-sac just two streets along from the street where Adrian and Yseult lived were going to sell a third of an acre plot which they owned a little further down from their own property and to invest the proceeds of sale to ensure some income for their future years in retirement. But they had not yet put the plot on the market nor made any publicity about it going up for sale.

Adrian could not believe what he heard and was greatly excited and encouraged when little inner voices seemed to tell him that this was the opportunity he was waiting for to build the villa of his dreams and he should not miss it. When he and Yseult walked round from their house to this nearby street and stood in front of the specific plot, he became even more excited and told her that this spot was the ideal place to build the Provencal style villa he so dreamed of and, to his relief, she concurred with him. They lost no time in contacting the elderly couple and were able to conduct the negotiations for the purchase to fruition and conclude the legal aspects of the purchase before a local notary public by spring 1990. They put their present villa on the market and had the good fortune of selling it to another couple with young children at a price which left them a reasonable profit after reimbursing their mortgage which enhanced the amount of the deposit they put down for the purchase of the new plot of land.

Adrian and Yseult received the recommendation to contact a reputable and experienced local architect who was also a very accomplished artist and created beautiful watercolour paintings. When they met with him and presented to him their first basic drawings and ideas for a Provencal style villa he came back to them within a week with his own drawings which were absolutely marvellous and had not only incorporated their concept but had introduced terrific elements which they would never have thought of and immensely improved the entire project. They included suggestions to landscape the garden in a better manner and to implant a lovely swimming pool on one side of the garden, which Adrian and his water-loving children truly wanted and of which Yseult also approved. As Adrian had an enormous amount of work at the office and also had to undertake a few business trips abroad, Yseult supervised all the building work alongside the architect and attended every one of the on-site meetings and the family was able to move into the completed, decorated and furnished villa in July 1991.

The year 1991 proved to be an exceedingly exciting and important year for Adrian and the family.

Shortly before Christmas 1990, when Adrian happened to be sitting at his desk at the bank and was not in a meeting or away on a business trip, his telephone rang and an unknown voice said, 'Mr Tunnington, you do not know me but I know you. It is not wise to give you my name and tell you over this telephone the purpose of this contact so would you mind giving me your home telephone number and allowing me to call you at home this evening when I can speak to you freely and openly?'

'Yes, by all means, that is fine for me,' Adrian replied, feeling most intrigued, and he gave the other person his home number.

During supper at home that evening with the family in their first villa, Adrian heard the telephone ring and Yseult heard it as well and got up from her chair to go to answer it.

Adrian said it was probably for him and he rushed over to take the telephone off its hook, leaving Yseult feeling very perplexed.

'Hello, this is Adrian Tunnington' he said into the telephone strongly and deliberately.

'Good evening, sir! My name is Rolf Pfister and I am a member of top management of one of the other international banks in Geneva, which are rivals of the bank where you work. We realise that we are one of the few banks in Geneva at the present time which still does not have its own Legal Department and we are spending large amounts of money paying legal fees to external lawyers in Switzerland and elsewhere for any and all legal advice and assistance which we require. The decision has been made that it is necessary and more efficient to hire an experienced lawyer to create our own internal Legal Department. As we know who you are and are fully aware of everything that you have accomplished successfully for your bank and of your excellent reputation in the field, we have decided to make a direct, discreet and confidential contact with you, rather than putting a search in the hands of a head-hunter, and ask you whether such a prospect could be of interest to you and if you would agree to come to meet us for discussions, for we feel that you would be the ideal person for this new position.'

'Thank you very much for your flattering remarks. This unexpected approach naturally takes me by surprise and I would like to have a little time to reflect on the matter. If you will give me your telephone number, I will call you back as soon as I can in the next few days.'

'Of course, I understand, but I would be grateful if you will come back to me as quickly as possible to tell me whether the prospect does interest you or not. I will give you my private telephone number where you can call and we can speak confidentially.'

After noting down the telephone number, putting the receiver on its hook again and returning to the dining room table, Adrian told Yseult that it was a business call. Later on, after reading stories to each of the children in turn in their separate bedrooms, hugging and kissing each one and saying good night

then going down to the lounge to sit with Yseult, he told her in a whisper, so that none of the prying ears of his curious children could catch his words, about the content of the telephone exchange.

'Wow, you have become more successful and have a better reputation on the market than I had realised! I bow to you in admiration, my lord! So, what is your first reaction to this direct contact out of the blue?'

'It is, of course, very flattering. However, I am very happy and content in my present position and am not sure if I really want to move to another situation right now. Let me sleep on it and think carefully about it over the coming few days.'

Adrian thought hard about the matter and, much to his surprise, he came to a decision within a couple of days. Whilst he was contented and satisfied in his present employment, he had always harboured the ambition to go as far as his intellectual and professional capabilities would allow and he liked new challenges, creativity and developments of interesting projects. He called back the other man, met up with him and two of his colleagues for lunch at a restaurant in a small village well away from Geneva, had further meetings with other top management members then the General Manager himself, was offered the new job officially, accepted it, explained the situation to his present employer, gave in his resignation and started in his new challenge in the early summer of 1991.

***

Adrian was ecstatic with joy when he read the short letter which arrived from his brother Justin in spring 1993 telling him that he, Maureen and the girls were going to fly to the United Kingdom for a month's holiday in July and would visit Aunt Clotilda at her bungalow in Pulham Market then go north to spend some time with the various members of Maureen's Yorkshire family.

He wondered whether it would be possible for Adrian, Yseult and their three children to make a trip over for a family reunion at the home of Aunt Clotilda. As the summer holidays of Steven, Tatiana and Justin would commence at the end of June, Yseult agreed that they could all drive through France in early July in their newly acquired, spacious French family car called the Renault Espace, take the ferry from Calais to Dover then drive up to Pulham Market and stay a couple of nights in a guest house then drive down to Devon to stay a few days with Mummy and her friend Catherine in the Devon long house where they were now living together.

In an ebullient mood, Adrian telephoned Justin and, in a short conversation, they agreed upon a specific date to meet up at Aunt Clotilda's bungalow. Justin said that he would contact her and knew already that she would be delighted to know that they were all coming to see her and would prepare a superb lunch for them all.

It was a wonderful family reunion and a great opportunity for Steven, Tatiana and Justin to meet their great-aunt Clotilda, Uncle Justin, Aunt

Maureen and their two elder cousins Lydia and Lynette, who were very pleasant, warm and great fun and played with them joyfully in Aunt Clotilda's garden after the lovely lunch. All of a sudden, whilst they were all relaxing on the lawn, as the weather was sunny and warm, they heard a car arriving near the front gate and a few minutes later Aunt Celestina and her daughter Roberta came round the house and greeted them all. This was a very pleasant surprise and Aunt Clotilda explained that she had told them about the upcoming family reunion and had invited them to come for tea and cakes in the afternoon to meet everyone.

When they had all hugged and kissed and made the introductions, Aunt Clotilda said it was such a pity that her other sister Aunt Patricia was not there with them as she had died a few years earlier. The other person absent from this happy gathering was Aunt Clotilda's and Aunt Celestina's brother Adrian, but nobody even mentioned the name of Justin's and Adrian's father who was unfortunately condemned as the black sheep of the family, despite Aunt Clotilda's attempt to push forward some extenuating circumstances for him.

After they said goodbye to Aunt Clotilda, Aunt Celestina and Roberta at the end of the afternoon, it was agreed that, as the weather forecast was also excellent for the following day, the two families would meet after breakfast then drive in their two cars to one of the resorts which Justin had known well on the Norfolk coast and would spend the day together on the beach with a picnic for lunch.

At the wheel of the Renault Espace, Adrian followed the hired car, which Justin drove, and they all spent a marvellous and sporting day down on the glorious beach on the North Sea coast. Lydia and Lynette were both very athletic and loved playing with Steven, Tatiana and Justin and running around with them all along the sandy beach and playing with them in the sea as they all swam gleefully together.

At one point, whilst Maureen and Yseult relaxed on their beach towels chatting merrily together, their husbands ran down the beach, plunged headlong into the waves and impressed everyone with their vigorous strokes as they swam far out into the sea, then swam back and treaded water as they conversed together, saying how happy they were to have the two families together and how much happier they would have been if Neil, his wife and their two sons had also been with them.

Justin told Adrian that he had liked Neil's wife Sheila very much. He said she was a pretty Irish girl, with a very good character and pleasant personality and she was a superb wife and wonderful mother to their two sons Neil and Peter. He said that he felt devastated when he learned from Neil that he was separated from Sheila, they were going to divorce and she was going to take young Neil and Peter with her to Ireland to live with her mother. Justin and Adrian both agreed that it was so awful that Neil betrayed his wife and his sons and had behaved so badly and they concluded that he must have had certain weaknesses in him which they did not have, for they both loved their wives and their children very deeply and were so happy in their family lives. Before

swimming back to the shore to be with the others, they both said how much they had loved Neil, how dreadfully they missed him still ten years after his tragic suicide and they would never forget him but would continue always to cherish his memory in their hearts.

The following morning after breakfast, the two families said tearful goodbyes and hoped they would be able to see one another again before too long. Adrian silently wondered how many years it would be before he would be able to see his beloved brother and his superb family again. Justin, his wife and two daughters drove north and Adrian pointed the Renault Espace south then west for the drive down to Devon. They arrived in the mid-afternoon at the Devon long house with its eight bedrooms standing in the countryside several miles north of Sidmouth and surrounded by forty acres of farmland, which Catherine rented out to a local farmer.

Her deceased husband Jack had been a farmer and they had bought this Devon long house thirty years earlier and had enjoyed living there working the land and developing a large vegetable garden. Shortly before his death, they had bought five glorious peacocks, which were still alive and were a wonderful sight as they paraded around the courtyard of the property. Catherine, who was several years older than Mummy, had met Granny and Mummy at some social events and had become very friendly with them.

After the deaths of her husband and Granny, she suggested to Mummy to sell Stenhill Cottage and come to live with her at her Devon long house, which sounded like an excellent plan and Mummy felt very contented and comfortable living in this huge house and having Catherine's company. As there were so many bedrooms, with Catherine and Mummy having a bedroom each, Adrian and Yseult slept in one bedroom and each of the children occupied a separate bedroom, leaving two other bedrooms still unoccupied, which the children thought was very grand!

A few days after their return to their six-bedroom Provencal villa in Switzerland, the telephone rang in the evening and Adrian was overjoyed when he heard the voice of Justin.

'Little brother, we are still up here in Yorkshire having a lovely time seeing all the members of Maureen's terrific family. We miss you all very much and we wondered whether, on our way back to New Zealand, we could fly over to Geneva and stay with you for a couple of nights and discover the dream house with its Provencal architecture that you mentioned so proudly to us in Norfolk?'

'Wow, this is terrific news! Of course you can come! I do not even have to ask Yseult, I will simply tell her and the children that you are coming! Just give me the date and time of arrival of your flight and I will come with our Renault Espace to collect you at the airport.'

Yseult and the three children were all very happy about this development and were extremely pleased to see Justin, Maureen, Lydia and Lynette again when they tumbled out of the Renault Espace and rushed through the front door of the villa to hug and kiss them all. Their short stay was a very joyful one and

during the first afternoon Justin tried to show off his prowess as a footballer when he played football on the large lawn with Steven, Tatiana and little Justin while the others sat watching and sipping mugs of tea and fruit juices on the long and wide terrace.

Suddenly, he trod clumsily on the ball, lost his balance and as his tall, large and heavy frame started to fall backwards like a felled sycamore tree he struck the heel of his right foot hard on the lawn. He emitted a loud groan, lay flat on his back for a moment and, when he started to pick himself up and tried to stand on his right leg, he let out a painful shriek and limped over to a chair saying that there was something wrong with his right heel. After a while the pain did not subside and it seemed that the heel had swollen badly, so Adrian helped him to his car and drove him to the closest clinic, where an x-ray showed that he had splintered a bone in the heel. A thick plaster cast was placed around the heel and part of his calf and he was given crutches to use in his movements and the doctor told him that the small splinter in the bone would heal by itself in a few weeks' time and there was no reason why he could not take the aeroplane flight back to New Zealand.

When he arrived back with Adrian at the villa and strode across the terrace swinging on the crutches he was greeted with a mocking cheer and clapping of hands in applause by the others like a brave wounded soldier returning from the battlefield. When they all went inside and sat in the lounge, Yseult told them in the conversation that Tatiana was a very keen ballet dancer and never missed any of the ballet lessons with the terrific teacher, who had been a star with the ballet of the Opera of Paris when she was younger. When they begged Tatiana to give them a demonstration, she went up to her bedroom, changed into her ballet leotard, tutu and ballet shoes and back in the lounge she danced and pirouetted and swirled gracefully around the room, almost tripping over Uncle Justin's outstretched right leg with its plaster cast at one moment in her enthusiastic movements.

When Justin, Maureen, Lydia and Lynette said goodbye to them all the next day with tears in their eyes, Adrian thanked them all profusely and warmly for having come to stay with them and see where they lived. After their departure, there was a deflated atmosphere in the villa and Adrian wondered to himself how long it was going to be before he would see his beloved and cherished brother again.

***

The summer ended all too quickly and Steven, Tatiana and Justin returned to their classes, sporting events and other activities at school. The months passed by very quickly and they all spent a marvellous Christmas break in the Valais with Yseult's parents and several other members of her family. The children's spring term at school went well and Yseult was very pleased when she received a telephone call from Christiana, her au pair friend in London two decades earlier with whom she had maintained a casual contact, who was now married

to an Italian and lived with him and their two small children in the industrial town of Reggio Emilia in Italy.

She invited Yseult, Adrian and the children to spend a few days with them in their large house after that Easter in April 1994 during the children's holiday. As Adrian felt very tired from all his professional activities and was going to have to prepare a new business trip which would take place in the last week of April, he told Yseult to go by train with the three youngsters to Reggio Emilia and he would stay behind at home and would cope very well on his own. He drove them all to the railway station in Geneva, gave them a fond and warm farewell and wished them a very enjoyable four-day Italian adventure.

When they built the Provencal villa, Adrian and Yseult decided that they did not want to have the television in the lounge and they agreed with the architect and the electrician to place the electrical points and the television itself, as well as one of the telephones, in one corner of the beautiful, long and curved mezzanine on the first floor which the architect had imagined and designed and which the whole family loved and enjoyed.

In the early evening of April 17th 1994, Adrian was sitting on one of the comfortable armchairs on the mezzanine watching the Swiss news on the television when the telephone rang. He lowered the sound of the television and replied to the call.

He heard, at first, a croaking sound of a broken female voice, an attempt to clear the throat then sobbing which became louder as a feeble voice said to him, 'Uncle Adrian, this is Lynette. I am calling from home here in New Zealand as it is impossible for my mother to speak to you right now and she is being comforted by one of her best friends in the house next door together with poor Lydia. I told them that I would call you. The most unbelievable, tragic, catastrophic thing has happened. My wonderful father died late afternoon yesterday April 16th!'

She stopped talking as her emotions got the better of her. She wept down the telephone and the sound she emitted was heart-rending as she poured out her tears. Adrian was tetanised as if he had been struck by a thunderbolt and he could not move or react or say anything.

After some seconds Lynette came on the line again and told him with a wretchedly sad, grieving voice, 'You remember the fourth bedroom upstairs in our house which my father used as his office? Well, I returned home yesterday afternoon from a volleyball match, went up the stairs and, as I passed the office, I saw Dad sitting at his desk working on the computer. I said hello to him and he waved back to me and asked cheerily if I had had a good game. I told him our team had lost the match then I went into my bedroom along the corridor to fetch something. I was in my bedroom only two minutes but when I came back past the office, I was shocked to see Dad slumped forward over the computer keyboard. I rushed over to him, but when I tried to pull his body upright he crashed heavily down onto the floor. I screamed and called down to Mum who was cooking our supper in the kitchen. She ran up the stairs and, when she tried to take his pulse, she told me there was no pulse and she then

tried one or two other tests and told me with tears streaming down her cheeks that he was dead! Can you believe it? I was in my bedroom for only two minutes and in that flash Dad had died! Mum called the doctor and when he examined Dad he said that he must have had a sudden, massive heart attack.'

'Please forgive me, I cannot go on. We are still trying to cope with this terrible shock, but I had to tell you. Mum asked me to say that she will call you as soon as she feels capable of doing so, perhaps tomorrow. I know how much you loved your brother, we all loved him very much, he was a truly wonderful and loving person and he told us often how much he loved and admired you. I am so very sorry.'

Then she hung up and a strange silence hung in the air.

Adrian was completely shocked. His whole being was devastated and blown apart by a blinding deflagration like a bomb exploding in a minefield. He let the telephone drop, slumped down onto the floor and remained curled up in the foetal position for at least two hours as his body wracked with pain. He wailed out loud for quite some time against this injustice and terrible loss and he wept so many tears that he became totally exhausted. All of a sudden, he thought of Yseult and his children, looked at his watch and said to himself that he had to find the mental, emotional and physical strength to get up and out and drive the car to Geneva railway station to collect them in a short while after their return journey from Italy.

When he arrived at the railway station some forty minutes later, he did not know how he had actually managed to drive the car and concentrate on the road, for his mind was thousands of kilometres away. When he saw Yseult walking towards him and his three children running to him on the platform he used his play-acting ability to disguise his pain and smiled at them all as he wrapped his arms around the children and gave his lovely wife a big hug and kiss. She was surprised when he asked her to drive the car back home and, when she glanced at him sitting glumly and silently beside her in the car, she sensed he was acting bizarrely and asked if anything was wrong.

He whispered that he would tell her at home after putting the children to bed. Later on, she was totally horrified to hear what had happened and wrapped her arms around him in bed and tried to comfort him and commiserate with his loss as he wept many more tears and could not disguise his grief and distress any more.

Maureen telephoned the next day and, as she spoke with Adrian, demonstrated just how brave and strong a Yorkshire lass she was in her efforts to cope with this terribly sudden, shocking and tragic loss of her beloved husband. She told Adrian that an autopsy of Justin's body would be made that day and she would send to him a copy of the death certificate and the autopsy report as soon as possible. She added that it had been decided with Lydia and Lynette to organise in the next few days a ceremony and the cremation of Justin's body at the North Shore Crematorium in Albany, the same one where his mother had been cremated.

When the copy of the death certificate and the autopsy report arrived a week later together with a poignant short letter from Maureen, Adrian read on the death certificate that the cause of the brutally sudden heart attack had been an ischaemic heart disease and the autopsy report provided the technical and medical details relating to the fatal disease.

Adrian could not prevent himself from dwelling over and over again on the three different destinies of his two brothers and himself. Neil had been exceedingly fragile mentally and emotionally and totally unable to cope with all the wounds, pain and suffering he had so cruelly endured and had ended his life brutally at the young age of thirty-nine. Justin was strong, reasonable and wise and had developed a love of life and had succeeded, like Adrian, in coping to a certain extent and in the best way possible with all the unhappy aspects of their childhood and in making a happy marriage and family life and a positive professional career. He was strong and full of life but had been suddenly, mysteriously and unjustly cut down and killed at the young age of forty-seven by a secret, insidious illness which had developed unknown to anyone inside his impressive body. Adrian was the youngest and smallest of the three brothers but he was the sole survivor. He had enormous difficulty in getting to grips with and comprehending this. He found it to be a very cruel destiny and, on top of all the festering feelings of guilt that he carried constantly inside him relating to his family's breakdown and the suicide of Neil, he started inexorably and with great, uncontrollable pain to feel an even heavier guilt about having survived his two brothers and being the only one unjustly still alive.

Adrian was very nearly destroyed and demolished by the death of Justin. He had become very closely attached to his second brother, much closer than he had been to Neil, as he felt that he and Justin were fairly similar in some ways, were on the same wave length and understood each other very well. Whereas he had loved and hero-worshipped Neil with ardour when they were younger, he had developed an even deeper, more tender and overwhelming love for and admiration of Justin and had been so looking forward to the happy occasions when they could be together again in the future years. He had looked on Justin as an indestructible oak tree bound to live to a very ripe old age. How horribly and calamitously wrong he had been! He was so thunderstruck, devastated and distraught over the shockingly brutal and cruel death of Justin, and so sorry and sad for Maureen, Lydia and Lynette at their terribly tragic loss, that he had to attempt to cope with and fight against a deeply depressed state.

Adrian's enormous and persistent sadness festered inside him like an infected, seeping wound for a very long time and he just could not avoid dwelling mentally and emotionally on the past and encountered again very severe difficulties to concentrate on various elements and subjects pertaining to everyday life. His wife, his two sons and his daughter were very badly affected by all of this. Yseult had to speak to Adrian on many occasions and to help him psychologically and emotionally to let both Neil and Justin go and to accept

their deaths and move on by living in the present and not remaining dragged down by continuous thoughts of the past unhappy events and tragedies. It took a very long time, stretching over several years, but Adrian did find his excruciating pain over the deaths of his two brothers subsiding gradually. He managed, finally, to accept their tragic destinies, to let them go and to live more and more in the present in his happy, protective and positive family cocoon developed and encouraged by his wonderful and impressive wife.

Chapter 11

Betrayal, Treachery and Rejection in Professional Career

When Adrian started his new employment in summer 1991 at the subsidiary in Geneva of another international bank, with the mission to create and develop a new Legal Department from scratch, his direct superior, the General Manager of the bank, was a tall, slim, handsome, blonde-haired, blue-eyed forty-five year old aristocratic banker, who was only two years older than himself.

Adrian soon discovered that his boss was a true French aristocrat who was a genuine Count from a long-standing aristocratic lineage with a posh surname containing the very important particle "de" in the middle, which was the upper-class equivalent in France of the hyphen in the middle of Adrian's original Welsh double-barrelled family surname Walton-Mornick.

Adrian did not divulge to his boss or to any other colleagues at the bank that his own ancient aristocratic family had also had a few Counts in their long lineage over the centuries nor that his birth surname of Walton-Mornick had been changed and down-graded to the simple, hyphen-less English surname Tunnington by his adoptive parents when he was a young teenager. Whilst he did not feel aristocratic at all, partially due no doubt to his detestation and rebuttal of his birth father's superior, arrogant and overly self-confident manner and partially due to his continuing inferiority complex, insecurities and feelings of lack of self-esteem and lack of much value or worth, he somehow felt on the same wave length as his boss in terms of intellectual understanding and had a good, harmonious and fruitful professional relationship with him.

He was fully supported by the boss, who authorised him to engage two other lawyers and two assistants, in addition to his own personal secretary, in the two years after his creation of the Legal Department, due to the bank's impressive expansion of its activities in trade finance, general credit, project finance, private banking and other sectors. In early 1993, the General Manager also asked him to create a Compliance service and to be the Head of Legal and Compliance for the bank. When the boss announced to him and several other top managers of the bank in mid-1993 that he had received a promotion and was going to leave Geneva within a month to take a summer holiday with his family then commence in a new position in the bank's world headquarters in another country, Adrian felt sad, disappointed and frustrated as he had greatly appreciated the intelligence, leadership qualities, moral integrity, honesty and

positive human qualities of this superior with his mild manner and collegial and respectful attitudes towards all of his subordinates.

The banker who replaced the former boss was a direct opposite of him and a stark contrast in many ways. This man, in his early fifties, was somewhat shorter than Adrian, was dark-haired and one could sense from his abrasive attitude and manner that he was possibly from a lower middle class origin, had a big chip on his shoulder and had a great need to prove to everyone in the bank how well he had succeeded by lauding it over them. He had small, weasel-like brown eyes with a rather unpleasant, untrustworthy, cynical expression and a rough, tough and uncouth manner and language and a harsh, ruthless way of imposing himself and dominating others. Adrian and many other colleagues soon said among themselves that this boss made them think of the French dictator Emperor Napoleon Bonaparte, who was also small in stature, no doubt had a chip on his shoulder vis-à-vis the self-important Parisians, as he was born and brought up on the small, insignificant island of Corsica lost in the Mediterranean Sea. And he probably had a great need to prove himself, to impose himself and dominate others and show that he was completely and solely in command.

It soon appeared evident that this new boss derived a real sadistic pleasure from putting down, insulting and embarrassing members of staff in front of others and treating some of the heads of departments with a harsh, grating, snide, domineering and contemptuous attitude and behaviour, as if to elevate himself by pushing them down. He was especially unpleasant towards Adrian, who began to wonder after a few months whether this French boss was perhaps a racist and had a contemptuous and even hateful feeling against British managers. Whenever Adrian was in a meeting with the boss and other departmental heads, the boss seemed to enjoy singling out Adrian for nasty, nit-picking, unjustified criticism and derogatory, negative, bullying and humiliating treatment, as if he had sensed and was playing on Adrian's fundamental weaknesses, hypersensitivity, fragility and vulnerability.

It was not long before Adrian's underlying psychological and emotional complexes and difficulties rose to the surface yet again, and the feelings of increasing self-confidence and self-esteem which had begun to develop in his relationship with the former General Manager started to diminish then evaporated very rapidly. This caused him to suffer from lack of sleep, deep anxiety and a painful, constricting lump in the throat as he travelled to the office each morning and as he worked during the day, compounded by a renewed and huge difficulty to concentrate, so that his efforts during the working day to overcome such difficulty completely exhausted him mentally and emotionally.

When he arrived home each evening he was so distressed and tired that he was not able to participate fully enough in the conversations with his wife and his three children and became unfortunately distanced therefrom, missing out on certain aspects of the evolution and development in each child's life. Whilst Adrian attempted to put into practice his determination not to allow anyone to

bully him again, the aggressive, menacing, overpowering and domineering comportment of this superior wore him down so much in his efforts to stand up to the mistreatment that he had to consult his family doctor in Geneva on several occasions and was obliged to take medicine, including vitamin pills, to be able to cope with an increasingly difficult and painful professional situation.

In the spring of 1997, the General Manger convened a small meeting of just a few managers, including Adrian, a specific project manager and a specific account manager, and told them that the bank was developing an interesting and mutually beneficial business relationship with the government of one of the Eastern European nations, which had been one of the satellites of the former Soviet Union and had gained its independence after the fall of the Berlin Wall as from November 1989 and the subsequent dismantlement of the Soviet Union.

He told them that this country, like several other Eastern European countries, had the good fortune to possess vast, unexploited oil and gas fields and was engaged in important negotiations with certain very well established and highly experienced American, English, French and Italian oil and gas companies in order to sell various concessions to the highest bidders in public auctions for exploitation of such oil and gas fields and the sale of the extracted gas and oil on the world market.

The General Manager explained that the bank had been negotiating for many months with this country's government the terms and conditions under which the bank would play the important role of establishing and administering some bank accounts in the names of the country's Ministry of Oil and Ministry of Gas for the receipt on such accounts of the payments to be made by the successful Western oil and gas companies for their purchase of the concessions granted by the country's government and for the onward transfer of such funds, which would amount to several hundred millions and eventually billions of United States Dollars, to various ministries and departments in the country pursuant to the government's payment instructions for use in the development of the country's infrastructure and the benefit of the country's growing population.

The General Manager told Adrian, the project manager and the account manager that they were to be the members of the bank's delegation which would fly to the country's capital in ten days' time with the mandate to finalise the negotiations and the contracts with the representatives of the country's government and concerned ministries, to ensure the signature between the parties of the necessary contracts and other banking documents and to bring all such signed documents back to the bank so that it could start fulfilling its designated role under the strict and exclusive supervision of the General Manager and the account manager.

Finally, he told them all that the commissions which would be earned by the bank for its services over the coming few years would be very substantial and rewarding.

When Adrian, the project manager and the account manager arrived in the country's capital, they spent the first two days in intense and interesting meetings with various representatives of the government and the concerned ministries. On the morning of the third day, they were taken in a chauffeur-driven limousine to the building where the Minister of Oil had his office for a meeting with the Minister himself and a couple of his deputies. When they walked into the Minister's office, they were very impressed by the huge size of the room and the luxurious decoration and furniture and beautiful paintings on the walls. They were also impressed by the Minister, who was tall and handsome with jet-black hair and a full black beard and a very pleasant and smiling manner. He was wearing a magnificent, dark tweed suit, which was exquisitely cut and must have been very expensive, and a luxurious looking blue shirt and yellow tie. He greeted each of them with a firm handshake and warm welcoming words.

As he stood in front of Adrian, his large, dark brown eyes gazed warmly into Adrian's blue eyes, then he looked down to Adrian's tie and said to him in a rich, deep, very virile voice, 'You know, I really like your red and blue tie. It is evidently of very good quality and I would be very pleased to buy it from you, if you would like to name the price.'

Adrian was so taken aback and amused by this entirely unexpected and unusual approach that he almost burst out laughing. However, he said to himself that he must show utmost respect towards the Minister, so he merely replied coyly,

'Your Excellency, I thank you very much for your kind remark and your offer. However, this tie has a great sentimental value for me. You are right, it is of first-class quality, being a Hermes tie. My secretary bought it for me for my last birthday, so I treasure it as a personal gift and feel that I must keep it out of respect for my secretary.'

'A Hermes tie? I might well have guessed it! You see, I have good taste and a great interest in ties of excellent quality. However, I quite understand that you feel you must decline my offer and keep this tie, so be it. Well, gentlemen, please take your seats and we will get down to discuss the business at hand.'

The Minister looked warmly into Adrian's eyes again, gave him a broad, charming smile and patted him on the shoulder in a friendly manner without any trace of condescension.

All the further meetings over the next two days went very well and the three members of the bank's delegation flew back to Geneva with the necessary signed and stamped documents, then met with the General Manager, who congratulated them on a successful mission and took possession of all the documents. Adrian did not receive any further information during the next two years from the General Manager or the account manager as to the development of the bank's relationship in that matter with the government of that Eastern European country.

**

In accordance with the provisions of the Swiss Law on Cooperation in International Judicial Procedures, all the banks in Geneva, Zurich and the other major banking centres in Switzerland received from time to time official notifications from the competent judicial authority in each Canton that it was cooperating with a judicial request for information emanating from various parties on various criminal matters under investigation.

In his capacity as Head of Legal and Compliance of his bank, Adrian received each such request on his desk and it was up to him and his team to cause the competent technical and administrative services inside the bank to verify in the bank's computer systems whether any of the parties targeted by such a criminal investigation held any accounts at the bank. If so, it was incumbent upon Adrian to reply to the judicial authority and follow up the matter in conjunction with that authority in application of the modalities of the law. Since he had joined the bank, Adrian had dealt with several such matters of varying degrees of size and importance.

It so happened that during 1999 all the banks in Geneva were obliged to spend an inordinate amount of time and effort in treating several matters of cooperation with international judicial requests, some much more important than others. One day in June, Adrian opened an envelope containing a specific request for information emanating from the judicial authority in Geneva and was totally shocked and flabbergasted by what he read. It sounded so unbelievable that he had to read the full contents of the request two or three times.

After he had dispatched copies of the request to the competent technical and administrative services and to the bank's General Manager, he was even more shocked when he received information several days later from the technical and administrative services indicating that their pain-staking searches showed that several individual persons mentioned in the request of the judicial authority held accounts at the bank through several offshore companies, Trusts and other legal entities of which they were declared in the account-opening documents to be the beneficial owners. These individuals recorded as the beneficial owners were prominent members of the well-known family which ruled the Eastern European country which Adrian and two of his colleagues had visited for a few days two years earlier, and they included the dictator himself who was the authoritarian President of that country. When Adrian fulfilled his duty of mentioning these dramatic findings to the General Manager, the latter expressed only mild surprise and the detached manner in which he reacted did not sound true but had a false ring to it and Adrian had a distinct feeling that the boss was hiding something from him.

When Adrian replied to the Geneva judicial authority that he had discovered to his shock and horror from his internal investigation that the President of the country and certain prominent members of his family held some accounts at his bank through offshore companies, Trusts and other legal entities, he was informed by the Geneva Public Prosecutor, whom he had known professionally for several years, that the whole affair had started

because the Prime Minister of the country had begun to oppose some of the very authoritarian and oppressive policies and methods of the President, who had sacked him. The Prime Minister had just managed to flee to Geneva before the President was going to have him arrested and flung into gaol, which was the fate that had already been suffered by several opponents to the dictatorial regime. The exiled former Prime Minister had filed a criminal complaint to the Geneva judicial authority, stating that he knew that the President and some members of his family had embezzled huge amounts of money from the country's coffers and had transferred illicitly such funds to bank accounts opened in the name of various offshore companies and entities at some banks in Geneva but he did not know which banks were involved. Consequently, the Geneva judicial authority had dispatched the request for information to all the banks in Geneva.

Adrian started working closely with the Geneva judicial authority in an attempt to find out more about how such accounts could have been established at his bank and how much money had been deposited on each of the accounts. Suddenly, near the end of the year 1999, Adrian and many other managers at the bank were astonished to learn that the General Manager had left Switzerland and had taken up a new position at the head of one of the group's Asian operations, in a decision made with the top management at the bank's world headquarters, and would be replaced by another banker, about ten years younger than him, in early January 2000.

The new General Manager had to spend many months after his arrival familiarising himself with all the facets and complications of the bank's overall operations and projects conducted from the Geneva offices. For his part, Adrian was submerged by an enormous amount of work on multifarious legal and compliance matters related to the various operations and projects and on the treatment of several requests for cooperation on international judicial procedures, including among them an enormous affair concerning billions of dollars of public funds of a large, oil producing West African country which had been embezzled by that country's dictator and members of his family and held on accounts opened by various offshore companies, Trusts and other legal entities with several banks in Geneva. Adrian was appalled to discover that two such accounts had been established at his bank during the years when his former boss was the General Manager and two of that dictator's sons were the beneficial owners of the offshore companies and entities which had opened those accounts.

Adrian could not understand how it had been possible that his Legal and Compliance Department had never been informed earlier of nor been able to become aware earlier of the existence of the accounts held by the offshore entities of which the President of the Eastern European country and his family members were the beneficial owners nor those accounts held by the offshore entities of which two of the sons of the dictator of the West African country were the beneficial owners.

In attempting to conduct internal investigations in the concerned technical and administrative services of the bank to find answers to his questions, Adrian encountered certain silences, obstructions and difficulties but after many months was able to discover that the former General Manager, who was now in Asia and no longer there to face his queries, had secretly given strict instructions to the manager of the information services department controlling all computer accesses to restrict any access to all of those particular accounts solely to the General Manager and a specific account manager, who Adrian discovered was the same account manager who had accompanied Adrian and the project manager on the trip to the Eastern European country in 1997 and who had become very close to the former General Manager.

Consequently, due to the secret access restrictions imposed by the former General Manager, in blatant violation of established written regulations, directives and procedures, it had been absolutely impossible for Adrian or any other member of the Legal and Compliance Department to become aware of the existence of all such accounts before the arrivals of the judicial requests for information relating to the Eastern European country and the West African state.

On top of all his other normal work leading his department and handling many files and projects as to their legal and compliance elements, Adrian continued over many months in 2000 and 2001 to work with the Geneva judicial authority and also the Head of the Legal Department at the Swiss Federal Banking Commission in Berne in order to try to get to the bottom of the scandals around the West African state's dictator and his family and the Eastern European country's dictator and his family as regarded the involvement of his bank and the actions of certain managers. In his internal investigations inside his bank, he discovered to his shock and dismay that one of the accounts held by an offshore company, of which the President of the Eastern European country was the beneficial owner, had received several transfers of many millions of United States Dollars each time and the total amount held on that account was almost one hundred million dollars. He notified the Geneva judicial authority of this discovery and the authority ordered immediately that this account be totally blocked. Another disturbing discovery happened after Adrian received a request for information from the Geneva judicial authority concerning yet another offshore company which Adrian had never heard of, for the result of the internal investigation showed that this offshore company also held an account at the bank with secret restricted access and the beneficial owner of that offshore company was the same account manager who had worked very closely with the former General Manager. Adrian was astounded to discover that this account had received a payment of two million dollars from a source in the specific Eastern European country. Under the pressure of interrogation by Adrian and another, female in-house lawyer named Georgina, the account manager admitted that he had received this under-the-table, illicit payment from that source as an inducement and gratitude for allowing the accounts ultimately controlled and owned by the individual persons, namely

the President and certain members of his family, to be opened and kept secret inside the bank. Adrian notified the Geneva judicial authority of this unpleasant discovery and the account was immediately blocked. Adrian reported this new discovery as well to the new General Manager, who had no choice but to suspend the account manager from any further work or activity at the bank.

During some months in 2001, Adrian began to sense that the new General Manager was adopting a progressively hostile and bullying attitude towards him and creating difficulties and complications for him in his overall role as Head of Legal and Compliance. He began to hear rumours inside the bank that this man was the close friend and protégé of the former General Manager, who was the godfather of one of the younger man's children, and that the new General Manager owed his rapid ascension and several promotions inside the bank's operations in Italy and France to the older man, who had arranged with some complicit top managers in the world headquarters to have himself transferred to a safe haven in an operation of the bank in Asia, thousands of miles away from Geneva, when the shit hit the fan with the two official requests for information on the Eastern European country's and West African state's criminal matters, and to have him replaced in Geneva by his younger friend who would be loyal to him and do his utmost to protect him from any recriminations during the criminal investigations undertaken by the Geneva and federal judicial authorities.

After the Geneva and federal judicial authorities discovered that the account manager had received two million dollars in the matter concerning the Eastern European country's President and his family, they requested Adrian to attempt to push his investigation further to see whether the former General Manager may have also received payments; they suspected that, if the account manager had received two million dollars, it was likely that his boss would have received a much greater amount of money as inducement and gratitude for his complicit actions.

One day, a senior member of the federal judicial authority told Adrian firmly over the telephone, 'To us here it seems obvious why the former General Manager arranged to be relocated all that way to Asia, to keep him out of the grasp of the Swiss banking and criminal authorities. As he has at the very least violated all his legal, moral, ethical and banking duties through his actions, let alone any potentially criminal aspects, if he were still working in Geneva I for one would have made it my business to ensure that he was sacked and forbidden to exercise any further activity whatsoever in the banking and financial field!'

During his next contact with the Geneva public prosecutor, Adrian informed him of the words expressed by the senior member of the federal judicial authority.

The public prosecutor replied, 'I agree with that assessment. However, I would also add that it appears fairly clear that the prime motivation of the former General Manager was to make as much money for himself as possible. It is understandable and reasonably acceptable that he undoubtedly received

increasingly large bonuses at the end of each year as the legitimate business relationship with the government of the Eastern European nation grew, the amounts transferred to the accounts at the bank of the government ministries increased to huge sums with sales of concessions to international oil and gas companies and the commissions earned by the bank for its services became very important.'

'However, the inordinate greed for money of this man seems to be demonstrated by the fact that, not only did he violate all his banking and civil duties, he also committed the criminal offenses of complicity in acts of corruption and laundering of dirty money arising from such corruption on the part of the dictator and members of his family in order to swell his bonuses paid by his superiors inside the bank, due to all the huge ill-gotten funds corruptly embezzled and transferred to accounts at the bank, but he was in all probability paid in addition substantial sums from the said dictator and his family as an inducement for allowing their dirty money to be managed on secret accounts at his bank.'

During the October 2001 holidays, Adrian, Yseult and their three children enjoyed a marvellous and relaxing ten-day stay at the Club Med named Djerba La Douce on the lovely island of Djerba just off the Mediterranean coast of Tunisia. After Adrian returned to the office, he sensed within a few days that the General Manager's attitudes and behaviour towards him had become even worse and particularly more aggressive and bullying than before.

Adrian's disappointment and frustration at this negativity and lack of support, in a situation where he was only doing his job properly and fulfilling his legal, ethical and moral duties professionally and to the best of his ability in all aspects of his work, were compounded when he received on his desk at the end of October a letter of resignation, with the legal two months' notice period, from Georgina, the female lawyer in his department who had been working side by side with him in the difficult, arduous and tedious investigations in the matters relating to the requests for information on judicial procedures concerning the Eastern European country and the West African state.

When he called Georgina to his office the next day and asked for an explanation as to the reasons for her totally unexpected and regrettable resignation, which he was very sad to receive, she put a finger in front of her mouth and blew softly on it as if to say *shush*, pulled out a pen and a sheet of white blank paper from her trouser pocket and wrote on the paper: *cannot speak right now; I suspect big boss has had your office and telephone bugged during your absence on holiday and he wants to break you and has obtained the connivance of Crisselda, the female lawyer who is your deputy for legal matters. I am on your side. I must go now.*

After Adrian had read the message, she put the pen and paper back in her pocket, turned on her heels and walked rapidly out of his office. Adrian sat back on his chair feeling dumfounded and confused and wondering what was going to happen next.

He did not have to wait long, for two mornings later, Crisselda, a very short woman with a small, round face and dark spectacles and a slightly plump body, who was ferociously ambitious, told Adrian and the other three lawyers in the department that she wanted a meeting between them that afternoon in Adrian's office as she had certain complaints to make about his way of leading and managing the department and wanted a full-blown discussion on the matter.

It seemed significant to Adrian that she wanted the meeting to be in his office and not in the department's conference room, where the monthly meeting to take stock of all ongoing files was always held, suggesting to him that if his office had been bugged she was fully aware of that and had agreed on such a ploy with the General Manager who would become aware of everything that was said during the meeting.

Adrian acquiesced readily, as he had absolutely nothing to hide and nothing to be ashamed of in his manner of managing his department and he felt intrigued as to what specious and fabricated arguments his ambitious deputy would bring forward, as he had already felt for some time that she would absolutely love it if he left the bank and she became the head of the department.

They were in the middle of the meeting, sitting around the table in Adrian's office, and his deputy Crisselda had come out with some preposterous, ridiculously trumped up and rebuttable complaints against him, leaving the other lawyers astounded, speechless and shaking their heads, when the telephone rang on his desk.

Adrian apologised to them all and said that he must reply as it might be a call of some importance on some aspect of any ongoing file. When he picked up the receiver he recognised the unpleasant, grating voice of the Head of Human Resources, a very unlikeable, cynical, calculating man who only did in his function what the General Manager wanted him to do with no concern whatsoever for the wellbeing of and fairness towards members of staff.

The voice at the other end said to Adrian in a contemptuous and aggressive manner, 'Apparently there are some issues concerning the way in which you run and manage your department and the General Manager has received some complaints from the lawyers reporting to you. As this concerns administrative, personnel and management issues, he has asked me to deal with this and to sort it out with you. As it is now Friday afternoon, I would like you to come to my office next Monday at four in the afternoon so that we can discuss the best ways in which you can reorganise and improve the way your department is handled in the future.'

Adrian almost laughed as he put down the receiver and whispered *the plot thickens* to himself under his breath. He told the other lawyers around the table exactly what the Head of Human Resources had said and he asked purposefully how many of the lawyers had made complaints against him to the General Manager. Whilst Crisselda remained silent but went bright red in the face, looked embarrassed and squirmed on her chair, the other lawyers, including Georgina who had given him her notice to leave the bank, told him that they had not made any complaints at all to the big boss and had been wondering

why this meeting had been called. While fixing Crisselda with a long, hard stare, Adrian said they could end the meeting there and then and he would let them all know what recommendations he could make to them about improving his administration and management of the department in the future after his meeting had taken place on Monday afternoon with the Head of Human Resources and he wished them all a very pleasant weekend. As the lawyers left his office, Adrian could not help but notice the very unpleasant and frankly nasty look that Crisselda shot at him as she walked out. He said to himself that if looks could kill he would drop dead that very instant.

On Monday morning, Adrian received a telephone call from Crisselda saying that she was ill in bed so could not come to the office. After wishing her a speedy recovery and saying he hoped that she would be able to come to work the next day, he spent a very busy day working on several files and attending some meetings on both legal and compliance matters. A little before four in the afternoon he walked up the stairs to the next floor and went to the office of the Head of Human Resources.

As soon as he had sat down on a chair in front of the man's desk he was greeted immediately, without any preamble, with the following astonishing words, 'I am sorry to say that I have the duty to inform you that the General Manager has decided to terminate your contract of employment with immediate effect.'

A heavy silence ensued as Adrian attempted to take in these appallingly shocking and entirely unexpected words and felt very groggy as if he had been punched hard on the side of the face.

As he tried to regain his composure, he shook his head, stared hard at the other man's harsh, unpleasant looking and unfeeling face, which showed no trace of emotion but looked like a rough piece of granite, and said forcefully, 'Wait a minute! You called me last Friday and said you wanted to see me this afternoon to discuss the best ways in which I can reorganise and improve the way my department is administered and managed in the future. All the other lawyers in my team are witnesses to that, as we were having a meeting requested by Crisselda my deputy when you called, and I told them straightaway the exact words you said. Over the weekend I have thought about the matter and I have written on this sheet of paper several suggestions I can make so that you and I can discuss the subject and foresee the future.'

'You can put away that sheet of paper, for we are not going to have any discussion and there is no future for you here. I have in my hand two signed originals of a letter notifying you of the termination of your employment contract with immediate effect and saying that the bank will pay you an indemnity amounting to six months' salary. A generous gratuitous gesture, but you must take all your purely personal items and effects from your desk, leave the premises immediately this afternoon and not come back to work tomorrow as you are being relieved right now of any duty to continue working at the bank. This is normal practice in the bank when a top manager's employment is

terminated. Please read this second original and hand it back to me countersigned by yourself signifying your agreement with this process.'

As Adrian took the short letter and read its contents, the stupefaction, anger and indignation which he felt vehemently began to rise and boil like bubbling molten steel. He tried to keep a cool head and when he read the letter a second time he spotted with his lawyer's eagle eye and mind that this notice of termination of his contract with immediate effect with no stipulated period of notice was invalid and illegal. For, firstly, it violated the terms of his employment contract which required that he be given two months' notice to terminate his contract in the absence of any misconduct committed by him. Secondly, it violated the legal requirement that a dismissal with immediate effect must state clearly the motivation thereof. And, thirdly, the letter was only signed by the Head of Human Resources whereas under legal regulations and procedures it also had to be signed by the General Manager for the dismissal of a high-ranking officer like Adrian who was the head of a very important and essential department in the bank.

He threw the letter back in the face of his tormentor and with his eyes blazing he spat out venomously like a hissing snake, 'Do you take me for a fool? There is no way I am going to countersign this piece of rubbish! It is an insult to my intelligence! This is an unfair and illegal dismissal with no valid motivation. Your mention on Friday of my administration and management of my department was obviously a crudely fabricated and dishonest pretext to get me to come up to your office. I insist that you call the General Manager and that he comes down here immediately to face me and to talk to me in your presence about what his real motivations are for wanting to get rid of me, as both you and I know that I have absolutely nothing to reproach myself for. You are a pathetic, weak puppet in the hands of this man being used to execute his dirty work for him by trying to execute me!'

The Head of Human Resources went bright red in the face and, as he saw the flaming fury in Adrian's steely blue eyes, he changed his attitude and tone a little and said with a slightly more conciliatory voice in an attempt to appease Adrian, 'The General Manager is away on business in Rome today and will only come back to the office tomorrow after lunch. I know that he will be extremely busy and tied up all afternoon and on Wednesday and I cannot say when he will be free to see you over the coming few days. So just countersign the letter by way of acceptance and be grateful to him for accepting to give you an indemnity equivalent to six months' salary.'

Adrian stood up abruptly, pushed the chair back violently and said ominously with a snarl, 'You really do take me for a stupid nincompoop! Get it in your thick skull that this letter of dismissal is unfair, invalid and illegal. You must get the General Manager to see me together with you before the end of the afternoon tomorrow or I will go to see one of the best lawyers in Geneva and you and the General Manager will have a lawsuit slapped on you!'

Adrian turned on his heels, slammed the door very hard, making it shake on its hinges, and ran down the stairs. As he passed the open door of the empty

office of Crisselda, he suddenly realised in his greatly muddled, suspicious and troubled mind that she had deliberately pretended to be sick that day so that she could be absent from the premises as she must have known beforehand that the Head of Human Resources was going to give him a letter of dismissal.

This confirmed that she was in cahoots with the General Manager and the Head of Human Resources in their attempts to axe him, no doubt in return for a promise to promote her to be head of the department after he was ousted. He picked up his briefcase and coat in his office, not bothering to turn off his computer, and closed the door with a violent bang, so that everyone in his department would hear the noise.

And, as he strode rapidly and angrily along the corridor to the exit, he shouted at the top of his voice so that all could hear, 'I have been stabbed in the back with a treacherous, murderous dagger!'

As Adrian left the bank's building and stepped out into the bustling street, the November air was bitingly cold, it was drizzling with slushy sleet and it had become pitch dark as the evening approached. He felt in a completely dazed, mixed up and lost state, as if he had just had his sense of identity criminally stolen from him by a pack of mischievous robbers.

As he started to walk aimlessly along the street, without any purpose and not knowing where he was going, the delayed shock to his hyper-sensitive and fragile system of the betrayal, treachery and rejection which he had just suffered hit him painfully hard like a large, round, wooden cudgel slamming with brute force into the solar plexus. He doubled over and fell headlong onto the pavement, where he lay sprawled out for a minute until a pair of kindly hands picked him up under each arm, asked if he was all right as he stood shakily, swept the wet mud from his soiled winter coat then went on their way as he nodded unconvincingly.

Adrian continued to amble slowly and shuffle along, dragging his feet like a drunkard in an alcoholic haze. All of a sudden, he felt extremely sick as he was crossing the large square named Place du Molard and he just had time to reach the public toilets, crash down the stairs holding onto the bannister on the men's side and rush into one of the empty cubicles before he vomited and retched violently several times. After hauling himself hesitatingly up the stairs again with the help of the bannister, he slumped down with his back propped up against a wall, then started sobbing with his hands over his eyes as if his whole world had just crashed down.

As his chest heaved painfully and an overwhelming feeling of depression suddenly and uncontrollably started engulfing him and he sensed the immediate danger quickly from his previous experiences with depression, he pulled himself up with difficulty, walked as rapidly as he could to a nearby telephone box on the edge of the square and dialled the number, which he knew by heart, of his family doctor, a kind, understanding and very humane person, who had his practice in a street in the area of Carouge situated a few kilometres from the city centre. When he told the assistant that it was an emergency and he needed to speak urgently with the doctor, the latter came on the line, listened to Adrian

for a quick moment and told him to take a tram and come to see him straightaway.

During the consultation, after Adrian had explained everything in detail, the doctor told him that this new situation of betrayal, treachery, rejection and abandonment on the part of certain unscrupulous, dishonest and cynical persons at his bank was exceedingly bad for his psyche, which was already extremely damaged and vulnerable from the past tragedies in his life.

He reminded him that all the pain and suffering stemming from his very unhappy childhood and the sad experiences in later years had left him badly scarred for life and the deep wounds in his system, which he had spent so many years and exceedingly tiring efforts to heal, would probably never heal entirely, unavoidably be opened and bleed again as a result of this latest dreadful and unjust suffering in his professional career.

He saw intuitively, from the gravity of Adrian's personal family history and from his vast medical experience in general and with other difficult cases, that Adrian, with his excessive hyper-sensitivity, continued insecurity, lack of self-esteem, doubts about his capabilities and worth, emotional fragility and overall vulnerability, had been totally floored by this new, entirely unexpected treachery and was on the verge of a grave new depression which would rapidly overpower and devour him.

He agreed with Adrian that he would give him on the spot a medical certificate stating that he was ill as from that early evening and entirely unfit for work for an unlimited period of time.

As it was patently obvious that the letter of dismissal was completely illegal, invalid and the product of a dishonest and immoral machination, both Adrian and the doctor knew that the labour law in Switzerland forbade any employer from sacking any employee who was under the protection of a medical certificate, so the doctor assured Adrian that his medical certificate would give him protection for as long as was necessary. For his employer could not issue another letter of dismissal, however properly worded and respectful of the legal requirements in its tenure, for as long as the medical certificate issued by the doctor remained valid.

It was also obvious from every point of view that, whilst Adrian still remained legally an employee of the bank entitled to receive his salary each month, he should not set foot again inside the premises of the bank, after so much betrayal, treachery, dishonesty and rejection perpetrated against him.

The doctor told Adrian to request his wife to take the medical certificate early the following morning and deposit it at the reception of the bank in an envelope marked to the urgent attention of the Head of Human Resources. The doctor also urged Adrian to consult a good lawyer as quickly as possible and give him the mandate to represent his best interests in the unavoidable forthcoming battle with the General Manager of the bank.

When Adrian arrived home later that evening and explained in detail to Yseult the afternoon's events and his visit to the doctor, making him feel even more despondent, guilty and exhausted, she was completely shocked and

outraged and could not believe what had happened nor the extent of the unscrupulousness, deceitfulness, hypocrisy, depraved nastiness and criminal actions of the General Manager, the Head of Human Resources and Adrian's deputy for legal matters Crisselda, whom Yseult knew as she had met her on certain social occasions during the past few years.

Despite her sadness, anxious state and trepidation about future developments, Yseult put on a brave and strong front and did her best to commiserate with Adrian and, sensing that he was already feeling very guilty and blaming himself in part for this disaster, she attempted, albeit unsuccessfully, to reassure him that he was an innocent victim and was not to blame for this new tragedy.

The next morning, in a bleary state after a fitful and sleepless night, she took the train to Geneva, walked from the Cornavin railway station to the premises of the bank and deposited the envelope containing the medical certificate at the reception saying that it must be given very urgently to the Head of Human Resources.

A few weeks later, about two weeks before Christmas 2001, Adrian received a telephone call at home one evening from Georgina, who had handed him her letter of resignation at end October. She was a Swiss lawyer in her mid-thirties with great integrity, a solid, steady, well-balanced, scrupulously honest and reliable character, personality and outlook on life and she shared with Adrian a deep hatred of injustice. She was happily married to another lawyer, with whom she had two young children. They were living in a reasonably spacious and comfortable rented flat just one street behind the central street of Geneva.

After enquiring about Adrian's health and asking him how he was bearing up in the very unfortunate, unpleasant and unjust circumstances, she confided the following elements to him, 'After the appalling injustice you suffered and you fell understandably ill a few weeks ago, I told the General Manager that I did not want to continue working my two months' notice period and wanted to leave the bank immediately as I found the situation unbearable and intolerable. He felt obliged to let me go and I have had the good fortune to find a new employment in another bank in Geneva, a Swiss bank this time, and I will start my new job in early January.'

'I can tell you now that I suspected several months ago that the General Manager was becoming horrible towards you, was bullying you and making your life unliveable upon instructions he received from his friend that monster, the former General Manager, now cowardly ensconced in a safe haven in Asia, because they saw how diligently and professionally you were carrying out your investigation in cooperation with the authorities. And they feared that you would get closer and closer to the truth and discover in what way and how much the former General Manager had received in under-the-table, illicit financial payments from the corrupt dictator and members of his family in the Eastern European country. I feel sure that their aim and hope in mistreating, bullying and pressurising you was that you would get so fed up, frustrated and

demoralised that you would hand in your resignation and leave the bank. When they saw that this did not happen and you continued to work hard, correctly with great diligence and very professionally in the investigation, the former General Manager told his buddy here to break you and throw you out by terminating your contract with immediate effect.'

She paused as she listened for any reaction that Adrian might emit but he said nothing and just let out a long, heavy sigh, so she continued, 'I can also tell you that while you were absent on holiday this October, the General Manager called me to his office and I was surprised when I got there that I was alone with him. He started to flatter me and tell me how pleased he was with all my work and my great contribution to the good functioning of the Legal and Compliance Department and the bank's overall positive development. It was obvious he was buttering and softening me up, like one caresses the hairs on a dog's back in the right direction, but I could not see to what purpose. He continued in this vein for another minute, then he suddenly changed his tone. He said that he had encountered some difficulties with you and was very disappointed by some of your attitudes and behaviour.'

'He ordered me bluntly and forcefully to write an internal memo addressed to him and copied to the Head of Human Resources accusing you of various reprehensible acts which he dictated to me orally and asked me to note down on my pad so that I would mention them correctly in my internal memo. He said such action would be greatly appreciated by himself and the Head of Human Resources and, as a reward, I would receive a handsome bonus at the end of the year and a big promotion to Head of the Legal and Compliance Department, with an appreciable salary increase, after your departure from the bank.'

'I was completely flabbergasted, taken aback and disgusted and realised on the spot that he intended to break you and was attempting to use me as a complicit weapon to help him strike you down and to buy my cooperation in the dastardly plot. I stood up and told him that I was an honest and decent person with full integrity and I could not accept to write such an unjust and untruthful memo, as I knew that you had never committed any reprehensible acts of any kind. I was so shocked and angered by the General Manager's dishonesty and depravity that I decided I would resign in protest and that is the reason why I handed you my letter of resignation at end October.'

'What the former General Manager and his buddy here have done to you is frightfully unjust, unwarranted and unpardonable and I urge you to file a lawsuit against them with the assistance of a very competent lawyer here in Geneva. Whilst it does not seem appropriate or sensitive to wish you a happy Christmas, I wish you and your family most sincerely all the very best and a much more pleasant and positive year 2002. Oh, one last thing. In any lawsuit that you may decide to bring, you can count on me and I will gladly come to court as a witness, testify in your favour and bring out the true facts about the dastardly machination and injustice perpetrated against you.'

After Adrian recounted to Yseult all that Georgina had told him, she felt encouraged and emboldened. Although she knew he was in the grips of and trying to battle against an awful depression, she managed without much effort to obtain his agreement that he should think carefully about who would be a suitable, good and reliable independent lawyer in one of the top law firms in Geneva that they could consult in early January.

Adrian said that in the meantime, over the period of Christmas and New Year, he would find moments here and there to write down by hand, in the shortest time that his grave difficulties to concentrate would permit, the full story of the truly dishonest and reprehensible actions of the former General Manager, the complicit account manager, the current General Manager, the Head of Human Resources and Crisselda his deputy for legal matters so that he could give the sheets of paper to the lawyer that he would decide he should consult.

A few days after New Year's Day, Adrian and Yseult had a rendezvous in the spacious and comfortably decorated office in the centre of Geneva of one of the best known and reputable lawyers in the city who had been recommended to Adrian by another lawyer in a smaller firm whom he had known for several years but to whom he did not mention any reason at all why he wanted such a recommendation.

After the first few minutes of polite introductions and conversation, Adrian gave the lawyer a concise oral description of the whole matter then handed to him the several pages setting out the full hand-written story.

After listening to Adrian then reading the pages in a very concentrated manner, the lawyer frowned, shook his head and murmured softly to himself as if in disbelief at the execrable injustice done to Adrian, looked first at Yseult then at Adrian and said to him, 'I am so sorry to learn what you have endured and suffered in this matter. In my opinion, you have very good grounds to file a lawsuit before the Geneva court claiming substantial damages for unjust harassment, attempted unfair dismissal and moral tort. However, it is necessary to bear in mind that there is no guarantee that the court will grant your claim or give you the level of damages we want and, if it does, the top management of the bank will be entitled to file an appeal against the judgement to the appeal court in Geneva and, if that court dismisses their appeal, they will have the right to appeal to the Swiss Supreme Court.'

'In all the litigation could drag on for several years and will cost you a small fortune in legal fees and court costs, with no guarantee of success. I recommend that in the first place I write a firm letter to the General Manager stating that you have mandated me to represent your interests, you have a strong and valid legal claim against the bank and him personally and, in the absence of a positive reaction on his part offering to negotiate an amicable settlement, I reserve the right to file a lawsuit on your behalf. My aim should be to negotiate with the General Manager the highest level possible of indemnities that he will accept to pay you, taking into account as well that you are now fifty-three years old and it may be extremely difficult for you to obtain

a new employment in the banking and financial field at the same top level that you had at the bank. I will send you by e-mail my first draft of my letter and, as soon as we agree on the final text, I will send the letter to the direct attention of the General Manager.'

Over the next four months, the lawyer conducted a difficult on-and-off, stilted and jittery negotiation with the General Manager, keeping Adrian and Yseult fully informed at each stage in his exchanges with the banker, who did not seem disposed to admit that he had committed any illicit acts or wrongful deeds against Adrian nor to accept to pay a very high or just level of indemnities to him.

One day, Adrian received a telephone call from Loïc, the deputy for Compliance matters at the bank. Adrian and Yseult had been on friendly terms with Loïc and his wife for some time. After Loïc had asked Adrian how he was faring and how his health was, as he knew well that Adrian was suffering from a wretchedly deep depression, it became instantly clear to Adrian that the call had a second purpose when Loïc said almost in a whisper and an embarrassed tone, 'The General Manager has asked me to tell you that he pleads with you not to go ahead with the filing of a lawsuit and not to wreck his career.'

Adrian was completely startled and rankled to hear this and, after a moment's silence, he growled angrily into the telephone receiver, 'That ungodly, cynical, self-centred, overly ambitious and sinister bastard has wronged me and wrecked my career and now he is begging me not to file a justified lawsuit and not to wreck his career! What an unholy and bloody cheek! He is totally unscrupulous and contemptuous. You tell that whining, despicable devil from me that I will not agree to his pathetic request. And, after the disaster he has caused for me and my family, if he wants to avoid a disaster for his bank and himself it is entirely up to him to settle and put an end to this matter directly with my lawyer in a way that is acceptable to my lawyer and myself!'

By early May 2002, the lawyer told Adrian that he had managed to push up the General Manager in the negotiations to a level of indemnities, which the latter said was the highest which the bank was able to offer. Although it was well below the level which the lawyer and Adrian had hoped for, the lawyer recommended to Adrian to accept the offer in full and final settlement, as they were aware of the overall risks and costs involved in filing a lawsuit, the long period of time over which such litigation could be dragged out by the bank and the fact that it was better for Adrian and his family to receive a concrete sum of money in the immediate future rather than maintain a tenuous hope over several years of receiving damages one day then having such hope dashed by the courts or being granted damages at a lower level than the one now being offered by the General Manager.

So, with a heavy heart, an enormous anger and a bitter resentment against the arbitrary workings of the judicial system and the mean, nasty and treacherous General Manager and his even worse friend the former General Manager, Adrian instructed his lawyer to accept the very ungenerous and

unjust offer of indemnities and to sign the settlement agreement on his behalf. Further, as a face-saving manoeuvre and mechanism for the General Manager, it was agreed between him and Adrian's lawyer that the bank would distribute a message to all the personnel at the bank, the members of the Board of Directors and the top management at the world headquarters of the bank, stating that, after being absent from work since last November due to serious illness, Adrian had resigned his post as at end May 2002 and was going to give a new orientation to his professional activities when his state of health would allow him to do so.

During the first six months of that year, Adrian was crushed and bowed down under the heavy black cloud of the worst depression he had ever endured. In a way entirely beyond his control, all the hurt and the traumatisms he had experienced in his life spurted hauntingly, all mixed up, scolding and with great violence to the surface of his psyche again like red hot, molten volcanic lava. All the excruciating pain and suffering from the betrayal, treachery, lack of love, rejection and abandonment by his mother then his father, the horrible years in both orphanages, the mental and sexual abuse to which his brother Neil and he had been successively subjected, all the bullying, harassment and emotional torture suffered at school and university, all the complexes, insecurities, conviction of being worthless and without any value, all the lack of self-esteem and lack of love of himself, all the appalling and consuming feelings of guilt about the breakdown of his family and the deaths of his two beloved brothers and guilt at being the sole survivor of the three, as well as the new, all-powerful and destructive feeling of guilt and shame about being partially responsible and to blame for the bullying, harassment, betrayal, treachery, rejection and abandonment carried out by the specific individuals at the bank.

Adrian experienced anxiety attacks, fits of panic, physical discomfort and pains in his chest and throat, sleepless nights and recurring nightmares in which the dreaded, fearful dark grey vortex swirled round and round, faster and faster, then hurled him headlong down into the deep, dark and dismal bowels of the earth where he would be condemned to remain isolated from humanity, alone, loveless, cold, terrified and lost in the pitch black of nothingness.

The state of Adrian's deep depression had a terrible impact on poor Yseult and their three offspring Steven, now twenty-two, Tatiana, now twenty and Justin, now sixteen.

The situation became so miserable and the atmosphere in the house so heavy and negative that Yseult exclaimed to Adrian late one evening in bed, 'Life has become unbearable for you and for me as well. I just cannot go on like this. You must not continue living in a way where you are so fragile and vulnerable that any hard knock causes your past traumatisms and unhappiness to rear their ugly head again and make you crumble and fall apart once more. After this latest extremely hard knock, which I can see has torn you apart, I think the only solution and hope for a better future is for you to ask your doctor if he can recommend a very good psychiatrist in Geneva with whom you can

undergo a really deep and efficient therapy for as long as is necessary to help build up your mental, psychological and emotional strength, defences and resistance. If you do not accept to undergo such a psychiatric treatment I will divorce you!'

Adrian almost fell out of bed as if he had been struck by an electric shock. The last thing in this life that he wanted to have to contemplate was a divorce. His love, respect and admiration for Yseult were extremely deep and genuine. Over the past twenty-eight years of their marriage, he had felt frequently the nagging fear, with his lack of confidence, lack of self-esteem, inferiority complex and regular pangs of jealousy when he saw how some men desired his wife, that Yseult would turn her back on him and would leave him for some other man.

He felt amazed, humbled and very grateful that she had put up with his insecurity, instability, hyper-sensitivity, excessive need for love and awful jealousy during all these years and was still by his undeserving side. He had just now heard her pronounce the dreaded word "divorce" and even as he felt very pained to hear it he understood fully her reason for threatening to go ahead with a separation and divorce.

So he cleared his painful throat and replied softly to her, 'My darling, you are absolutely right. I agree with what you have just said and I accept fully to ask my doctor to make an introduction for me to the best psychiatrist he knows in Geneva to see if I can follow a psychiatric treatment with him.'

When Adrian went to see his doctor two days later and explained the situation to him, the doctor said that he knew personally the best psychiatrist in the city.

He telephoned him in front of Adrian, was fortunately able to talk to him for two or three minutes, then put down the receiver and said to Adrian with a smile, 'He is always extremely busy and taken up with urgent cases. However, I have obtained an appointment for you with him at the beginning of next week at the end of the afternoon. Please make sure you arrive on time for he will not put up with lateness, as his schedule is so busy and pressurised. I am confident that he is the right specialist to help you overcome your inner problems and difficulties. I can see that you are a resilient but in too weak a way, as you are a survivor and have been just coping with all your past traumatisms and unhappiness but need a much stronger resilience to withstand the negative repercussions each time you receive another hard knock.'

'What do you mean by "resilient"? What is resilience? I must admit that I do not know that concept.'

'Resilience is the ability in a human being to become strong, healthy or successful again after something bad has happened. Resilience is the capability to recover from or adjust positively to misfortune or a negative change. Resilience is the wonderful capacity to remove any obstructing cause, no matter what, such as the destructive impact of an unhappy childhood, and find the way to have confidence in the first and basic principles of true hope, real happiness and enjoyment of life.'

'The specialist will try with the therapy to help you to remove all your obstructing causes and build you up to be a strong resilient and not just a survivor who is merely coping in life but remaining very fragile and vulnerable with a weak psyche, which has evidently been your case up to now. I wish you all the best and a great success with this therapy. The psychiatrist will keep me informed of the progress you are making as time goes by. In the same way that Rome was not built in a day, as the popular saying goes, you must keep in mind that a positive result of this psychiatric treatment will not be achieved quickly and may take quite a long time, so the key for you is to be patient and persistent.'

The psychiatric treatment was difficult and very intense, with two hourly sessions of psychoanalysis each week, and continued for several months. The psychiatrist was like a car mechanic who had to take the engine of a car totally apart, clean out all obstructions, dirt and impediments then re-build the motor again so that it would function properly, smoothly and reliably.

He used a similar approach to Adrian's mind, psyche, mental state and emotional make-up, de-constructing them and taking them apart, using the therapy to clean out all the negativity and obstructions to mental strength, emotional security and psychic stability. Then assisting Adrian to build for the first time in his life a healthy and positive recovery from all the traumas, bad, sad and painful experiences, hurt and suffering that he had endured during the early and formative years of his life. He explained to Adrian that, among all his other deep and troubling psychological, mental and emotional problems, a big difficulty was that it was obvious he was living with a type of post-traumatic stress disorder, to which all his automatic flashbacks, recurring bad memories and renewed nightmares beyond his control about each traumatic event and suffering contributed in psychological and biological dimensions even more so than the actual traumatic event and suffering itself, as he experienced intrusive unhappy and negative thoughts and fears making him relive all the traumatic events and suffering in his psyche on a recurring basis and in a constantly vicious cycle. An important aim of the treatment was to cure Adrian of that post-traumatic stress disorder.

The psychiatrist helped Adrian to understand that a strong resilience was a psychological phenomenon which consisted, for a deeply traumatised and damaged person like him, in taking stock of past horrors and miseries in a clinical and matter of fact way without emotional fear of their recurrence, accepting as being in the past, discarding and putting to bed behind him once and for all the various elements of pain and suffering he had gone through in those past years in order to avoid having to relive depressions and feelings of hopelessness and to be able to reconstruct himself, develop self-esteem and love of and confidence in himself, be more secure and stable mentally and emotionally, and envisage the future with a more positive, pleasant and optimistic outlook. The psychiatrist drummed into Adrian's mind and inner being that the strong resilience to be achieved would be the result of the multiple processes being used in the psychoanalysis and psychiatric treatment

which would interrupt the negative trajectory deeply engrained in his system and counter and overcome the psychological and emotional vulnerability linked to Adrian's extremely traumatic past history.

After several, painstakingly difficult and exhausting months, and after using a variety of tests to gauge what progress had been made, the psychiatrist told Adrian that they had gone as far as was possible in the treatment and he was hopeful and confident that the whole process had been very helpful and beneficial for Adrian and that he would no longer suffer from the debilitating post-traumatic stress disorder and was on his way to being a strong resilient.

In their final session, he warned Adrian that it was not a foregone conclusion that he was now a strong resilient and would no longer have any of the problems, complexes, anxieties and insecurities that he had always lived with before the treatment. He told Adrian firmly that the ball was now in his court, he had been given the psychological aids and tools during the treatment but he had to remain very vigilant against sliding back into negative and destructive elements and had to continue working on himself constantly, tirelessly and with determination in order to be a strong resilient and to put into practice in his day to day life all the methods and ways he had learned in their sessions so as to live more happily, securely and positively.

When Adrian visited his family doctor again, the latter said that he had received the psychiatrist's full and final report and, after reading it, he was very pleased that Adrian had undergone the treatment and was confident that Adrian would henceforth live his life more positively and in a forward-moving way as a strong resilient and not as a mere survivor of various tragedies and twists of fate attempting to cope with all the bad and negative experiences that life in the past had thrown at him.

Chapter 12
Miraculous Contact with Half-Sister

A little while after the final session of the psychiatric treatment at end March 2003, as Adrian continued to assimilate in his psyche everything that he had been taught and given by the specialist, he began to sense deep inside himself some positive effects of the long, gruelling and deeply stirring treatment in three different ways.

Firstly, each time he was walking in the streets and in shops in Geneva or elsewhere and saw various couples of homosexual men ambling together holding hands, caressing parts of one another's bodies or kissing each other, he was unexpectedly amazed and secretly pleased to detect a total change of attitude inside himself towards such situations.

In past years, he had become extremely agitated, anxious, fearful and aggressive like a small neurotic terrier dog each time he had encountered couples of homosexual men due to the awful traumatisms to his system caused by the horrible, depraved and violent sexual abuse perpetrated on his brother Neil at the orphanage and on himself at the college. As a consequence of those hideous and unforgettable sexual assaults, he had automatically developed, in a way beyond his control, a dreadful fear of and a very badly negative reaction against the idea of any erotic and sexual behaviour between members of the male gender and any penetration of a male body by a male penis which he saw as an aggressive, destructive dagger-like weapon causing both bodily and mental harm and damage in such a situation.

However, he felt now that he was thankfully becoming a strong resilient on that score as he sensed that he was recovering in a healthy, positive and successful manner from those traumatisms linked to the sexual abuse he and Neil had suffered, for all his anxieties, fears and aggressiveness were becoming dissipated and were disappearing each time he saw a couple of homosexuals.

He was now able to realise for the first time that, contrary to the violent, unloving and sadistic sexual abuse to which some males had subjected Neil and himself, the couples of homosexual men that he saw in public demonstrated genuine affection, consideration and tender love towards one another. He suddenly saw their attitude and behaviour as something humanly understandable, acceptable and not to be feared, judged or criticised.

He now said to himself, with a great and welcome sense of liberation from the former yoke of anxiety and fear, that any loving couples of the same sex, whether homosexuals or lesbians, should be allowed to live their loving

relationships freely and openly in a society showing tolerance and understanding. He had never mentioned to any family members, any friends or any acquaintances the fact that Neil and he had each suffered sexual abuse when they were young and he felt that he should not burden any of them with that at this stage and he would and could continue to live with the dark secret buried deep inside him. But he felt with immense gratitude that a dire, monumental weight had been lifted from his system by this new discovery inside himself of a much healthier, more positive, considerate and tolerant attitude towards homosexuals.

The second area where Adrian now detected a positive effect and a healthy change concerned his attitude towards the necessity of seeking a new professional activity. During many months, he had been so incapacitated and bowed down under the heavy black cloud of a vicious depression that he had lost all confidence in himself and felt again that he was utterly worthless and was devoid of any value. So that it had been impossible for him to face contacting or meeting anybody in professional circles or undergoing any interviews for a new employment.

However, in a better state of mind after the long treatment he found himself freed from the depression, reprimanding himself for his cowardice and telling himself over and over again that he did have some worth and value and that, instead of feeling miserably sorry for himself over the twisted googly ball that fate had recently thrown at him, he had to prove to himself, his beloved wife, his beautiful daughter and his two handsome sons that he was capable of pulling himself out of the wretched quagmire into which the sodden and ignominious bastards at the bank had thrown him and to put into practice all that the psychiatric treatment had taught him by bouncing back, putting the misfortune at the bank well behind him and acting as a strong resilient.

He discovered deep inside himself a renewed courage and energy and over the next six months he telephoned to and met with many professional contacts, wrote dozens of letters seeking an employment to many banks, financial institutions and companies and submitted himself humbly and modestly to a large number of interviews, making it clear to each potential employer that he did not need a job at the same high level as his last post at the bank and would be satisfied with and grateful for any interesting employment even at some lower level.

However, he met with refusals everywhere and was told on countless occasions that the obstacles to him finding a new employment were that he was too old, at the age of fifty-four, and was over-qualified and over-experienced for each and every job which was vacant. With a feeling of bitter frustration and disappointment, as well as a certain anger against the prevailing unjust system, both Adrian and Yseult became obliged to accept the fact that the chances were almost nil of him being able to obtain a new employment.

Although he was beset by a certain feeling of despondency, Adrian repeated to himself that there must be a light at the end of the tunnel and he must not concede to defeatism but must act as a strong resilient and find a

solution to his professional predicament and a way to recover and to restore his personal dignity and his confidence in the future. After much reflection, soul-searching and praying at home and at his local church he imagined suddenly one day that he had seen a flash of bright light before his eyes. He told Yseult with a firm voice and with a look of gritty determination in his steely blue eyes that the best solution for him was to establish his own law office, for he had no intention to take a terribly early and unacceptably premature retirement and to sit at home twiddling his thumbs. He said he knew it would be difficult and he might not be able to earn very high sums of money each month, but he was going to take his courage in both hands and give it a try. She encouraged him to go ahead with this project and he contacted the Law Society in Geneva and obtained their authorisation to be admitted to their section of foreign lawyers in Geneva, distinct from the section of Swiss lawyers, and to open his own law office as an international lawyer, use his own letterhead and have his own visiting cards printed. He was able to rent a small office with a miniscule adjoining meeting room in a smart building in the good area of Malagnou in Geneva and opened his tiny, one-man law firm in early December 2003 on his own without a secretary for the first time in his whole career. He could not believe his good fortune when he was able quite rapidly to sign a contract with a commercial company in the centre of Geneva, having business interests and investments in certain countries and in several areas, including in telecommunications, to be their international legal consultant and to be paid a retainer fee at the end of each month which amounted to almost one-half of the monthly salary that he had received in his post at the bank. When the ink of the signatures on the contract was barely dry, he sensed little inner voices calling softly to him and he felt sure that they were the voices of the souls of his beloved brothers Neil and Justin speaking to him from Heaven and reassuring him that they were watching over him and interceding to Divine Providence for him and his family and that he was protected and could envisage the future with confidence and optimism and should banish all fear and insecurity from his mind. Indeed, Adrian felt hopeful that over the ensuing period he would be able to obtain various other mandates, on top of the first very important one, which would provide him with some interesting and intellectually satisfying legal work and some legal fees on top of the retainer at the end of each month.

The third area where Adrian sensed an important, healthy and better change concerned his attitude towards his birth father. His mother had died some seventeen years earlier in 1976 and he had been able since then to dissipate his grievances and feelings of hatred against her and had managed to forgive her for the wrongs she had committed against her three sons. He had continued to harbour very sore, angry, negative, unforgiving and hateful feelings about his father, not only over his sins against the three boys but also his extremely bad treatment of poor Anita and the baby she was carrying in 1955. However, he now started to feel that he could not go on hating his father and he began to think about him in a more pining, nostalgic and softer manner and to wonder where he was in the world, what he was doing and with whom he might be

living, if he was still alive, for he knew that his father would now be eighty-five years old. He mulled over in his mind all that Aunt Clotilda had told him about his father's own difficult childhood and the extenuating circumstances she had put forward in his favour to excuse him to some extent for his bad behaviour towards his wife and three sons. Adrian had been told by his cousin Roberta that his paternal grandmother, her maternal grandmother, had died in 1971, her mother Celestina had died in 1998, their Aunt Clotilda had died in 1999 and their Aunt Patricia had died some years earlier. He said to himself that, if his father was still alive, it would surely be a positive step in his healing process and his attempt at recovery from all the traumatisms of his unhappy childhood if he could find out where his father was now living and try to establish a contact with him before he would in his turn leave this earthly life.

Adrian mentioned the subject of his father several times to Yseult. She saw that the subject was deeply troubling him and was constantly on his mind. She concurred that it would be beneficial for him if he could now establish a contact with his father, if he was still alive. She took it upon herself to conduct searches and she started by contacting the General Register Office in London in June 2003, requesting them to search on the Register of Deaths in order to determine whether Adrian's father, who was a British national, may have died at any time in the United Kingdom during the past years.

She received a buff-coloured envelope one day in late July 2003 bearing an English postal stamp and, after having opened it and read its contents, she put it aside until Adrian came home that evening after a hard working day at his office.

After he had relaxed his tired head and sore eyes sitting comfortably on the couch in the lounge, she handed him the envelope with trembling hands, as she was fearful about how he would react after reading the contents, and she whispered gently that she had read them.

He sat upright, extracted the sheet of paper from the envelope and let out a long, slow, mournful groan as he saw that it was a certified copy of a registration of his father's death and he read the essential elements:

Registration district Brighton; administrative area County of East Sussex; born on March 25 1918 in Bournemouth; died on November 25 1987 at Royal Sussex County Hospital in Brighton; occupation Civil Engineer (retired); usual address a house in the town of Rustington in West Sussex; informant of the death Mrs Joanna Barker living at the same house who was having his body cremated; cause of death acute renal failure and ruptured abdominal aortic aneurysm; signatures of Mrs Joanna Barker and the Registrar.

Adrian slumped back slowly on the couch, let the sheet of paper slip from his fingers, closed his eyes for what seemed to Yseult like a very long moment, then his body started shaking uncontrollably as large teardrops cascaded down his cheeks onto his blue shirt.

He croaked as he choked back the tears, 'The last time I saw him in July 1955 I was six years old. I had so hoped that he was still alive and I could establish a renewed contact with him and attempt to re-create some semblance of a father-son relationship at his advanced age, as the sole survivor of his three sons, and accompany him for the rest of his life until he died, which it was not possible to do for my mother.'

'He was my father and he remained my father, for God's sake, even after all the dastardly things he did to Neil, Justin and me! I feel right now just what a very thin line there is between love and hate. All these years I have harboured feelings of hate against him but I think that in reality I have never stopped loving him and most of my pain and suffering since being rejected and abandoned by him has come from the lack of his love, care and esteem for my brothers and me.'

'It is so terribly sad and unjust to learn now that he died all those years ago in 1987 at the relatively young age of sixty-nine and I cannot have any contact with him, tell him that I have forgiven him for his sins against Neil, Justin and me, that I still love him and ask him what he did in his life over the decades after he turned his back on his three sons.'

Yseult knelt down beside Adrian, with tears in her eyes, cupped his hands tenderly in hers, then looked up at him as he squeezed her hands fondly then retracted his own and wiped away his tears and hers with them and gave her a blank look with his watery blue eyes as if to say there was nothing to be done. Suddenly, Yseult's beautiful, brown, velvety eyes seemed to light up as she said to him, 'You cannot ask your father himself about his life during all those years but you can surely ask Mrs Joanna Barker about them, can't you? The copy of his death certificate indicates that he was living at the same address as her at the time of his death. If you wish, I can find out easily from the English directory enquiries what her telephone number is, call her and explain the situation and ask whether she would accept that we pay her a visit.'

'My darling, would you do that for me? It is a brilliant idea and I will be very grateful if you will try to talk with this Mrs Joanna Barker and ask her if she will see us.'

With her usual, impressively abounding energy, dynamism and efficiency, Yseult lost no time in obtaining the telephone number of Mrs Joanna Barker. When she rang her number one evening, with Adrian sitting on tenterhooks wringing his hands together at the other end of the couch in their lounge, she was immensely gratified that the lady at the other end listened politely and attentively to the story she told without making any interruption, then said in a very pleasant, soft voice that she commiserated and sympathised greatly with Adrian's very sad family history and could willingly tell him certain things about his father's life during a certain number of years as she had been his father's last lover and companion and had had him taken by ambulance to the hospital in Brighton when he had become extremely ill and was at his bedside when he drew his last breath in hospital.

It had already been agreed between Adrian and Mummy that he and Yseult would take a holiday in early September and spend a few days staying with Mummy at her lovely cottage in the small, pleasant country hamlet of Metcombe some five miles out of Sidmouth and celebrate her eighty-fifth birthday with her. So, Yseult agreed with Mrs Joanna Barker that she and Adrian would drive in a hire-car from Bristol airport down across to Rustington to visit Mrs Barker before driving over to Mummy's cottage where they would arrive just in time for supper.

When the day arrived, Adrian was as nervous as a jumping circus flea as he drove the car down from Bristol airport to Rustington, which was a small town by the sea at a midpoint of the West Sussex coast of the English Channel and midway between the county town of Chichester and the larger town of Brighton. Using the detailed directions which Mrs Barker had given him by telephone, he easily found the pretty bungalow with its large, well-tendered garden filled with the magnificent colours of a large variety of summer flowers, including many rose bushes in full bloom.

As he parked the car in the driveway, Adrian jokingly said to Yseult that he already had something in common with Mrs Barker as the rose was his favourite flower. When the front door opened, they were greeted by a tall, slim, impressive-looking lady with a lovely hairstyle who appeared to be in her seventies but whose face and figure must have been most attractive and even beautiful when she was younger. Adrian said to himself that he remembered that his father had excellent taste in women and he did not feel at all surprised that he had fallen for this very becoming lady all those years ago when she must have been some years younger than him at the time they first met. Her manner was very warm and friendly and her engaging smile put Adrian and Yseult at ease very rapidly. After showing them into her cosy and well-furnished living room, she brought a large tray with a huge teapot and a plate of biscuits from the small, well-appointed kitchen and over the next hour and a half she told them how she had met Adrian's father at a social occasion when she was much younger, how he had seduced her with his Welsh charm, handsome face, irresistible, large blue eyes, lovely deep voice and aristocratic, confident manner and how she had become his last lover and companion up until his death. She looked at Adrian with soft, kind brown eyes and said she could see some of his father in him, with his own handsome face, lovely blue eyes, attractive voice and natural charm, which made Adrian purr like a Cheshire cat and feel very flattered! Due to his complexes, insecurities and lack of self-esteem, Adrian had always felt during these past decades that he was ugly and not at all attractive and here was this lovely lady telling him that he was almost as handsome as his impressive and charming father. He sat there smiling and thinking to himself that he would willingly lap up some more compliments of that nature!

Mrs Barker gave them a very critical appraisal of Adrian's father's difficult, very self-centred character and awkward personality beneath his suave and self-confident veneer. She told them how she had discovered what a

spoilt brat and extremely selfish sod he was, devoid of any sense of responsibility. Adrian laughed at this and told her that he had always felt from his very tender age when they lived in Kenya that his father was very selfish and unfeeling about others' needs. And he had always concluded that one reason why his father had rejected and abandoned his sons and callously shoved them off into the hands of his sister Clotilda was that they were an obstruction, impediment and hindrance to his very selfish plans for personal pleasure and he did not want the responsibility of raising them.

She agreed with this and explained to Adrian and Yseult how Adrian Senior would at regular intervals leave her alone in the bungalow, pretexting that he had to go to Nigeria or some other exotic far-off country on a work assignment as an engineering consultant, and would be away for several months on end, without sending her any news. Then he would arrive back unannounced at the bungalow and expect her to resume their life together as normal and cater to all his personal needs as if nothing untoward had happened.

Whilst she felt certain that he was enjoying himself in the company of other women while he was away, as soon as he returned he would put on the charm with his seductive manner and she could not resist letting him come back into her life and her home. She said that she was fully aware that he was using her and taking advantage of her softness, kindness and weakness and, although she contemplated on a few occasions throwing him out and ending the relationship, she could not bring herself to do so, she let the situation drag on and on and then his illness took over their lives.

Whilst she omitted to show them her own bedroom where she had slept with Adrian's father over many years, she showed them the bedroom he occupied with its single bed during the long months of his awful illness, during which she acted as his carer and nurse, until it became no longer possible and he had to be transported to hospital where he was cared for properly by doctors and nurses during the last few weeks until he died.

Mrs Barker showed Adrian and Yseult an album containing some photos of her and Adrian Senior. As he scrutinised his father's face on some of the photos, Adrian was struck to see how sad the look was in his father's eyes and how much older his father looked than his real age. He could not help but wonder whether the sad look emanated from regrets about his past actions that his father might have had and a certain sense of guilt and sorrow that he might have harboured about the fact that he had missed seeing his three sons and his daughter growing up.

With tears glistening in his eyes as he looked long and hard at the photos, he asked Mrs Barker whether he had showed any signs of regret over his rejection and abandonment of his three sons and his separation from Anita when she was carrying his daughter. He felt wretched, bitterly angry and immensely saddened when she replied that his father never talked to her about his feelings concerning his three sons and his daughter. Adrian ended the conversation by telling her how struck he was by the stark contrast between his mother and his father, for he had been extremely moved to receive a copy of

his mother's will leaving all her assets to her three sons, showing that she did care for them, whereas his father had done nothing at all demonstrating any love for his children.

As Mrs Barker escorted them to the front door on their way out, she hugged each of them in turn, gave them a soft kiss on the cheek and said she would be very happy if they would maintain the contact with her and come back to see her again at any time they wished and could do so. On the drive down to Metcombe, Adrian thanked Yseult warmly for having taken the initiative to arrange the meeting with Mrs Barker and said that he was very pleased to have met her and to learn more about certain years of his father's life.

He added that he liked Mrs Barker very much, felt that she had been stoical and even heroic in putting up with his dreadful father during all those years and he very much wanted to keep up the contact with her and see her again. He said finally that he felt his father had not deserved Mrs Barker in the same way that he had not been worthy of the lovely Anita. Yseult concurred readily that she too had liked Mrs Barker very much and thought she was a very fine, friendly and loveable lady.

***

By the end of the first quarter of 2004, Adrian felt concerned that he was not receiving many more mandates over and above the first important mandate for his small law practice and the amounts of fees he was earning were not at the level that he had hoped. He spoke to Yseult about the fact that he could not be over-confident for the ensuing years of an increasing success of his endeavours as an independent lawyer, his future prospects appeared somewhat precarious and he felt they should be very prudent on the financial level.

They discussed the matter carefully and took into account the fact that Yseult's small, independent activity as a real estate consultant carried out on her own from her small office in the villa over the past twelve years was not a very secure activity either and only gave her some commissions on very few occasions each year if and when she managed to sell a villa or a flat or rent out any properties for clients.

After much deliberation, they came regretfully to a mutual decision that it would be wise to leave their large, roomy and beloved Provencal villa and find a flat to rent somewhere in the area. They had spent thirteen very happy years living there and bringing up their offspring in that delightful and privileged home, but their two sons and their daughter were growing up fast, with Stephen now living in a small rented flat in Lausanne during his studies to become an industrial designer. Tatiana now living in a tiny rented flat in Geneva while she studied at the Art School. And Justin now in his final year at the higher school in Nyon, studying to obtain his baccalaureate and hoping to go to university to study Law. It seemed evident that their six-bedroomed villa was becoming too large for them in any case.

Adrian felt deeply hurt, upset and emotionally destabilised at the prospect of having to leave this lovely home, which had been the villa of his dreams. He experienced an enormous anger, grudge and resentment against the specific persons at the bank who had wronged him so badly and destroyed his successful career, thereby causing him to have to take up a risky and precarious activity as a solitary independent lawyer, in a city where there were already far too many independent lawyers practising and too much competition for mandates, and obliging him and his wife to leave their much loved home.

However, he repeated constantly to himself that it was paramount that he put into practice all that the psychiatric treatment had brought him and he had to act as a strong resilient who was capable of assimilating and recovering from this new blow of having to leave the villa of his dreams. He felt bolstered and reassured when Yseult told him that she saw no reason why they should sell the villa and that the right and intelligent plan was to rent it out to a family for as high a rent as she could obtain and find a reasonably comfortable flat that they could rent for a much lower amount, so that the difference would provide them with a revenue at the end of each month to supplement whatever sums each of them was able to earn in their respective, small independent activities.

They both agreed that it was very important for them, emotionally, sentimentally and financially, to remain the owners of the property and to manage to meet their mortgage interest payment commitments through receipt of a rental income for as long as possible and not to lose the ownership at this stage of their much loved villa. Adrian felt strongly that if they achieved this it would give him a small victory over and a sweet revenge against those nasty bastards at the bank who, whilst having damaged his career, would not have succeeded in breaking and destroying him altogether. With her usual positivity, strong character and enormous energy, Yseult threw herself into looking for tenants for the villa and a suitable flat for them to live in somewhere in the area.

One evening in May 2004, after they had cleared away the supper and were sitting on the comfortable brown sofa up on the mezzanine watching a programme on the television, the nearby telephone rang and Yseult walked over to it.

After a few seconds, she walked back and told Adrian, 'It is a male voice asking to speak with you. He did not tell me who he is.'

'Sounds mysterious,' Adrian replied as he stood up reluctantly, for he was enjoying the subject of the programme.

He walked nonchalantly over and said into the receiver with a grave, business-like voice, as he thought it might be some man calling him about a legal matter, 'Adrian Tunnington here. Can I be of any service to you?'

'Hello, Uncle Adrian. I am your nephew Neil, the elder son of your eldest brother Neil. We have never met but you have always sent Christmas cards each year to my mother Sheila, my brother Peter and me and you wrote your home telephone number and your e-mail address on one of them. I hope that this is not a bad moment and I am not disturbing you?'

Adrian was so shocked to hear his nephew's voice that his body wobbled like a shaking jelly, his legs became weak and he sat down with a hard bump on the floor, very nearly letting the receiver drop. This voice was so similar to that of his beloved brother Neil that he saw an ethereal, ghost-like image of his brother's face floating before his eyes and he choked as he felt a painful lump in his throat and tears warming his cheeks.

He tried to calm down and replied gently, 'Dear Neil, you are not disturbing me at all. It is wonderful to hear your voice. I am very sorry that we have never had the opportunity to meet yet, but I do hope we can remedy that and get together before too long. How are you and how are you faring generally in life?'

'I am doing all right. I work as a commodity trader in a medium-sized company on the outskirts of London and I live with my girlfriend together with her daughter from a previous relationship and the six months old baby boy, your great-nephew, who we have had together. As for my brother Peter, he is studying at the University of Glasgow to become a chartered surveyor. We do not manage to see one another very often. My mother has been living in a little house in Londonderry in Northern Ireland for many years now. However, I am ringing you for a specific purpose. The fact is that I have recently received a telephone call from your half-sister Philippa, who told me that she is looking for you.'

It was fortunate that Adrian was already sitting on the floor, otherwise he would have fallen down like a heavy sack of potatoes. He gulped and felt his head whirring like a fast-revolving spinning top. He shook his head, thumped his forehead with the palm of his free hand to stop the spinning, cleared his throat and said almost in a whisper, 'This is absolutely incredible! Can you repeat what you have just said, for I do not understand?'

'I can well imagine that this must come as a bolt out of the blue. I was extremely surprised when this lady called me at home one evening and told me that her name was Philippa Mornick. She said that she was told by her mother many years ago, when she had a different surname, that she had three half-brothers, having the same father as them, she had not done anything about it before but, after her mother's death, decided to use her father's surname and decided also that she wished to search for her half-brothers.'

'She had looked up every person in the United Kingdom bearing the same surname Mornick, had telephoned each one over a period of several weeks and had been told by each one that they did not have one or two brothers or other relatives fitting in with the story she told them. As my surname is Mornick, she telephoned me one day and, after piecing together the parts of the puzzle, I told her that I was the elder son of her half-brother Neil and both Neil and Justin had died but her last half-brother Adrian is still alive. As I told her I have your telephone number, she begged me to call you and ask if you will accept that I can give it to her and tell her that she can call you directly. Would you mind my doing that?'

'My dear nephew, I am completely thunderstruck! This is a miracle! Can you imagine that I knew Anita, Philippa's mother, for a few months when I was six years old and she was expecting a baby by my father Adrian, your paternal grandfather? I loved Anita dearly and hoped very much at the time that she would become my substitute mother but sadly it was not to be, for she left my father several weeks before the birth of the baby, because he was utterly selfish, cruel and totally impossible for her to live with, and I never saw her again.'

'I discovered many years later from your father, my beloved brother Neil, that he had kept a vague contact with Anita over some years while he was serving in the Royal Navy and she had told him that we had a half-sister named Philippa. However, your father lost contact with Anita and, whilst I have thought of Philippa on many occasions over the years, I had absolutely no way to make contact with her for I did not know what her surname was nor the surname of her mother. As I saw Anita leave our father in a very angry and distressed state in May 1955 and I believe she never saw him again, I would never have imagined that she would give his surname to her daughter and from what you say she did not do so. This is an incredible, wonderful and miraculous development that Philippa has now taken our father's surname and searched for her half-brothers! Please telephone Philippa as quickly as you can, giving her my number and telling her that yes, yes, yes I will be delighted if she will call me and if we can meet up somewhere at some time.'

After saying goodbye tenderly to his nephew, Adrian placed the telephone receiver gently on the floor and stayed seated for several minutes with his body rocking from side to side and his hands over his eyes as he wept silently whilst thinking of his deceased brothers and his half-sister Philippa who was thankfully very much alive and was miraculously on the verge of entering into his life.

Whilst his mind was miles away deep in thought and was seeing the beloved faces of Neil and Justin and wondering what Philippa's face looked like, he felt a hand rubbing his left shoulder and the voice of Yseult asking him, 'Are you all right? Have you just received some more bad news?'

'Oh, no! No bad news. Quite the contrary! I still cannot believe what has happened and I think you will have difficulty believing it. I have just received the most unexpected, incredible and wonderful news! Do not ever say that miracles do not happen, for a marvellous miracle has occurred!'

As he attempted unsuccessfully to stop his body rocking and to stop weeping whilst he wiped away the tears with the paper handkerchief which Yseult gave him, he gestured to her to sit down beside him and he recounted to her with a very emotional voice the full contents of the conversation which he had just had with his nephew Neil. She was so moved that she started weeping as well and, as they hugged one another, clung on to each other and dabbed away each other's tears with a succession of paper hankies, she kissed him lovingly on the cheek and said,

'This is in effect a totally unexpected and incredible miracle! I know that you have been thinking very often about your half-sister over all these years and have been trying to come to terms with the awful thought that, having endured the dreadfully painful loss of both your brothers, you would sadly never have a way of finding your half-sister. It is so fortunate and wonderful that she has undertaken the steps and has now found you. I am so happy for you. We must just wait until she gets around to having the time to telephone you. This will be a good exercise in patience for you!'

The wait lasted a few weeks, during which time Adrian encountered great difficulty of concentration and a big problem of managing to deal with the few legal matters and files which came his way at his little office in Geneva, for he was mentally and emotionally agitated, disturbed and distracted and found himself thinking constantly about his half-sister who was born forty-nine years earlier and with whom he was now very impatient to establish some form of contact.

One evening, the telephone rang; Yseult took the call, spoke to the person at the other end for a few seconds then came running over to Adrian and whispered to him excitedly that it was his half-sister Philippa. He took the telephone in trepidation and with his hand shaking and his heart beating so strongly against the wall of his ribcage that he felt Philippa would no doubt hear the sound like the loud beating of a big drum. He felt very anxious, but he had no cause to be for the lovely female voice put him at ease very rapidly and they chatted cheerfully to one another for many minutes as if they already knew one another. Adrian felt very gratified as he sensed very positive vibes circulating between them. She told him, among many other things, that she worked as a roaming journalist for one of Great Britain's largest newspapers based in Fleet Street in Central London and that she was due to fly to India during the coming week on a specific mission. She said that she did not know when it would be possible for them to meet physically as she had to travel abroad very frequently in her job. However, they promised mutually that, having established a first contact after a huge hole and lack lasting forty-nine years, they would try to keep in contact as much as possible by telephone until such time as they could actually meet and she ended the conversation by telling him that she would call him sometimes from her home near London in between her trips on assignments to various countries.

After saying goodbye to Philippa, Adrian felt overwhelmed by many mixed emotions and saw in a flash before his eyes the excruciatingly painful, fateful image of beautiful Anita forty-nine years earlier, with her large, rounded belly, as she said a final goodbye to the three ten, eight and six year old brothers and walked out of their lives forever carrying her soon to be born baby after he had pressed his tear-stained little face and short arms against her heavily pregnant belly, had kissed that life-bearing belly and had whispered softly to the unborn baby wishing him or her the very best of luck in life and a much happier life than he and his two brothers were living. He then shook his head to evacuate the image and, collecting his spirits, walked to where Yseult was standing

nearby, took her in his arms, hugged her lovingly, stood back and looked deeply into her superb brown eyes as he said, 'I have lost both my much-loved brothers, but I have now gained a sister! Whilst I will never stop missing Neil and Justin and thinking about them, I am really looking forward to being able to develop a lovely and pleasant brother-sister relationship with Philippa. This is a truly miraculous and happy development!'

***

Adrian, Yseult and their three young visited several flats to rent in the area over a two-month period, but found each time that something was missing, was not to their taste or was lacking.

One day, Yseult told Adrian that there was a spacious, duplex flat for rent on the top floor beneath the roof of a small building in a village situated not very far from the town of Nyon. She said that the real estate agent had told her they should go to visit it quickly as he felt sure there would be several candidates interested in renting it. On the day that he had fixed an appointment with Yseult for a visit, she was not free due to a last-minute commitment in one of her own real estate matters, and all the three young were taken up with other activities, so Adrian agreed that he would visit the flat by himself and report back to them.

Barely had he entered the flat and met the present tenant, who was moving with his wife and their two young children to a small villa which they had managed to buy, that he started to feel very positive vibrations which had been totally lacking during visits to all the other available flats. After the tenant showed him the open kitchen giving on to the dining room area, the large living room with its very high ceiling and three wooden beams just below the roof of the building and the stairway up to the second floor with a mezzanine at the top, the two bathrooms and separate toilets and the comfortable, spacious bedrooms, Adrian stood beside the tenant and said smiling, 'As the real estate agent said, this is a very spacious and comfortable flat, with a lot of charm, especially with that high, cathedral ceiling in the lounge, making it somewhat special. I could definitely live here with great pleasure!'

When he walked around the flat a second time, Adrian felt sure he heard soft inner voices talking to him. He stopped walking, listened very attentively and it seemed clear in his heart and mind that the souls of his brothers Neil and Justin were sending him the message that this flat was where he, Yseult and eighteen year old Justin were destined to live. He left the premises in a buoyant mood and when he returned to the villa he told Yseult how much he had liked the flat and how he had heard the inner message transmitted to him by his brothers' souls. She was very pleased to hear that he was enthusiastic about the flat but she felt very sceptical about any soft voices sending him messages from Heaven and she said to herself and to him that her dear hubby was going rather soft in the head!

Both Adrian and Yseult were very disappointed and frustrated when they received a telephone call from the real estate agent a few days later, after Yseult had visited the flat and had told him that they wanted to rent it. He said that a young couple with three young children had visited the flat that day, had begged him to allow them to rent it, as it was ideal in size for a family of five people, and he had decided that he should ask the owner of the flat to grant the new lease to this family. Whilst feeling sad that they could not have the flat, Adrian and Yseult agreed that this family should be given the priority and should be able to live in that flat and they requested the agent to let them know if he found any other suitable flat for them to rent.

Yseult just could not believe it when the agent called her about a week later, informing her that the family in question was not going to rent the flat after all, for some mysterious reason, and she and Adrian could have the new lease and move into the flat when it suited them, if they were still interested. When she told Adrian this unexpected and incredible good news over supper that evening, after his return from the office, he jumped up, danced around the table whooping loudly like a Red Indian doing a war-dance and gloated gleefully, 'Aha! You took the mickey out of me when I told you that my little inner voices said that this flat was destined for us and you treated me like a deluded madman! As I have told you before, if I listen carefully to my little inner voices and act upon what they tell me I never go wrong and never make a bad decision. I am convinced with my deep Christian faith that it is the intervention and the assistance of Divine Providence that has brought us this flat and the souls of my brothers communicated to me the message that the flat was destined for us. I trust that you have already told the agent that we do want to contract the lease and move into this flat, as it is definitely the right decision. This is a second happy development this year, after the miraculous surprise of having that first contact with my half-sister!'

Yseult managed to find tenants for their villa, a very friendly young couple with two young children. She, Adrian and younger son Justin moved into the rented flat near end July and the new tenants moved into the villa during August. Each time that elder son Steven and daughter Tatiana visited them they each agreed that this was a spacious, comfortable and pleasant flat with a certain charm and their parents had been very fortunate to obtain it. Yseult still found it incredible and very mysterious that it had been Adrian who had first seen the flat on his own and had told her that he had received a spiritual message while on the premises that this flat was destined for them, which it had then turned out to be. She pondered silently on this mystery and decided that in the future she would have to treat any mention by her husband of his little inner voices with greater respect!

A third happy development occurred in July 2004. Justin, who had just turned eighteen, was successful in all the examinations and obtained his baccalaureate at the higher school in Nyon, in the same way that Steven and Tatiana had done before him. He told his parents that he desired to go to university to study Law but wanted to take a sabbatical year first in order to do

some odd jobs to earn some money then to travel overseas and discover parts of the world. Adrian explained to Justin that he had started at university straightaway after obtaining his low-grade A Level exams at St Boniface's College then the higher grades of A Levels at the Technical College in Exeter, so as to remain mentally and intellectually in the studying mode without interruption, and had only enjoyed a sabbatical year after obtaining his Law Degree at Exeter University. He suggested to Justin that it might be wise and better overall if he went first to university then took his sabbatical year after obtaining his Law Degree, but Justin insisted, with his forceful character, that he was going to enjoy his sabbatical year first then go to university afterwards, to which youthful and stubborn insistence his parents reluctantly capitulated.

In late autumn that year, a fourth happy development came out of the blue and in an unexpected manner. Adrian received an e-mail from his niece Lynette, the younger daughter of his brother Justin, informing him that she and her boyfriend Jeremy, known popularly as Jerry, had become engaged and were to wed in a lovely, romantic place near Auckland in February 2005.

She wrote that she wanted Adrian to give her away in the place of her beloved and sorely missed father, if he would accept to do so and if it would be possible for him to take the time to make the journey. Adrian was completely overwhelmed with joy and when he showed the e-mail to Yseult he told her firmly that nothing was going to prevent him from going down under, for it was extremely important for him to accede to his beloved niece's touching request and to give her away at her wedding and to celebrate this wonderfully happy event as well with his marvellous sister-in-law Maureen and his second beloved niece Lydia.

He suggested to Yseult that they could take a lovely holiday of two weeks or so around the wedding together with all their three young and pay for it out of some of their hard-earned savings. She agreed, but when they broached the subject with their offspring, the only one who was free and able to make the trip with them was Justin, as both Steven and Tatiana were unfortunately tied up with their respective activities and commitments and would not be able to take off the time for such a trip in February.

So, Adrian, Yseult and Justin flew down to Auckland and enjoyed a fantastic, very romantic and happy celebration of the wedding of Jerry and Lynette and a supremely joyful holiday with them, Maureen, Lydia, her steady boyfriend Arthur, some of the members of Jerry's family and various friends. On the day of the wedding, as lovely Lynette walked beside him holding his arm as they approached the bridegroom Jerry and the pastor who was marrying them, Adrian could sense strongly with deep emotion the spiritual presence of Lynette's father Justin walking with them.

Later on, at the beautiful, warm and friendly reception at a delightful location, when it was Adrian's turn to make a short speech in front of everyone, he told Lynette lovingly and very emotionally that he knew that the soul of her wonderful father was looking down on them happily from Heaven, that he was very proud of her and that he would always watch over and protect her and

Jerry and their future children, as well as Maureen and Lydia, together with any family of her own that Lydia would have in the future.

On the day of the departure of Adrian and Yseult to Geneva, they were escorted to Auckland airport by Maureen, Lynette and Jerry, Lydia and Arthur, whom they liked very much, as well as their son Justin who was going to stay in New Zealand for a few weeks before flying over to Australia. After having said very moving, loving and highly emotional goodbyes to Maureen, Lynette and Jerry, Adrian took Lydia warmly into his arms, whispered to her how very much he loved her, stepped back, looked at Arthur then said firmly to Lydia,

'You will hang onto Arthur, won't you, my dear? I can see that you have found a very fine fellow. It appears clear that he is good for you and I wish you both the greatest of happiness together. Please remain in contact with me by the occasional e-mail and keep me informed of the development of this lovely relationship.'

***

Over the period of several months, Adrian received an occasional telephone call from his half-sister Philippa between her journalistic missions abroad and they happily chatted and exchanged news.

However, during all this time Adrian kept wondering anxiously and impatiently when it was going to become possible for them to meet. Suddenly, one evening at end May 2005 Philippa telephoned and told him that she saw an opportunity coming in the near future for her and Raymond, her long-standing boyfriend, to meet up with Adrian and Yseult in Switzerland. She explained that Raymond's mother was half-Swiss and his family possessed a flat in the village of Murren.

'Murren, you say?' Adrian interjected. 'I must admit I have never heard of it but perhaps Yseult has an idea about it.'

'Murren is a pleasant mountain village in the Bernese Oberland situated at 1,650 metres above sea level,' Adrian heard Philippa's lovely lilting voice saying at the other end. 'It is a very popular tourist spot in both summer and winter. From the village there is a spectacular view of the Eiger, Mönch and Jungfrau, the three famous impressive and legendary mountains. The railway station in Murren is the terminus of an aerial tramway and a connecting narrow gauge railway. A large cable car goes up to the summit of the mountain called Schilthorn and the revolving restaurant named Piz Gloria. Did you see the James Bond film *On Her Majesty's Secret Service*, which was released in 1969? The Piz Gloria restaurant was the principal filming location of that movie in which Bond, played by George Lazenby, escaped from the headquarters of the criminal Blofeld, played by Telly Savalas, and fled from his henchmen in a car driven by his girlfriend, played by Diana Rigg.'

'This is fascinating. You are a fountain of cultural knowledge, my dear sister, which I suppose is not surprising as you are a professional journalist! I did see the film but had not realised that it was filmed near Murren and at the

Schilthorn restaurant. However, for what reason exactly are you telling me about Murren?'

'The fact is that Raymond and I are going to stay in mid-June at his family's flat in Murren for several days and we wondered whether we could travel by train to Geneva in the morning of our departure from Murren and meet up with you and Yseult?'

'How fabulously wonderful! That is a tremendous idea, which I will mention immediately to Yseult. Just call me much nearer the date and tell me exactly on which day and at what hour your train will arrive at Geneva railway station. I will e-mail to you a recent photograph of myself and please will you e-mail a photograph of yourself, so that we will be able to recognise one another on the platform? Both Yseult and I are looking forward with great anticipation and immense pleasure to meeting you and Raymond. We will take you for lunch at one of my favourite restaurants on the outskirts of Geneva. One last thing before I say goodbye – if you and Raymond go up to the Piz Gloria restaurant during your stay and discover that some gangster is holed up there, just give me a call and I will contact James Bond and have him fly over there to deal with the rascal and rescue you straightaway!!' Just before the telephone went silent, Adrian smiled as he heard his half-sister chuckle out loud at his pathetic joke!

After Adrian had sent his e-mail with a fairly recent photo of him attached, he was delighted to receive a short and chatty e-mail back from Philippa with her photo attached. He printed the image, sat down in the lounge of the flat and looked intensely at this photo of his half-sister, put it down when it was time to go to the dining table for the supper that Yseult had prepared, then picked it up again eagerly after supper and perused it again for a long moment. He loved that face immediately with a tender affection and felt deeply emotionally stirred as he felt hot tears pricking his eyes and cast his mind back to that very last moment with Anita fifty years earlier when he had hugged her swollen belly and whispered his very best wishes to her baby nestling inside her as he felt a desperately despondent conviction that he would never, ever have the chance to meet that boy or girl during his life.

He expressed whisperingly to the photo his deepest gratitude to Philippa that she had taken the initiative to search for her half-brothers and had found him, which he repeated to himself constituted a true miracle. He seemed to perceive some traits of their father's handsome and charismatic face in her pleasant and attractive face and said to himself that she had no doubt been a very pretty young girl. He felt sad as he tried to recapture in his mind the features of her mother's face, in order to sense which of her features Philippa had inherited, but he could only recall that Anita was beautiful and the exact shape of her lovely face and of her features had regrettably become somewhat blurred in that space of fifty long years.

One evening a few weeks later near end June, Philippa called and gave Adrian the time at which their train would arrive at the Geneva railway station at Cornavin the following morning. He tossed and turned in bed all through the

night, being highly agitated and extremely excited at the upcoming event of meeting his half-sister finally after fifty years.

At the railway station the next morning, he left Yseult standing still as he saw a couple descending from the train, recognised Philippa from her photo and rushed forward impulsively to greet them like a forlorn young schoolboy running headlong to meet his parents after a long term away at boarding school. He was met halfway by a rushing Philippa with wide open arms, a loud cry of joy and floods of tears and multiple kisses on each cheek as they fell into each other's arms, stayed locked together for long seconds, separated and looked at one another with genuine happiness and appreciation as they stroked each other's face gently with their fingers as if to verify that this was not some fake dream in their sleep but the incredible reality of the end of a terribly long lack, absence, search and wait.

When she felt sufficiently recovered from these emotions, Philippa introduced Adrian to her boyfriend Raymond, who was a very pleasant-looking, friendly and smiling man. By this time, Yseult had almost reached them along the platform and Adrian joyfully introduced his beloved wife to Philippa and Raymond.

As the four of them drove in Adrian's car from the underground railway station carpark into bright sunlight, down the street called Rue Chantepoulet and then down Rue du Mont-Blanc towards the Mont-Blanc bridge spanning the wide River Rhône as it left Lake Geneva and flowed on down through part of the city, Adrian told them gleefully,

'As the weather forecast yesterday predicted a beautiful, warm and sunny summer day today, I have reserved a table for us on the terrace of a restaurant called La Belotte, which is one of my favourite restaurants in the whole area to eat at during the fine summer period. Over the years, I have been there for business lunches with various contacts, colleagues and clients as I love the situation, the food they serve and the calm. Yseult has also been there with me on one or two occasions. I do hope that you will enjoy it, Philippa and Raymond.'

After crossing the Mont-Blanc bridge and passing the delightful Jardin Anglais on their left, they had a most pleasant drive of about two kilometres along the left bank of the lake, "*La Rive Gauche*" in French, with a beautifully stunning view of many yachts and some larger boats on the lake as well as the prestigious buildings lining the road on the opposite, right bank of the lake, "*La Rive Droite*".

Then, as the car started to climb the long ramp towards the village of Vésenaz, they saw a large sign indicating La Belotte on the left. After going down the short driveway Adrian parked the car in the restaurant's private car park and they were shown to their table as near as one could possibly be to the lake on the very spacious and leafy terrace with its line of magnificent and decorous plane trees providing very welcome shade from the strong sun.

During their meal of specialities of the area, the two couples conversed in a very relaxed and friendly way as if they already knew one another and gave

each other many titbits of information about their lives. Among other details, Philippa told them that, after having been brought up by her mother Anita, she had married quite young an Englishman whose surname was Cockle and they had together a son named Brian. Unfortunately, she discovered that she had made a dreadful mistake, as Mr Cockle turned out to be a rather distasteful, unpleasant and difficult man, so she left him, then divorced and brought up Brian on her own. At some point, her mother had a serious relationship with a man and they had a daughter named Clarissa and a son named Albert whom they raised together until his unfortunate and untimely death. Philippa said that she was very close to her half-sister Clarissa, who was married with two daughters, and they saw each other as often as their respective activities and commitments permitted. She said that it was after her mother Anita's death that she decided to assume the Mornick part of their father's surname, without the first part Walton, as she did not wish to have a double-barrelled surname, and to search for her three half-brothers. Her son Brian had always continued to keep his father's surname Cockle, but he had a very strained and distant relationship with his father, who was living in France with a woman that Brian had never taken to.

After the most pleasant time together at La Belotte, they drove to Geneva airport at Cointrin from where Raymond and Philippa were going to fly back to Gatwick airport on the outskirts of London. During a very emotional and tearful farewell, they promised to keep in touch as closely as possible and Adrian and Philippa in particular swore that they would do their best to meet up again at the next earliest opportunity.

The following important event on the calendar of Adrian and Yseult was the return home near end July 2005 of their younger son Justin after a six-month absence undertaking some very exciting travels during his sabbatical year. They had received some postcards from him as he toured New Zealand first, then Australia, flew over to New York to meet up with one of his best friends, then drove down with that friend to Florida and the Everglades area, flew down by himself to Chile, where he toured around over several weeks, and went finally to Argentina where he also discovered the way of life and many important places before flying back to Geneva.

Once back at their flat, he spoke to his parents about some of the exciting adventures he had experienced and showed them all the wonderful photographs he had taken with his small camera. Naturally, he felt completely disorientated being back in Switzerland after discovering the wonderful sites and multi-cultured people down under and in North America and Latin America and he groaned at the idea that he would have to start studying Law at the University of Fribourg in about six weeks' time. He was especially irritated when his father reminded him pedantically and somewhat contemptuously that he had warned him that it would perhaps be wiser to obtain his Law Degree first before embarking on a sabbatical year and exotic adventures!

One morning, when Adrian was working on a file in his little office in Malagnou, Justin telephoned him and asked if he could be free to have lunch

together either that same day or the following day. Adrian could sense from the tone of Justin's voice that it was important for him to speak with his father about something. He looked out of the window, saw that it was a bright, sunny, cloudless day, and told Justin that he would immediately reserve a table for the two of them on the terrace of his favourite outdoor restaurant La Belotte and would meet him with his car just outside the front entrance of the Cornavin railway station at quarter past noon, as Justin could take a train from a local station into Geneva.

When they were seated on the delightful terrace at La Belotte, just one table away from the one where Adrian, Yseult, Philippa and Raymond had enjoyed their wonderful lunch together a few weeks earlier, Justin started to recount to his father a myriad of details concerning some extraordinary, hair-raising, dangerous and even near-death experiences and encounters that he had had in some of the countries he had explored.

From the way that Justin spoke, the look in his eyes and his overall aspect and manner, Adrian could tell that his beloved nineteen-year-old son had been profoundly shaken, traumatised, changed and matured by all these mishaps and adventures. In particular, Justin explained in minute detail to Adrian what had happened to him in Chile. He had taken a bus from the capital Santiago up to the north of the country, where he spent some time exploring certain towns, villages and a part of the countryside. However, instead of taking a bus back down to the southern part of the country, he decided to buy a second-hand motorbike and to cross a nearby desert in order to reach a small town which he saw on his map of the whole country was situated just on the southern edge of that expansive desert.

'I have for several years felt a great attraction for deserts and a big desire to explore some of them. I discovered that this particular desert was a mixture of sand, medium-sized boulders and smaller stones, there were not many already existing tracks to follow and as I ventured further into the desert it became somewhat arduous and slower to ride the motorbike along the sand whilst avoiding hitting large boulders. All of a sudden, I had to twist the handlebar sharply to the left to miss an obstacle, I fell off the motorbike and the engine stopped. It was the middle of a very hot day with a scorching sun blazing down on me. I had taken with me a jerry can full of fuel and some provisions of food and bottles of water in two saddlebags attached on each side of the back wheel. I kick-started but the engine would not start again. I kick-started again but to no avail. I waited for a while, as I did not want to flood the engine, kick-started again unsuccessfully, waited a while, kick-started, waited again and this process carried on for what seemed a very long time. I was becoming increasingly hot, tired and thirsty, with sweat pouring down my face and I had to drink a fair amount of the water because the desert air was so dreadfully hot, dry and dehydrating.'

'After the umpteenth time of kick-starting and failing to get the engine going again, as I was feeling completely exhausted I became panicky and

desperate and felt sure that I was going to die in that desert, for no other living soul had passed by since I had entered the desert and I was completely alone.'

'I collapsed and lay down in a fit of wretched exhaustion and defeat, but I started thinking of you, my mother, my brother and my sister and I said to myself that I could not do this to you all, I could not let myself die in that goddam, forlorn desert thousands of miles from my home. I stood up, took my jacket out of one of the saddlebags, spread it out on the ground and proceeded to take the engine apart and lay each part carefully on the jacket to avoid any sand or grit getting into it. Luckily, one of my best friends at school had always had an interest in car and motorbike engines and was training to become a car mechanic. He had a motorbike of his own and had taught me on some occasions how to take an engine apart and put it back together again. So, I tried to recall from memory what he had taught me, I cleaned each part meticulously with a handkerchief, put it back in its right place and reassembled the engine. I kick-started but nothing happened; I checked the whole engine, as I feared I may not have put each part back properly, but felt sure that I had done the job correctly.'

'However, when I kick-started, waited a while, kick-started again and so on, the engine just would not start. After a very long moment of continued failure, I was completely spent and resigned myself to the horrible fact that I was destined to die in that desert, for the nearest village was still dozens of miles away and if I started walking I would simply collapse and die after a while. I knelt down on the ground, started weeping wretchedly and regretted not having taken the bus as my folly was going to kill me and I would never see my family again.'

'All of a sudden, something inside me told me not to give up but to try to kick-start the engine again. I stood up wearily, kick-started and the engine miraculously came to life with the sweetest purring sound I had ever heard! I then rode the motorbike extremely cautiously and slowly to avoid another accident and I made it to the village which was my intended destination.'

As Justin looked emotionally across the table at his father, his eyes were full of tears. Adrian, whose own eyes were very moist, stretched his left hand across the table, caressed Justin's right hand with it and said very gently as he looked deeply and warmly into Justin's eyes, 'My dear son, you were not alone in that desert. You were not destined to die in that desert. You were watched over, protected and saved by an invisible, higher spiritual force, for you have a life to live.'

'Yes, I know you are right.'

'Well, we have had enough emotions for one day! Let us now order our drinks and some food and celebrate your safe return home! Just promise me that in the future you will behave more sensibly and avoid taking any inordinate, reckless and foolhardy risks in your various activities.'

Whilst driving the car after their lunch, Adrian said no more about the terrifying and life-threatening experience that Justin had encountered. However, with his deeply engrained spiritual faith he sensed through little inner

voices that it was the souls of his two brothers who had saved their young nephew and he sent up a silent prayer of thanks to God Almighty and the spirits of his brothers for such intervention of Divine Providence which saved his son from certain death. Later on, when he told Yseult about the incident she was greatly moved and shaken and, on the next occasion she had, she pleaded with Justin to be more sensible, mature and careful in the future.

A few weeks later in mid-August 2005, Adrian and Yseult helped Justin transport his belongings and install himself comfortably in his room in the large, three-bedroomed rented flat that he was going to share with two other friends in the city of Fribourg who were also going to study Law at the University of Fribourg. All three of them chuckled in amusement as they reminisced about the happenings one year earlier, when Justin had told his parents that he was interested in applying to study Law at one of the colleges at the very historic and prestigious Cambridge University and, after some research, he had decided he wanted to apply to Sidney Sussex College. This college was the Alma Mater of the very famous and controversial Oliver Cromwell, an English military and political leader of the "Roundheads" who opposed the monarchy. He was one of the signatories of the death warrant of King Charles I in 1649 and he was the Lord Protector of the Commonwealth of England & Wales, Scotland and Ireland from 1653 to 1658.

When Sidney Sussex College had its Open Day in early September 2004, Adrian accompanied Justin over to Cambridge, where they had agreed with Adrian's Cousin Roberta and her husband Lionel that they could sleep in a guest bedroom in their charming house near the centre of Cambridge. During the next morning and part of the afternoon, Adrian and Justin had the fascinating experience of attending the Open Day, listening to various speeches about the college, the syllabuses and other important subjects, and talking with some of the college professors, staff and students. Justin was given the appropriate forms to fill in to apply for a place in the Faculty of Law. A few weeks later, he received a letter from the college summoning him for an interview in ten days' time. This time Yseult accompanied her son to Cambridge, they slept at Lionel and Roberta's house and Yseult went with Adrian to the college for his interview. However, she was shocked and indignant when she saw that morning that, instead of wearing a smart shirt, a tie, decent trousers and a proper blazer, which seemed the right attire for an important interview, Justin was only wearing a casual open-necked shirt and scruffy blue jeans with no jacket at all. When she complained, he told her that his way of dressing corresponded to his personality and he was confident that the interviewers would understand and respect that. Needless to say, Yseult laid into Justin with a strong verbal tirade when he received a notification from the college later on telling him that he had failed the interview and was not being offered a place. She said it appeared just as well that Cambridge had refused him, for if it had accepted him his arrogance would have rocketed sky-high and his head would in its pride have swelled so much that it could not have passed through the door! Feeling somewhat chastised and humbled, he had to agree

with her that he had been far too complaisant, arrogant and over-confident and it was justified that he had been brought down a peg or two and he would be satisfied with a place at the much less prestigious but still excellent University of Fribourg.

During autumn, Philippa and Adrian managed to speak over the telephone once or twice and it was agreed together with Yseult that, as Adrian's adoptive mother Margaret was coming over to spend Christmas 2005 with them at their flat, Philippa and her son Brian would fly over from Bristol airport to Geneva on Boxing Day to be with them all for a week. It was not possible for Philippa's boyfriend Raymond to come over as he had to spend Christmas and New Year with his elderly parents.

Steven had driven over from his little flat in Lausanne, Tatiana had come from her tiny flat in Geneva and, as Justin had his bedroom at the flat and Mummy was able to occupy a spare bedroom, they all enjoyed a very pleasant and happy Christmas Day celebration together. The excitement continued the next day on Boxing Day when Philippa and Brian arrived. It was marvellous and emotional for them all to meet one another and they were all very impressed and moved to see, when Steven, Justin and Brian stood side by side, how similar Brian looked to both Steven and Justin ; the similarity was so striking that one could have thought that Brian was their brother ! He told them that he had obtained a Law degree and was now studying to become a solicitor. Adrian pricked up his ears and said how uncanny this seemed, as he was an Anglo-Saxon solicitor and his newly found nephew was also going to be a solicitor!

It had been agreed that, on the next day, Mummy and Yseult would stay together at the flat and Adrian, Steven, Tatiana, Justin, Philippa and Brian would all drive in two cars to the mountain chalet and spend a few days there. As the chalet was small and only had three bedrooms, Adrian had managed to reserve two bedrooms for Philippa and Brian in a house near the centre of the village where the lady owner had a Bed & Breakfast activity. It took Philippa and Brian only three minutes to walk after breakfast up the hilly road covered in snow to the chalet at the top and enjoy the spectacular view over the snow-covered village and across to a large ski resort on the opposite mountains which were completely white and fairy-like. Adrian had started to teach his three children how to ski when each one was only two and a half years old, as each was a summer baby, and they were all very proficient and skilful skiers. However, they had over the past few years almost given up skiing in favour of the trendy snowboard and each was now a very accomplished snowboarder. Adrian hired a snowboard for beginners and the right-sized boots for Brian from the shop in the village selling and renting winter material and Steven, who was the same height as Brian, lent him appropriate clothes, gloves and goggles. Each day during the week Steven, Brian, Tatiana and Justin rode in a tele-cabin up to the top of the ski slopes and Brian had the good fortune to be given free snowboarding lessons by three expert instructors in nifty rotation! He was very sportive and fit and his three admiring cousins told Adrian and Philippa how

very impressed they were with the rapidity of his progress, and the fact that he was soon able to snowboard down the full length of the blue easier ski slope from the very top to the snow-covered garden of the chalet with only one or two tumbles. While the young were enjoying themselves on their snowboards, Adrian and Philippa enjoyed each other's company and getting to know more about each other and their respective lives.

Their short holiday up in the mountain village flew by far too quickly and they were all a little sad when they left the chalet and drove back to the flat, but they were very pleased to be with Mummy and Yseult again. Two days later, after Adrian and Yseult had driven Philippa and Brian to Geneva airport for their flight and they had all said emotional and tearful goodbyes, Adrian smiled to Yseult in the car going back home and said cheerfully,

'Not long ago I said that I had lost both my brothers but I had gained a sister. Now I can say that I have also gained another nephew! Brian is a splendid fellow, he got on extremely well with Steven, Tatiana and Justin and it was extraordinary how much he looks like Steven and Justin. I do hope that we will be able to see much more of both Philippa and Brian in the coming years for they are wonderful and much loved additions to the family!'

Adrian was very touched and highly emotionally affected when he received from Philippa some weeks later a small photo album containing various photos which moved him greatly. There was a black and white photo of Anita standing beside six-year old Adrian and holding his hand and another black and white photo of little Adrian standing by himself with the treasured garden shed behind him in the lovely garden of the house called "Paddock Gates" in Caterham. There were also two black-and-white photos of Anita sitting beside Adrian's father at a restaurant table in what appeared to be a happy pose, she looking so beautiful and elegant, and he looking so handsome and distinguished. All these photos must have been taken with Anita's own camera and Philippa wrote in her covering letter that she had found the photos in her mother's belongings after her death and had had copies made of them for Adrian. There were also a few coloured photos of Philippa when she was younger and when Adrian showed them to Yseult she agreed with him that Philippa was indeed a very pretty and attractive girl. As he looked intently at all the photos, he was reminded with nostalgic sadness of the very lovely, gentle and kind Anita and his hope at the time that she would become his second mother and the way in which his dreadful father had dashed that hope through his appalling attitudes and behaviour. He looked lovingly at the photos of Philippa and felt so grateful to his sister that she had done the necessary to find him, make contact with him and become an essential, warm and everlasting part of his life.

Chapter 13

Renewed Confidence in Life and Serenity
with Family

In early January 2006, Adrian became very dismayed, disappointed and concerned for his future professional activities when the commercial company which had given him a mandate with a retainer fee two years earlier told him that they would no longer require his services as from end January.

However, he felt blessed and protected when he was soon approached through some contacts by a Mr Duncan Worburg, the owner of a small but highly profitable group of financial and asset management companies in Geneva, who asked him to go to see him at his office as soon as possible. When he arrived, Mr Worburg explained that he needed the urgent advice and negotiating and drafting skills of an Anglo-Saxon solicitor with international experience for an important international commercial and financial project that one of his companies was involved with. As it became clear to him during their discussion that Adrian possessed all the necessary skills and experience to be of efficient assistance to him, he gave the mandate immediately to Adrian and agreed an hourly basis legal fee that he would earn in accordance with the number of hours he would work on the project and record on a specific time-sheet opened for that matter.

In the second part of January, Adrian and Yseult were delighted to hear from Alan, the eldest of Lionel and Roberta's three offspring. They had known Alan for quite a few years as he had come to stay with them on holiday in his late teens at their Provencal villa. He had undertaken horticultural studies and had set up his own gardening business in Cambridge when he was in his early twenties. As he had a special interest in Eastern European countries and culture, he had spent some time in Budapest, the capital city of Hungary, where he had met a delightful and highly intelligent Hungarian girl named Elspeth who was working as a lawyer in a prominent law firm in Budapest.

On his last short stay with them in the villa a few months before they rented it out, he had told Adrian and Yseult that he had established a new gardening business in Budapest and he loved Elspeth very much but he was not at all sure that she returned his deep feelings.

However, when he sent his e-mail to them in January 2006, he announced the marvellous news that their relationship had developed well, he had proposed to her and she had accepted to become his wife. He told Adrian and

Yseult that he was going to send them an invitation to the wedding, which would take place in Budapest in two months' time on the last Saturday of March and he hoped that they would like to and would be free to come. He added that his parents, his sister Isadora and his younger brother Lawrence with his Japanese wife Etsawa would all be coming and he was arranging suitable accommodation for them all and would do so as well for Adrian and Yseult if they were coming. Adrian had a deep affection for Alan and was delighted for him. Both Adrian and Yseult flew over to Budapest, attended the lovely and happy wedding celebration in Elspeth's parish church and the ensuing reception together with her mother and other members of her family and all the members of Alan's family and some local Hungarian friends. Adrian and Yseult took the advantage of having a relaxing holiday in Budapest as well and did some pleasant sight-seeing together with Alan, Elspeth, Lionel, Roberta, Isadora, Lawrence and Etsawa, and were especially happy to strengthen and deepen those family ties.

After he had finished the first mandate for Mr Worburg and the project was successfully completed by the end of April, Mr Worburg told Adrian that he was so pleased and impressed by Adrian's ability, rapidity and efficiency as a solicitor that he wanted to entrust to him a second very interesting, complicated and quite demanding mandate, which Adrian accepted with alacrity. When he had accomplished that task by end June, Mr Worburg told him that, due to its flourishing and satisfying expansion, his group of companies needed to engage a good internal Head of Legal & Compliance and he offered Adrian the job and pleaded with him to accept it. After serious reflection and discussion with Yseult, he decided to accept the post as it would provide him with a steady flow of work, a reasonable salary and pension benefits and overall job security, all of which were lacking in his tiny, one-man law office. He would not have a secretary but that did not bother him. Mr Worburg told him that he wanted him to start his new employment at the beginning of October, which would allow him to enjoy a pleasant and relaxing summer. Adrian informed the Law Society in Geneva that he was closing his law office and he started to anticipate entering into the new employment with great enthusiasm.

Shortly after mid-July 2006, Adrian and Yseult set out on a most unexpected, very welcome and extremely pleasant adventure for a few days, filled with deep emotion for Adrian in particular. Three months earlier, Adrian had been surprised and absolutely delighted to receive a warm message by email from Peter, the second son of Adrian's deceased and much missed eldest brother Neil. Peter had announced that he and his fiancée Sally were arranging their wedding for the third weekend of July, were inviting Adrian and Yseult to come to the wedding, if it was possible, and, hoping for a positive response, he was looking forward with great pleasure to meet his uncle and aunt for the first time, as this was the first occasion which had arisen over the years for a get-together to be concretised. He had added that it would also enable Adrian and Yseult to meet his mother Sheila and his elder brother Neil for the first time, as well as Sally's parents, her younger sister Jamesina and other members of her

family and some of their friends. He had divulged that the wedding would take place on Kirkwall, the largest island of Orkney, the archipelago of islands north of mainland Scotland, as all the members of Sally's family lived up there and Sally had been born and raised in Orkney and had met Peter when they were both students at the University of Glasgow in mainland Scotland. It had only taken Adrian about two minutes to obtain Yseult's agreement to make the trip and Adrian had had several email exchanges with his nephew Peter concerning various aspects of the forthcoming trip and stay in Orkney.

A few days before the date of the wedding, Adrian and Yseult flew from Geneva to Edinburgh and were fortunate to be able to sleep for two nights in the spacious and comfortable flat owned by a couple of close friends who lived near them in Switzerland. They played the curious, relaxed and happy tourists during those two days and visited the principal sights that the beautiful city of Edinburgh has to offer, including the impressive castle built in the 12th century standing majestically like a wary sentinel up on its great rock, formed after a volcano erupted over 340 million years ago. Holyrood Palace situated at the bottom end of the Royal Mile at the opposite end to the castle, which was built between 1671 and 1678 and is the official residence of the British monarch in Scotland. The present Scottish Parliament building located in the Holyrood area of the city and constructed in 2004. The Sir Walter Scott Monument, erected by public subscription in Binny sandstone from West Lothian from 1840 to 1844 to commemorate Sir Walter Scott who was hailed as one of Scotland's greatest novelists, with 287 steps to the top which provides an amazing spot from which to view the city.

Adrian and Yseult flew from Edinburgh to Aberdeen, then travelled in a small, two-propeller aeroplane with just twenty-six other passengers, were most impressed by the lovely view of the sea which was very close on the right side of the aeroplane as they descended to the somewhat miniscule airport of Kirkwall about three miles from the city of Kirkwall and were interested to be told by the pilot that the archipelago of Orkney is separated from mainland Scotland by Pentland Firth, a mere six-mile wide seaway. The islands are mainly low lying with rugged cliffs on some western coasts and have a notable absence of trees mainly accounted for by the amount of winds and their immense force and speeds, especially during the long winter months.

Adrian and Yseult met Peter, Sally, Jamesina, their parents and Peter's mother Sheila for a copious lunch at a hotel near the port of Kirkwall. It was an extraordinarily emotive moment for Adrian and he embraced Peter then Sheila, about whom he had received very laudatory comments from his deceased and much missed middle brother Justin. Adrian felt very sad that he was not able to meet his second nephew, Peter's elder brother Neil, as he had unfortunately been prevented from coming up for the wedding due to some unforeseen last-minute circumstances. After the pleasant lunch, Sheila, Adrian and Yseult were taken for a walk by the others to visit some of the main sites of Kirkwall, originally a Viking town founded in 1040 A.D., now Orkney's capital and the islands' largest city, including the imposing Saint Magnus Cathedral dating

from the early 12th century constructed from local red sandstone, the Bishop's Palace and the Earl's Palace, administrative buildings dating from the era when the Vikings ruled the Orkney islands, and Highland Park Distillery, the most northern whiskey distillery in the world where the peat distilled single malt whiskey is truly fabulous.

The following day, the day of the wedding, was marvellous with a very joyful atmosphere and Adrian and Yseult were impressed by the friendliness and warm, generous hospitality of all the members of Sally's family and their numerous friends. In the evening, after the splendid dinner, it seemed, as the large building continued to become fuller and fuller with dancing and singing people, that the entire population of the island had been invited to participate in the energetically rousing, head-spinning, ankle-tiring, cheerfully noisy and magnificent Scottish ball!

When Adrian saw the announcement in a legal journal that an international conference on legal areas which were of great interest to him would take place in a hotel in London at the end of that July, he contacted Philippa and asked whether it might be possible for him to meet up with her and Raymond somewhere in town during his two-day stay at the hotel in London. She soon came back with the most unexpected, generous and very welcome invitation for him to spend the two nights staying with her and Raymond at Raymond's two-bedroomed flat situated in Battersea, which would not only be great fun but would avoid him the expense of paying for a hotel room. The conference was highly interesting and instructive and his stay at the flat in Battersea was extremely pleasant and one evening he took Raymond and Philippa out for a lovely meal at one of their most favourite Chinese restaurants. Philippa had also mentioned that, whilst she stayed at Raymond's flat from time to time, she did not actually live with him there and she had her own home together with Brian in a small cottage that she was renting in the picturesque village of Plaxtol very near Sevenoaks and not very far from Tunbridge Wells and she had invited Adrian to go there with her after his conference, see Brian again and stay for a few nights. When they arrived at the cottage, Adrian and Brian were delighted to meet again and Brian introduced his uncle to his then girlfriend who happened to be visiting at that time. Later on, when Brian and his girlfriend had gone out for the evening and Philippa and Adrian were chatting alone together in the lovely living room whilst sipping a glass of cool, delicious white wine, Adrian reminded his sister that he and Yseult had mentioned to her and Raymond the visit that they had made in September 2003 to Mrs Joanna Barker at her home in Rustington. He said that he had looked at a map and had seen that Rustington was about sixty-eight miles south-west below Plaxtol and he thought that Rustington could be reached within one and a half hours by driving down on the motorway M23. Before he could say anymore Philippa took a large gulp of her wine and, with her lovely large eyes almost popping out, she asked excitedly,

'Are you suggesting that we could drive down together during your stay to visit this Mrs Barker?'

'Yes, my dear, that is exactly what I want to suggest! This is a golden opportunity for you to meet her and for me to see her a second time. She was our father's last lover and companion. She is a very lovely and friendly lady and I am sure that you will take to her immediately. I have her telephone number and her address with me in my little diary. I can call her here and now and ask if she would mind our visiting her tomorrow. What do you say? Would you like that?'

Philippa stood up hastily to go to the fridge in the kitchen and take out the wine bottle in order to refill their glasses and as she walked back into the living room holding the bottle she put her free hand on Adrian's shoulder, bent down and gave him a tender kiss on the cheek then said,

'Yes, it is a wonderful and thoughtful suggestion, dear brother! I will be most happy to meet the lady who was the last important person in our father's life. You can call her using my home telephone sitting on the small table over there.'

Mrs Barker was quite taken aback but very pleased when she heard Adrian's voice and said she would be delighted to welcome them for a cup of tea at about three o'clock in the afternoon the next day. On the following morning, Philippa told Brian that she and Adrian would be leaving after lunch in her car to drive down to visit Mrs Barker. When she reversed the car out of the garage, Adrian almost squealed with boyish joy when he saw that it was a black Mazda MX-5, as this was his favourite sports car of all in the category of affordable sports cars, since the car of his dreams, the classic E-Type Jaguar, was way beyond his means. It was fortunately a bright, sunny summer day and they drove cheerfully with the hood down and a warm breeze caressing their hair and their faces. The traffic was light, Philippa drove fast and skilfully as if she had been a Formula One racing driver in earlier years and they arrived on the outskirts of Rustington after a mere one hour and fifteen minutes. It took a little time to find the correct street, as the last time Adrian had come to the town he had approached it from the north-western side, as he and Yseult had come down from Bristol Airport, and he felt a little lost and disorientated by this approach from the north-eastern side. However, they finally reached the bungalow and Adrian was delighted to see the lovely garden again with all the colourful summer flowers and the beautiful rose bushes in full bloom.

The hour and a half chatting easily and emotionally with Mrs Barker, looking at her photos, sipping tea and partaking of her tasty ginger biscuits flew by all too quickly. When Adrian and Philippa said goodbye to her, Mrs Barker embraced them both very warmly and told them how happy she was to see their father's daughter and sole surviving son together and she complimented Philippa on how clever she had been in managing to find and make contact with Adrian. The drive back to Plaxtol was pleasant and without any encumbrances or hitches and Philippa told Adrian very emotionally how strange she felt at having actually been for the first time in her life in a place where her father, entirely absent from her life, had lived, loved, breathed and slept. She also told him how uncanny it felt to see how very much like her

mother Mrs Barker was in physical appearance, stature and elegance. Having known Anita briefly when he was a six-year old boy, Adrian conferred willingly with her assessment, especially after having seen those photos of Anita in the album that Philippa had sent him and having a romanticised and enhanced image of her natural beauty and elegance in his mind.

Two mornings later, after Adrian had said farewell to Brian and his girlfriend, Philippa drove him to Gatwick Airport and, when they embraced in a tearful and highly emotional farewell, she thanked him profusely for having arranged for her to meet Mrs Barker and for including her in and sharing with her the sentimentally important relationship with their father's last lover and companion in life.

Within the first two months in his new employment, Adrian discovered a completely unexpected, unpleasant and frustrating situation, very different from what he had expected. Whilst he had worked for Mr Worburg's group as an independent legal adviser, Mr Worburg had treated him with a certain respect and deference. Once he was in the man's clutches as one of his employees, he was treated very harshly and with a total lack of respect.

Adrian saw rapidly that Mr Worburg was a Dr Jekyll and Mr Hyde type of character who bent over backwards to please, flatter and grovel to clients and external consultants in his dealings with them but behaved inside the offices in a very disrespectful, dictatorial, bullying, threatening and mentally cruel manner towards all the employees. He quickly subjected Adrian to immense stress and pressure and rude, oppressive and denigrating remarks and actions.

Further, he had engaged Adrian as the group's Head of Legal & Compliance but when it suited him he reacted to Adrian's legal advice and opinions on the compliance aspects as if they were not worth anything, had no value or pertinence and were to be ignored or discarded, saying that he was the big boss and could do whatever he wanted.

Instead of acceding to compliance with the prevailing laws and regulations in financial, stock exchange and other business matters in pursuance of Adrian's correct advice, recommendations and warnings, he acted frequently in total conflict of interest between his own personal money-making and investment affairs and the business conducted by the group's companies. Adrian discovered to his horror that the boss was acting illegally and in flagrant contravention of clear regulations on certain occasions. Under the bullying, harassing, disparaging and denigrating attitudes and conduct of Mr Worburg Adrian started over the next few months, with his hyper-sensitivity and mental fragility, to suffer again slightly, in an automatic way entirely beyond his control, from the mental, psychological and emotional problems, insecurities and complexes that he had painfully endured in previous years and an increasing lack of confidence, difficulty to concentrate and a feeling once more that he was rather worthless and without much value.

In January 2007, Adrian's niece Lydia sent him an e-mail saying that she had followed the advice he had given her after her sister Lynette's wedding, she had hung on to Arthur and they were going to get married in Auckland in

early March. Just as Lynette had requested for her wedding, Lydia asked Adrian if he would be able to come to the wedding and give her away in the place of her father Justin. Adrian felt elated that the relationship between Lydia and Arthur had developed and deepened so well that they were now going to be united by the sacrament of marriage. He and Yseult planned to fly down to Auckland together for the wedding and to take a holiday to spend some time with the family members. However, two unexpected problems interfered with their plans. Firstly, Mr Worburg nastily and cruelly forbid Adrian from taking any holiday at all and ordered him to return back to Geneva after only three days in Auckland around the wedding, on the pretext that he needed Adrian's presence in some meetings involving negotiations for a new project. Secondly, poor Yseult fell ill with a terribly bad bronchitis just a week before the scheduled date of their flight down to Auckland. As she was far too unwell and weak to make the trip, it was agreed that Justin would replace his mother, take the few days from his studies at university and accompany his father on the trip. Lydia and Arthur had chosen another beautiful location for their wedding and the reception and, as it had been at Lynette's wedding, it was a lovely and highly emotional reunion for Adrian and Justin with them all, especially as Philippa was able to fly down from England and to join them all in the happy reunion and festivities.

After returning home following the wonderful but regretfully far too short three-day long weekend in Auckland, Justin returned to the rented flat in Fribourg and Adrian, now beginning to feel the onslaught of the jetlag, got up wearily the next morning, drove down to the local railway station, left his car there in the carpark as usual and took the early express train to Geneva. However, as he walked through the Cornavin station on his way to the office building, which was only three streets away, he started to feel very unwell, collapsed suddenly, fell headlong and banged his head on the hard floor. He lay very dazed as he slowly regained consciousness then felt the strong arms of two men lifting him up and helping him to stand. As there was a pharmacy very near that spot, they helped him to walk into the pharmacy, where he was given a chair to sit on. The pharmacist measured his blood pressure with his apparatus and told Adrian with a shocked voice that his blood pressure was extremely and even dangerously high and he needed to be checked straightaway by a doctor. He said that there was an emergency medical centre very near the railway station in Rue Chantepoulet and, after Adrian had remained resting on the chair for a long moment, an assistant held Adrian under an arm as she accompanied him on foot to the medical centre.

After a doctor had given him a thorough check-up and undertaken some necessary analyses, he asked Adrian if he had very recently had any extremely exerting, tiring and stressful activity. When Adrian mentioned his long, very tiring flight down to Auckland, his three-day stay on the spot then the long, exhausting return flight, the doctor told him that was undoubtedly the cause of his collapse that morning. He said that the two long flights with such an inordinately short time to recuperate in between had put an extreme stress,

strain and pressure on his heart and he could have suffered a life-threatening heart attack and it was because he kept himself physically fit through running and other exercise that he had a strong heart and had had a mere alert but not a heart attack. He said that if one flies down to Australia or New Zealand one must always stay down there for at least ten days to two weeks in order to allow one's system to adjust and to avoid any heart problem. He gave Adrian a medical certificate and ordered him to return home and rest completely for two days before returning to work. When Adrian explained the type of boss he had and the fact that he expected him back at work that morning, the doctor noted his name and telephone number and told Adrian he would telephone him quickly explaining what had happened and tearing a strip off him for his harsh and cruel attitude towards an employee which could have had very dramatic consequences.

When Adrian returned to the office after resting two days, he was greeted by a very angry, indignant and aggressive Mr Worburg who, with his authoritarian, inconsiderate and arrogant manner, said he had not at all appreciated the telephone call he had received from the doctor. His behaviour towards Adrian became immediately much worse than before and under the barrage of bullying, scathing and denigrating attitudes and psychologically oppressive conduct Adrian became rapidly very despondent and started to feel depressed. However, he told himself that he must not cave in, for he had undergone a long, in-depth psychiatric analysis and treatment and had been given the mental and emotional tools to be a strong resilient and to react with forceful and positive resistance against a negative, bad and potentially destructive situation. He said to himself and to Yseult that he would no longer tolerate all this ghastly, unjust and damaging mistreatment like a cowering, beaten dog but was going to bite back. So, acting as a strong resilient, he defiantly handed Mr Worburg his letter of resignation at end March, only having to give one month's legal notice within his first year on the job. And he slammed the big boss's door and left the group at end April 2007, after just eight months working as an unfortunate employee of this abominable, twisted and impossible man.

In order to celebrate their thirty-third wedding anniversary on May 4th, and to give them a change of environment and ideas, Adrian reserved a bedroom for himself and Yseult at a lovely Bed & Breakfast for a few days in the countryside near the wonderful town of Gorde in the Luberon part of Provence in southern France, an area which they had always loved and which they were able to reach easily by car.

On the second day, as they sat on the sunlit, warm terrace consuming their breakfast, Adrian divulged that he did not feel sad at all about the end of his job but was, on the contrary, very relieved at having left the unsavoury and negative situation and he felt a renewed confidence in life and in the future by acting as a strong resilient should. And he was convinced that he would find another suitable employment before very long, as there was no question of going back to be an independent lawyer.

As she looked at her husband, Yseult detected that there was a big change in him and she felt very gratified and relieved that he had accepted to undergo the psychiatric treatment, which from appearances seemed to have been quite successful as she saw his much less anxious and more positive and confident approach about future prospects.

In early September that year 2007, during Justin's summer holiday break from his studies at university, he and his parents flew over to England and enjoyed a most pleasant holiday visiting Mummy for several days and celebrating together her eighty-ninth birthday at the charming small house where she was now living near the centre of the town of Sidmouth.

When she was in her mid-eighties a few years earlier several friends and the parish priest at the Roman Catholic Church in Sidmouth, of which she was a most ardent and active parishioner, had urged her to start thinking about finding a suitable house in Sidmouth itself and selling her cottage in the countryside, as once she had to stop driving her car due to advanced old age or any other impediment she would be very cut off and stranded living out in Metcombe and would find it difficult going to church for Mass and other celebrations and visiting all her friends and the shops in town.

In mid-2006, she had telephoned Adrian and had glibly announced to him in a very matter-of-fact manner that she had bought a small house with a pleasant terrace and tiny bit of garden in a lovely situation very near the centre of Sidmouth, within easy walking distance from the church, and was about to complete the sale of her cottage in Metcombe! Adrian had been very impressed and immensely proud of Mummy who had done all that by herself without requesting any assistance from him or Yseult. She had told him that local removers and some friends were helping her make the move from the cottage to the house in Sidmouth and she was having some items of furniture put into storage, as she had no room for them at the two-bedroomed house. As it was during Justin's summer holiday, he and Yseult had flown over and helped Mummy undertake the move. When Adrian had come over to stay with her in her new home and to celebrate her eighty-eighth birthday in September 2006, she had been very worried that he might not like the house and might say she had made a mistake in buying it. She had had no cause for worry, as he had said he liked the house immediately and thought it was ideal for her and in such an excellent and suitable situation. She had told him that she had been informed at Mass one Sunday by the lady who lived in the house next door, who was also a parishioner at the local Catholic church, that the lady who owned this house was having to go to an old people's home and her family were going to sell the house. But luckily, they had not yet put it on the market, so Mummy should speak directly to them, having an inside track, and offer to buy the house, which she did. With his deep spiritual faith, Adrian had told Mummy that he felt convinced that the intervention of Divine Providence had brought her this new home and she had concurred immediately with his assessment.

Philippa told Adrian in an e-mail in June 2007 that both she and Raymond were moving, she from Plaxtol and he from a flat he was renting in the tourist

village of Dunster on the north coast of the County of Somerset, in order to live together in a house which they were renting in the centre of the small village of Stogumber nestled in beautiful countryside about ten miles south-east of Dunster, several miles north of Taunton, the capital town of Somerset, and on the eastern flank of the picturesque Brendan Hills. When Adrian informed Philippa that he, Yseult and Justin were going to visit Mummy in September and celebrate her eighty-ninth birthday with her, it was agreed that after their stay, on their drive in the hire car back to Bristol Airport to return to Geneva, they would make a deviation and visit Raymond and Philippa in their new home. When the time came in September, as they arrived in the village of Stogumber and drove up the High Street they saw when they read the name of the house on the front door that it could not have been more in the centre of the village as it was two doors down from the essential, all-important village pub and across the road from the village church. It was a very old, quaint and charming house with a lovely garden out at the back, where they all sat around a small table on the terrace sipping tea and chumping biscuits as they chatted and caught up on their respective news. Adrian thought that it was a sizeable garden, but Raymond and Philippa told them they were renting this house so as to see whether they liked the life and people in this village and, although they had been told that the house was going to be sold at some point, they did not want to buy it for they harboured a dream to acquire a property somewhere in the local countryside not far from the village with several acres of land upon which they would keep sheep and perhaps some other animals. Philippa said she would keep Adrian informed of the progress of their search for such a paradise.

***

After the gruelling, pressurised and exhausting years studying hard at the Cantonal School of Art in Lausanne, Adrian's and Yseult's elder son Steven qualified in the summer of 2007 as an Industrial Designer. He was still living in his small rented flat in Lausanne and began to obtain some interesting mandates in the industrial design field and, together with some of his friends who had also graduated from the same school as Industrial Designers, he started to make the annual pilgrimage each spring to the mecca of industrial design, the huge, foremost and reputable Industrial Design Show in the city of Milan in Italy.

As for Adrian's and Yseult's daughter Tatiana, she had graduated successfully in the summer of 2006 at the Art College in Geneva. She had then worked during the ensuing months in various short-term jobs, some reasonably interesting and others totally boring, with the sole aim of earning and saving as much money as she could for she had decided that she wanted to spend a year living and pursuing further art studies in Italy and taking courses learning the Italian language. In the summer of 2007, she bid a tearful goodbye to her parents and her two brothers as she boarded the train at Geneva railway station

bound for the magical and cultural city of Florence, the heart of the Italian Renaissance movement several centuries earlier and still a very important centre of art, as well as being a city flooded by hordes of tourists each year. After six months studying art and the Italian language in Florence, Tatiana moved to Milan for further courses in art and Italian. She was delighted when her parents were able to accompany Steven to visit the Industrial Design Show in Milan in spring 2008. She went with them to walk around all the stands and exhibits and admire the magnificent, varied and creative products made by a wide variety of industrial designers, including her own elder brother, followed by a visit to the Duomo, the majestic cathedral of Milan.

Adrian, Yseult and Steven were all able to doss down for two nights in Tatiana's spacious bedroom in the flat that she shared with two other girls also studying art situated in the basement of a block of flats not too far from the centre of Milan. They were all very happy to be able to spend this pleasant and joyful time together before her parents and elder brother had to leave her since she was staying in Milan until the end of her art and language courses in the summer.

After Adrian left the job with the group of Mr Worburg, he spent several months searching fruitlessly for a new employment. He found to his dismay and frustration that he was the victim once more of the three "overs" – over-qualified, over-experienced and over-aged!

However, he saw by pure chance one day a small advertisement in the newspaper placed by a small asset management company in Geneva searching for an experienced Head of Legal & Compliance. He replied straightaway without hesitation and felt very relieved and gratified when he was called for a first interview with a lady in charge of personnel matters. He was even more gratified and encouraged when he was asked to return for an interview with two of the asset managers then for a third and final interview with the general manager of the company, who was also one of the asset managers and the majority shareholder of this private company. He found it unbelievable, absolutely wonderful and almost miraculous when he was offered the post just a few months before his sixtieth birthday!

He thought back to that visit to the offices for his first interview, how pleasant he had found the offices, the overall atmosphere and how he had seemed to hear little inner voices whispering to him that he was going to work in those offices as he sat in a comfortable, leather-upholstered chair in the large conference room, waiting for the personnel lady to come in to interview him.

After he had signed the employment contract in the office of the general manager and had left the building with one fully signed original of the contract in his briefcase, he could not help but have a feeling deep inside that he had heard on that first visit to those offices the souls of his two brothers whispering to him and that it was Divine Providence that had come to his assistance and salvation yet again and had brought him this new employment.

With a very deep gratitude to the souls of his two brothers in Heaven and to Divine Providence and a clearly renewed confidence in life and a buoyant and

positive attitude Adrian commenced this last part of his professional career on May 1st 2008, just a couple of weeks after that lovely visit to Milan with Yseult and Steven and the extremely happy reunion with Tatiana.

Adrian was overjoyed to receive an e-mail from Alan, the elder son of Lionel and Cousin Roberta, informing him that Elspeth had given birth in early June 2008 to a girl, whom they named Julianna, and he and Elspeth would be delighted if Adrian and Yseult could make the trip to Budapest for her baptism. He added that his parents and his sister Isadora would be coming over from Cambridge, but his brother Lawrence and his little family would not be able to come as they lived in Hong-Kong and Lawrence was not able to take time off his work to make the long trip. Yseult knew that contacts, whenever possible, with various members of his own birth family were extremely important to Adrian, even more so after the tragic loss of both his brothers. She realised that it was easy for her to maintain contacts with her own family as they saw different members, most notably her two brothers and two sisters and their own family units, each time they visited the Valais and stayed up at the family chalet in the mountains.

So, she agreed immediately that it would be lovely to go over for the christening and Adrian obtained easily the permission from his kind and very humane new boss to take a couple of days holiday around the weekend in early July to fly over to Budapest, participate in the joyful christening of Julianna and the most happy reunion with Alan, Elspeth, Lionel, Roberta, Isadora and members of Elspeth's family and circle of close friends.

Adrian and Yseult flew over to England that Easter 2008 and spent a few very pleasant days celebrating the Easter festivities with Mummy in her new home, being able to sleep in the second bedroom upstairs in her small house. They took her out for lunch on Easter Sunday to her favourite restaurant in Sidmouth and while they were all appreciating the excellent dessert Adrian said to her, 'Mummy, it will be your ninetieth birthday this September. We will organise a big party for you at that time at a restaurant of your choice and will naturally invite Uncle Patrick and Aunt Josephine, your brother and sister-in-law, their three offspring and their own families, our three young and all the friends that you wish to invite, just as we did to celebrate your eightieth birthday ten years ago. However, on top of that, as the ninetieth birthday is a very important milestone and you always told us that you probably would not reach it, but you have, Yseult and I are wondering whether you would like anything very special as a present to mark this very special birthday?'

Mummy thought for a moment, looked from Adrian to Yseult and said somewhat wistfully and sheepishly, 'Well, I visited Italy many decades ago with some friends in 1950 when I was thirty-two years old and have always cherished the wonderful memories of that trip. I even had the good fortune to participate in an audience at the Vatican in Rome with the then leader of the Roman Catholic Church, Pope Pius XII, who I remember well had an aura of saintliness about him. If I could, I would love to visit Italy one more time before I die, if that is not too much to ask.'

Adrian gazed at Yseult with a quizzical look and was delighted when she smiled and said kindly with her enchanting voice, 'That is an excellent idea, Mummy! As you know, Adrian will start a new job on May 1st, so I imagine it will be rather difficult for him to take time off this summer to travel with us to Italy and I know already that Steven will be working hard throughout this summer on important mandates that he must accomplish within a set deadline. I suggest you, Justin and I could all go to Italy for a week and meet up with Tatiana who will still be in Italy until mid-August. Leave it to me. I will speak with both Tatiana and Justin and I am sure he will be most happy to accompany us on the trip in mid-July during his summer holiday from the University of Fribourg.'

With her usual abounding energy, great dynamism and lively enthusiasm, Yseult organised the special trip in conjunction with Tatiana and Justin over the period of the next months. During the week after their return from the stay in Budapest, Yseult flew over to England, stayed a couple of days with Mummy, helped her pack her suitcase for the Italian adventure and flew back to Switzerland with her. On the day of their departure by train to Milan, Adrian drove the very excited trio of Mummy, Yseult and Justin to the Geneva railway station and waved a loving goodbye from the platform as the train drew slowly out of the station.

They were met by Tatiana at the Milan railway station some hours later and spent a fantastic and joyful week together with her visiting Milan, Florence, Sienna, Assisi where they attended Mass at the famous basilica of St Francis, several old, charming and romantic villages. And finally Pisa, from where the three of them took an aeroplane flight to Geneva airport, where Adrian met them and drove them back to the family flat. Tatiana returned by train to her digs in Milan, as she would only be returning home to Switzerland a few weeks later after her marvellous year living and studying in Italy.

After Mummy unpacked her suitcase, she showed Adrian with alacrity some of the items she had purchased in various places during their Italian tour. He was most impressed and amused when she put on the bright red leather jacket she had fallen for and just could not resist and he told her she would be the most rock-and-roll and youngest looking ninety-year-old granny in the whole of England when she went out on the town wearing that splendid, eye-catching and garish red leather jacket!

She had also bought a most fetching pair of red leather slippers and Adrian gleefully remarked that they were exactly the same type and colour of slippers that His Holiness the Pope wore and, if she ever had the chance to attend an audience with the current pontiff Pope Benedict XVI at the Vatican, she should not forget to wear those red slippers so she could impress His Holiness with their matching pairs! She thanked Adrian and Yseult profusely for their generosity and told them that they had given her the most enjoyable and unforgettable birthday present of her whole life.

The development of Adrian's deeper involvement in his own family's matters with his beloved wife and three wonderful offspring and in as frequent

contacts as possible in various ways with members of Yseult's family in Switzerland, Mummy's family and his own birth family in England, Hungary, Australia and New Zealand became of paramount importance and priority to him. He felt very sad, regretful and guilty about having missed out on so many aspects of his three children's evolution, progress, problems and achievements when they were very young and as they became gradually older, due to his very deep personal pains and suffering, mental and emotional problems, obsessions with the past and difficulties to concentrate on and live in the present after his dreadfully unhappy childhood and other bad experiences, as well as the appalling impact and nearly destructive effect on his entire being of the suicidal catastrophe of Neil and the tragic death of Justin.

After having undergone that vital, most necessary and salutary psychiatric treatment, whilst he could not swear that he had been completely and definitively cured of all his mental and emotional ills, fragility, insecurity and hyper-sensitivity, he was very gratified to see that he had gained a good degree of inner stability, security, self-esteem and normality, did not dwell on the awful past nearly so much and was beginning to be able to live more in the present and derive much more positive stimulus and enjoyment from the multifarious family events on a day-to day basis. He wanted to be there fully for his beloved wife and three offspring and do all he could to ensure the happiness of each one of them. The biggest drawbacks and handicaps in his healing process were that he could no longer support stressful situations and he still had to cope with and try as best he could to overcome certain difficulties to concentrate, but he considered they were somewhat minor aggravations as compared to the enormous progress achieved in many important ways through the psychiatric treatment.

During the past eighteen months, Tatiana had toyed with the prospect of attending one of the prestigious art schools in and around London. After a certain amount of research and some interviews, she decided that, after her year studying art and Italian in Italy, she preferred to study for a year to obtain a Master of Illustration at the University of Falmouth in the County of Cornwall in England. Tatiana was a very talented artist with a wonderful imagination and some of the paintings, drawings and illustrations that she had produced during her year in Italy were most impressive and proof of her outstanding artistic abilities. She knew that the arts department of the University of Falmouth had an excellent reputation and that it would be most beneficial to study there for the Master of Illustration.

So, at the end of August 2008, Adrian, Yseult and Tatiana all flew over to Bristol airport then drove down in a large hire car with Tatiana's packed suitcases, left those at the pleasant house in the town of Falmouth where Tatiana was renting a room and then took a walking tour around the campus of the university and visited the rooms and the art studio where Tatiana would be studying and working on her art illustrations during the forthcoming year. They were then able to drive up to Sidmouth where Steven and Justin, who had flown over from Geneva, joined them at Granny's house and a few days

afterwards, they all enjoyed a wonderful luncheon party at a very charming restaurant, together with all the members of Mummy's own family and her closest friends, in a very joyful and happy celebration of Mummy's ninetieth birthday.

When Tatiana returned home after the first term for her Christmas holiday, she confided to Adrian and Yseult that she had met a young man and they had started going out together.

'His name is Arawan, he is half-French with a French mother and half-English as his father, now unfortunately deceased, was an Englishman. I was sitting one evening in a corner of a pub in Falmouth with two girlfriends studying with me when one whispered to me that a very handsome and attractive-looking young man who was sitting at the bar had been glancing over at me for quite a while and seem to be interested in me. When I looked over at him as discreetly as possible I saw that he was indeed very good-looking and our eyes met. When I left the pub with my two friends, he simply smiled shyly at me but did not say anything. A few days later, I saw him again at the same pub and this time he ambled over, introduced himself and asked me if I would like to go to have a coffee somewhere with him the following day. When we met and were drinking our coffee, he told me he was studying for a Master of Photography at Falmouth University, and he has a brother who lives with his wife and two children in a small town in north Devon. We have gone out together several times since then and we will see how the relationship develops over the coming months.'

Their relationship developed very positively and a little while before the summer, when both would be graduating with their respective Master diploma, Tatiana left the boarding house where she had been staying and moved in with Arawan in the small and charming converted barn that he was renting in the grounds of a lovely farm which had a reasonably large and pleasant farmhouse, a second and larger converted barn rented by one of Tatiana's artist girlfriends, and several acres of gardens and fields with a magnificent view over the rolling Cornish hills and a glimpse of the nearby sea on a sunny day.

Adrian and Yseult flew over and attended Tatiana's graduation in the summer, were most impressed by the exhibition of all her illustrations and were very proud parents as she received her Master of Illustration diploma. They were introduced by her to Arawan and were able to admire all the photos he had taken for his exhibition and to applaud as he received his Master of Photography diploma.

Adrian and Yseult became prouder and prouder of their elder son Steven as his professional achievements and successes snowballed and his reputation on the industrial design market increased. In the first years, he worked on several interesting mandates designing and making different products in various materials. One thing led to another and, through the success of his industrial design work, he was approached by the management of an important museum in Geneva to be the scenographer imagining, designing and creating together

with the museum's technical team all the decor and supports for a large forthcoming exhibition.

When Adrian, Yseult, Justin and Steven's steady girlfriend Marianne were shown around the exhibition by Steven just before the opening ceremony they could not believe what they saw and were immensely impressed by the magnificent decor and supports which Steven had designed and helped to create and build. If Adrian and Yseult had always thought that their daughter Tatiana had great imagination, they realised that their elder son Steven had also been endowed with a wonderful imagination! The success of that exhibition gave a new orientation to Steven's career and he became steadily a very reputed scenographer with various mandates granted by well-known museums in several cities and towns in Switzerland.

When younger son Justin graduated from the University of Fribourg with his Bachelor of Laws, he told his parents that he had decided that he did not want to become a lawyer like his father but was very interested in sustainable development and the complicated problems relating to climate change, agriculture, water supply and treatment, culture of crops to make foodstuffs and the various scientific solutions to be studied in order to solve such problems. This was an unexpected but impressive re-orientation in Justin's thought processes and ambitions and, after undertaking wide research and discussing with several specialists, he told his parents that he was going to undertake the hard and complex studies over several years to become an Engineer in Agronomy at the specialised academy for such studies in Geneva. When he contacted the academy, he was told that before being accepted for the long, arduous and very tough course he would have to begin, as from the summer of the following year, several training periods for a few months each during an entire year working on-site at various professional establishments involved with grape-growing, fruit tree cultivation, market-gardening activities, agricultural farming and other agronomy-linked specialities. He spent many months searching for and obtaining such training periods, then underwent them all over the following year, took exams related to the scientific aspects in each training period, was given glowing marks and reports and was accepted by the academy in order to commence the complex, challenging and tough course in order to become an Engineer in Agronomy.

In early February 2012, Alan, the elder son of Lionel and Roberta, informed Adrian and Yseult that Elspeth had just given birth to their third child, a son named Victor, and he hoped very much that they could come to Budapest for his baptism in a few weeks' time. Their second daughter Shannon had been born in April 2010 but Adrian and Yseult had not been able to attend her christening because Adrian had been obliged to make a business trip abroad at that time for the asset management company now employing him. He was able to take a few days holiday and attend the baptism of Victor with Yseult and was over-joyed to be together again with Lionel, Roberta, Isadora, Alan, Elspeth and their gorgeous three young children. The shared happiness of that stay in Budapest was made even greater by the very pleasant presence among

them all of Raymond and Philippa, who had met Lionel and Roberta on a few occasions, especially in London, and had been invited by them to make the trip.

A few months later, a chatty e-mail arrived on Adrian's computer, copied to Philippa, from his beloved sister-in-law Maureen in Auckland giving him and Yseult the latest news of herself, Lydia and Arthur and their two children and Lynette and Jerry and their two children. Then, the message wrote that she was going to make a big trip on her own in two months' time to visit members of her own family up in Yorkshire and she had arranged with Raymond and Philippa that after her time in Yorkshire she would travel by train down to Somerset and would spend a weekend staying with them at the cottage which they had bought with an acre of garden on the outskirts of the village of Stogumber. They all hoped that Adrian and Yseult would be free to fly over and spend the weekend with the three of them. Adrian was very excited at this prospect, as he had not had the opportunity to see Maureen again since his attendance with his son Justin at the wedding of Lydia in Auckland in 2007.

As soon as he mentioned it to Yseult, she smiled and said she knew how important it was for him to be able to get together with Maureen again after such a long absence, as well as with Raymond and Philippa, and she accepted with alacrity to reserve their flights to and from Bristol airport as well as a hire car. After Adrian replied to Maureen and Philippa confirming they would be delighted to come for the specific weekend, Philippa sent him an e-mail a few days later, saying she would reserve a double room for him and Yseult at a pleasant and cosy Bed & Breakfast in Stogumber village, not very far from their cottage, as all the three bedrooms at the cottage would be occupied, for Maureen would naturally sleep in one and the third one would be occupied by her son Brian and his steady girlfriend Arabella who would also be visiting that weekend.

This was the icing on the cake for Adrian, who had not expected to be able to see his fine nephew again so soon. He and Yseult spent the most wonderfully happy weekend with them all and it was an especially moving occasion to be with marvellous Maureen again after so much time and to see the recent photos she showed them of the two young couples and their children. Adrian and Yseult were very happy to see Brian again and to meet Arabella, who was a very pretty, intelligent and pleasant girl whom they and Maureen liked very much.

Arawan was working very hard assisting in the development of various activities, as well as a lovely and unique café offering vegetarian food of which he was the manager and head chef in one of the three large greenhouses, at an expanding horticultural centre situated about a couple of miles from the converted barn on the farm. Tatiana was very active with her work on art and illustration subjects as well as helping out quite regularly at the horticultural centre.

Adrian and Yseult were absolutely over the moon and could barely contain their excitement when Tatiana announced to them in September 2012 that she was expecting a baby. During the following nine-month period, they managed

to visit Arawan and Tatiana, as well as Mummy, on two or three occasions, staying on each visit to Cornwall at a Bed & Breakfast a mile away from the farm. However, they were obligatorily at home in Switzerland when Arawan drove very heavily pregnant Tatiana to Truro Hospital, where she gave birth to a baby boy in mid-May 2013. They gave him the lovely Celtic first name Liam. When Arawan sent them by e-mail a short while later the first two photos of Liam he had taken in the delivery room just after Liam had been born, cleaned up and placed in his mother's arms, Adrian looked at the photos and exclaimed to Yseult with a broad smile on his face, 'That little fellow's face is the splitting image of his mother's face when she was a new-born baby! She was such a beautiful baby and has become a very beautiful woman. Our first grandson is going to be a really handsome boy!'

Adrian had been present at the delivery of each one of his three children and had taken many photos at the time of each delivery, had had them printed and had stuck them in a photo album for each child respectively. A few days before the expected date of Liam's birth, Adrian had looked once again at Tatiana's photo album and as he gazed at the first photos of Liam he saw that his face was almost a conform copy of his mother's face just after her birth.

Both he and Yseult looked at those first photos of Liam with absolute adoration and they took no time in arranging for a trip to go to see Arawan, Tatiana and their golden first grandson. They stayed at their usual Bed & Breakfast down the road and spent as much time as they could during the waking hours of each day with Arawan, Tatiana and Liam and helping exhausted Tatiana with her lovely little baby in every small way possible.

Adrian and Yseult could not get over how much they were blessed when their second grandson was born in late November 2013, six months after his cousin Liam. Steven and Marianne had moved from their small rented flat in Lausanne about two years earlier to a three-bedroomed rented flat in the lakeside town of Nyon. Whilst Adrian and Yseult were following Tatiana's pregnancy with great joy, anticipation and enthusiasm, they received a second wonderful gift when Steven and Marianne told them in March 2013 that she was expecting their first baby. She also gave birth to a baby boy and both Adrian and Yseult were delighted when Steven and Marianne announced that his first name was Kirwyn, another enchanting Celtic name.

When Marianne's mother told her daughter that she thought that Kirwyn looked very much like his father, Adrian felt he had to concur, for a couple of days before the delivery date he had taken out the photo album he and Yseult had made for Steven and he saw that Kirwyn's face resembled closely that of his father when he was a small baby. However, after some months Adrian and Yseult started to tell Marianne that it was when little Kirwyn smiled and laughed that they saw her in him, for he had a very similar smile and laugh to those of his pretty mother.

After the momentous and marvellously happy events of the births of grandsons Liam and Kirwyn, another important and life-changing event took place that year for Adrian and Yseult, for Adrian ended his career and took full

retirement at end November 2013 at the age of sixty-five, the legal retirement age for men under Swiss laws. He had worked contentedly and satisfactorily for the asset management company during the past five years and had been treated very well, kindly, fairly and with great respect by the general manager and the other colleagues in a humane and pleasant environment with a family-style atmosphere. He decided when he was sixty-four that he would retire a year later, whereas he knew that in many asset management companies it was quite a usual practice to carry on working well beyond the age of sixty-five. He explained to Yseult that he knew he could no longer tolerate stress and pressure and his whole system was completely exhausted by all those many years of trying to cope with and battle against the dreadful aftermaths of the unhappy childhood and other tragedies, most of all the terrible loss of his two beloved brothers, and his concentration difficulties were increasing with his advancing age.

When he told his boss and other top managers that he was going to retire, they said it was a great pity, for he was much appreciated inside the company and they would all be very happy if he would accept to carry on working there for as many more years as he would like. He felt very flattered, warmed and heartened by this kind compliment, especially after so many years of feeling inferior, useless and worthless. He was acutely aware of his good fortune of being able to work right up until the legal retirement age and even beyond if he so wished in an economic environment where he knew many professionals had lost their employments in their fifties and were not able to obtain any jobs again, causing immense distress and problems for them and their families. He thanked his boss sincerely for his extremely kind offer but he declined it and helped him to find his successor and trained the selected person over several months in order to ensure continuity in the function after he left the company.

During the first quarter of 2014, Tatiana rang her parents and told them that she and Arawan were going to get married and wished to have a very special and unique celebration in early July with them, Steven, Marianne, little Kirwyn, their own baby Liam and their dog, Justin, Arawan's mother Priscille and Arawan's brother, his wife, their two children and their dog.

While she and Arawan were wondering where would be a very special and unique place to celebrate their wedding, Arawan suggested Lundy Island, sitting some miles off the coast of North Devon where the Atlantic Ocean meets the Bristol Channel with nothing between the island and the east coast of North America. He said that he had fond and sentimental memories of Lundy Island, where he and his brother had gone on some summer holidays with their father when they were boys. Tatiana found this a brilliant idea and so did Adrian and Yseult when she rang them again to tell them.

Tatiana reserved the largest house on the island for their group, with just enough bedrooms for everyone, and the ferryboat tickets for them all to make the crossing from the quayside at Bideford over to Lundy Island.

At end June, Arawan and Tatiana were legally married in Falmouth and the next day everyone congregated on the Bideford quayside, with thirteen months

old Liam and seven months old Kirwyn comfortably held against their mothers' bosoms in the special baby holders with straps over each shoulder and firmly fastened on their backs. The sea was reasonably calm and the ferryboat crossing to the island was enchanting. They all stayed three very pleasant days and nights on the island, enjoyed clement sunny and warm weather and had the most marvellous, romantic and fun-filled family celebration of the wedding of Arawan and Tatiana. When they sadly took the ferryboat back to Bideford and saw the island becoming smaller and smaller behind them, they all agreed that this had been a wonderful, unforgettable family get-together and they should try to arrange some other year another occasion to return to Lundy Island for another happy family celebration.

The year 2015 was an important one for both Justin and Steven with regards to their professional activities and prospects. Firstly, after all those long years of very gruelling, tough and exhausting studies, laboratory experiments and on-site visits to various places linked to agronomy, Justin successfully passed all the exams and obtained his qualification as an Engineer in Agronomy in the late autumn. His professors were so impressed with and pleased by the excellence of his written work and scientific analytical results that they proposed that he should set about working in the coming weeks and months on drafting an article on a very complex subject which would afterwards be submitted for publication in an international science journal.

On his side, whilst Steven was in the middle of accomplishing a mandate relating to an exhibition in his capacity as an independent industrial designer and scenographer, he came across an advertisement announcing the search for a qualified and experienced person to become the chief scenographer for two important museums on a full-time employed basis. When he showed the advertisement to Marianne and his parents and asked their opinion, they all encouraged him to apply for the post as this could be a most interesting and positive development in his career. He sent his application, underwent a series of gruelling and testing interviews and was selected for the important job over several dozens of other candidates. He commenced his new employment in this challenging environment in late autumn and during the following year became involved in the conception, design and creation of some very important and fascinating exhibitions.

The year 2016 turned out to be an exceptional and joyfully happy one for Adrian and Yseult and the entire family. It started out with the participation in February of Mummy and Adrian in the lovely celebration of Aunt Josephine's one-hundredth birthday, surrounded by her offspring, her four grandchildren and her two small great-granddaughters. Then in the spring, there were the two romantic weddings of the son then the daughter of Yseult's middle sister and three babies were born to three young mothers on Yseult's side of the family during the space of four months.

In mid-May, Adrian and Yseult flew over to England, drove down to Cornwall to celebrate grandson Liam's third birthday and participated in a most enjoyable birthday party organised by his parents with several of his little

friends and their parents. A week later, they drove up to Sidmouth and stayed with Mummy for several days and on the last weekend of May they had the immense joy of participating near Tunbridge Wells, south of London, in the superbly organised, romantic and happy wedding of their nephew Brian and his lovely fiancée Arabella. They were delighted as well to be with Raymond and Philippa again on this joyful occasion of the wedding of her beloved son, and Adrian was extremely happy and moved to meet for the first time Philippa's half-sister Clarissa and her half-brother Albert on her mother's side as well as Clarissa's husband Ralph and their two very pretty daughters.

In December 2015, Steven and Marianne had given Adrian and Yseult the wonderful news that she was expecting their second child. Some weeks later Marianne told them that she had just discovered that morning that she was carrying their second and third children as she was expecting twins! This came naturally as a big shock to Steven and Marianne but both Adrian and Yseult were ecstatic with joy at this marvellous news.

In mid-August Marianne gave birth to non-identical twin boys and they were given the unique and special Welsh first names Terfel and Emrys by their parents, which moved grand-father Adrian immensely as he was of Welsh origin and Steven had told him that he was very proud of being half-Welsh and he loved Welsh culture, music and names, with which Marianne had been happy to concur.

The doting grandparents were very pleased to help Marianne in as many ways as possible each week with looking after the twins and their elder brother Kirwyn and they alternated with Marianne's mother, who lived in a nearby village, with undertaking the babysitting chores, which were not chores at all but a truly wonderful pleasure.

One day in the flat of Steven and Marianne, when Adrian looked tenderly at Kirwyn sitting beside him and at the two months old twins, nestled restfully in the loving arms of their mother and their grand-mother Yseult, he felt an immense joy and peace deep inside him as he thought to himself that these three brothers would not have to go through the pain, suffering and scars of an unhappy childhood like his two brothers and himself as they were surrounded by very loving, attentive and caring parents, grandparents and other family members and were living in a happy, stable, united, secure and normal family unit.

Each time Arawan, Tatiana and young Liam were able to come to Switzerland, Liam and his six months younger cousin Kirwyn were delighted to see one another again and revelled in each other's company and playing together and romping around and a very loving and strong bond had developed between the two cousins.

Tatiana flew over with Liam in July 2016 to stay at her parents' flat then attend the wedding of a close girlfriend with whom she had gone through school and ballet lessons during several years and had always kept in close contact. During their stay, Liam and Kirwyn saw one another several times and it was delightful for everyone to see them together and witness yet again the

close, loving relationship that existed between them. In mid-September, Tatiana came over again with Liam so that they could see the one-month-old twins Terfel and Emrys for the first time and Liam and Kirwyn fell into each other's arms again then tumbled about, wrestled like small sumo champions and played together with renewed joy.

In late November, Adrian and Yseult celebrated the third birthday of Kirwyn together with his parents at their flat in the company of his three months old younger brothers who could not care less about elder brother's birthday treat and were simply happy to be molly-coddled, kissed, caressed, fussed over and adored by their fawning and doting grandparents. Then, in December, Arawan, Tatiana and Liam all came over for several weeks and a wonderfully happy family reunion was enjoyed by everyone at Christmas and Liam and Kirwyn were overjoyed to share wonderful moments together on several occasions during those weeks.

Adrian was especially happy and contented to have lived, observed and participated in all the marvellous and joyful family events over the past several years and during that year 2016, including the wonderful news from his nephew Peter that the first daughter of Peter and Sally had been born in March 2015 and their second daughter had been born in November 2016. He felt a greatly renewed confidence in life and in people and a serenity with his family, which procured an immensely deep happiness for him and the hope of a positive and greatly satisfying future for all the members of his extended and expanding family wherever they were in the world.

His birth family unit had been blown to smithereens when he was a very young boy, causing so much unhappiness, guilt and deformity in his life, and later on the appalling deaths of both his beloved brothers had caused ravaging shock, grief and sorrow, terrible pangs of loss and long-lasting and agonising traumas which had very nearly destroyed his own life.

However, reconciliation with and acceptance of the awful, tempestuous and convulsive past had become possible and a bright, calm and happy future in the bosom of his present family could be envisaged. As he thought that, he sensed vividly deep inside him the soft, little inner voices of the souls of his beloved, never to be forgotten brothers Neil and Justin whispering to him that he was well on the road to a good, partial, even if not full recovery from the past traumas, anguishes, pain and suffering.

After the New Year's eve celebrations, as they lay side by side in bed and Yseult snuggled up to him and rested her head on his chest, he wrapped his arm tenderly around her, kissed her softly on the forehead and thought to himself how he loved, respected and admired his wonderful wife more and more with each passing year. Although he was not regretfully able to show it to her sufficiently well due to some hang-ups, drawbacks and failings remaining deep and silently inside him beyond his control as sore, pathetic vestiges of all the past distress, guilt and suffering.

They had celebrated their forty-second wedding anniversary in May and he felt eternally grateful to this exceptional and marvellous woman for having

298

stayed with him, stuck by him, endured and tolerated all the difficulties he caused due to his unhappy past and assisted him in so many ways with coping and then overcoming as many of his personal problems as possible. She was his rock and had been his very solid and faithful partner, so essential to his recovery, harmony and happiness, since their wedding day so many moons ago. She was the central pillar of their family unit and had never betrayed the trust placed in her by himself, their two sons, their daughter and their reliance on her to ensure that theirs was a truly loving, caring, stable, secure, and unified family nucleus.

As she lay comfortably in the crook of his arm, he ruffled her hair with the other hand, kissed her lovingly on the lips and then said in an excited flourish, 'You know, my darling wife, I am thinking that one's deep emotions are a great source of inspiration, one should not be afraid of those emotions or hide them and memory is the scribe of the soul, as Aristotle wrote. Consequently, I should perhaps make the effort and write a novel inspired by and based on the true story of the three brothers and our three different destinies!'

She looked intently into his blue eyes with her lovely, brown, velvety eyes, smiled with that glorious, charming and mischievous smile that he loved so much then replied with her great sense of humour, irony and sarcasm, 'That is an excellent idea, my dear husband. The task of writing about the gripping story of the three brothers and your three destinies will keep you well occupied and out of mischief, will keep you out of my hair, will help to improve your power of concentration and will keep your brain from being addled by dementia or Alzheimer during your retirement!'